S0-ACB-315

Breaking Up Is Hard To Do

Stories by Women

808.
83935
2
B828

Edited by
Amber Coverdale Sumrall

The Crossing Press · Freedom, CA 95019

The copyright notices listed below constitute an extension of the copyright page. Grateful acknowledgment is made for permission to use the following previously published material.

"We Visit a Poet and Ponder Life" by Alta is reprinted by permission of the author from *Deluged with Dudes* (Shameless Hussy Press, 1989).

"Rough Slice" by Reneé Ashley originally appeared in *Hayden's Ferry Review,* Spring 1989.

"Golden Chances" by Alice K. Boatwright originally appeared in *Penumbra* under the title "Elmo and Emily."

"Getting Out" by Thea Caplan first appeared in *Snake Nation Review,* Spring/Summer 1991.

"Cleft" by Martha Collins originally appeared in *Field* and is reprinted by permission of the author from *A History of Small Life on a Windy Planet* (University of Georgia Press, 1993).

"Mum and the Planet Earth" by Carolyn Cooke first appeared in *Sojourner.*

"One Day It Happens" by Silvia Curbello is reprinted by permission of the author from *The Geography of Leaving* (Silverfish Review Press, 1991).

"Monsters, His Monsters" by Terry Ehret is reprinted by permission of the author from *Lost Body* (Copper Canyon Press, 1993).

Continued on page 414

humca

Copyright © 1994 by Amber Coverdale Sumrall
Cover design and interior design by Sheryl Karas
Printed in the U.S.A.

Library of Congress Cataloging-in-Publication Data

Breaking up is hard to do: stories by women /edited by Amber Coverdale Sumrall.
p. cm.
ISBN 0-89594-655-6. — ISBN 0-89594-654-8 (paper)
1. American literature—Women authors. 2. Man-woman relationships—United States—Literary collections. 3. Separation (Psychology)—Literary collections. 4. Women—United States—Literary collections. 5. Love stories, American—Women authors. 6. Love poetry, American—women authors. 7. American literature—20th century. I. Sumrall, Amber Coverdale.
PS508.W7B74 1994
810.8'09287—dc20 93-41995
CIP

Damage Noted 08/04/00 10/cen

Contents

In the Box Called Pleasure

One Day It Happens

The Last Mr. Wrong

The Future Tense

For Wally Parham,
with love, for lighting the way.

Some say the heart is just like a wheel, when you bend it you can't mend it. And my love for you is like a sinking ship and my heart is on that ship out in mid-ocean.
—Anna McGarigle—

I saw this thing turn, like a flower, once picked, turning petals into bright knives in your hand. And it was so much desired, so lovely, that your fingers will not loosen, and you have only disbelief that this, of all you have ever known, should have the possibility of pain.
—Nadine Gordimer—

Preface

Endings are horrible, almost impossible. We are deeply instilled with the belief that love will last forever, even though the statistics give us quite a different perspective. I have had ten major breakups so far in my life and hope never to have another, but I'm far from confident. I am perplexed by the rapidity and ease with which passion, desire and shared dreams simply fade away or deteriorate into boredom and animosity. Last year I broke up with someone and believed I would never fall in love again. This year I've fallen in love with someone and believe we will never break up.

My last breakup was devastating, a phantom pain of the heart. I thought I'd never love or be loved again. I started smoking, took two-hour baths so I could cry without interruption, and listened to Nanci Griffith continuously. Days passed in which I was unable to eat, sleep, or leave my home. I thought I needed a jumpstart, some incredible jolt to my nervous system in order to feel alive again. What I needed was simply to grieve. For months. Many prior losses surfaced which I also grieved. My hypnotherapist, the support and love of my friends, my writing, my dreams and the passing of time pulled me through. Love comes with no guarantee. The alternative is to display my scars and close my heart. A price I'm not willing to pay.

Breaking Up Is Hard To Do is actually the mate to *Love's Shadow*. When I put out a call for work focusing on the dark side of love easily half of the manuscripts I received were about breaking up. So I divided the work into two books. For the writer the advantages of breaking up are similar to the advantages of falling in love—we get some great material. Also, writing is cheaper than therapy. The sixty-three stories and poems in *Breaking Up Is Hard To Do* unearth a variety of long-buried feelings: before, during, and after the breakup. They speak to a broad range of experience and circumstance. There is humor and heartbreak. Disbelief and relief. Betrayal and revenge. A determination and resolve to understand and survive. And most of all there is the feeling of déjà vu, as if we are standing, not outside the experience, but rather inside, with each woman who tells her story. We have all been here before; some of us, many times.

I am deeply grateful to each writer for her work in helping to create *Breaking Up Is Hard To Do* and to Elaine and John Gill for putting the book into print. To Ruah Bull I send my heartfelt thanks for walking me through, step by step. Thanks also to Neil Sedaka for the title.

—*Amber Coverdale Sumrall*
Santa Cruz, California, 1993

In The Box Called Pleasure

Love's a disease. But curable.
— *Rose Macauley* —

I am remembering you, my love, whoever you are, and I wave goodbye, because I think I finally understand the difference between love and thievery. I have turned my back on fear and pain, which I have named hell.
— *Rosalind Pace* —

Romance

Dorianne Laux

I know we made it up, like God.
But, god, it hurts. Like phantom pain
in a leg that's been taken, what's gone
throbs, aches. Nothing there
and still, the pain makes a shape.

Adrenalin

Cris Mazza

I

It wasn't fear that made Maureen wait so long to have her first lover. She just waited for someone who didn't make her want to spit, and it turned out to be Grant. Then she didn't have time to regret or be melancholy about the years she was alone because the relationship with Grant progressed too quickly and intensely for her to even worry about inexperience. Giddy instinct took over, for a while. Her virginity bothered her for a few days, but she put it aside and was able to ignore or perhaps not even notice the initial clumsiness. Then at least half of the time sex was her idea, and it became easier, although never climactic for her. She wasn't worried about that. She was too affected by the obvious effect she had on *him*: the sweat on his back and buttocks, his deep panting and the drowsy look on his face, sweat on his temples, his eyes half closed but still staring at her, his mouth involuntarily puckered because he had hyperventilated.

"I want a picture of this the way your face looks right now," she said once, her own face not even an inch away because he was lying on top of her, resting afterwards.

"Let's just hope you'll see me this way often enough," he said, still a little out of breath. "You won't *need* a picture."

"But if I had one I could look at it when we're *not* in bed."

"Why?"

She didn't have an answer that time, so she just wrapped her legs around his back.

She worked part-time in a hospital, typing, and he was a musician in a band that played several nights a week. But except for his gigs and her job, they were always together, either at his studio or her apartment. She wrote letters to him while she was at work, then brought them home to him and watched him read, waiting for him to look up at her, the few seconds before he pulled her close and kissed her.

When she was younger and lived at home with her parents, her mother used to spend the whole summer canning fruits and making jelly. The kitchen would be thickly filled with the pungent combination of hot fruit and too much sugar. Smelling it, even just walking through the kitchen and quickly out the back door, made her stomach burn and legs feel weak. That first summer with Grant she finally felt it again, even though his faint smell and taste was musky or salty. It happened when he looked at her.

His face was almond-shaped, thin, without prominent cheekbones, but his eyes, mouth and teeth were large, his lips full. His hair was straw texture and shaggy and hid his ears which stuck out slightly from the sides of his head. His chin was narrow and his neck long. She often watched his mouth when he talked. He had several different smiles. A few times she tried to describe one she liked, to get him to do it again, but although he tried to follow her description, it never came out quite right.

"I want a picture of you," she said again one day. She was dressing for work and he was half asleep in bed, having gotten in at two the night before. "Not like this," he mumbled.

"No," she laughed. "I mean just you, smiling or whatever. I need a picture on my dresser and one in my wallet so I can look at you while I'm at work or when you're at a gig."

"You sure it won't excite you too much?" His groggy voice was muffled in the pillow, but his eyes crinkled and laughed.

"If I'm lucky!" she giggled.

She bought some oak picture frames at a thrift shop, cleaned the glass parts and stained the wood. But the frames were laid aside and forgotten for a few weeks when Grant suggested they get married and have just one place to live. They did it as soon as they could get blood tests and a license. Maureen quit her job, which she hated, and bought a camera. "I never needed a camera before, but now I do."

"Why?"

"Now I have you and I don't want to miss any of it."

At first she just shot the photos of him while he was busy practicing his string bass or reading the newspaper or playing a game of scrabble or chess with her. Then she began to pose him, and she once again tried to describe the expressions she wanted.

Once Grant remarked that it made him a little uncomfortable to have pictures of himself all over, like living in a hall of fame or seeing his own head stuffed and mounted over the fireplace.

"I know, I used to wonder why hunters would want to do that," she said. "But now I understand. Imagine being out hunting and for days you don't see anything but footprints and turds. Deer are so beautiful and elusive that when the hunter finally gets one, he wants to preserve the moment when he first saw it gazing at him from a thicket."

He laughed and said, "Just don't start taking the camera to bed."

"Very funny."

But they didn't go to bed as often.

There were always pictures of him still on the film in the camera, and a finished roll of film at the drug store being developed into snapshots, and last week's snapshots spread out on a table with a magnifying glass handy constantly arranged and rearranged in order of best-to-worst while negatives of the best ones from the previous batch were already at the photo shop being enlarged to 8x10 or 11x14. In the meantime there were finished enlargements waiting for frames and frames waiting for varnish or paint to dry. Then there were the already framed photographs leaning against the back of the couch as she analyzed the walls to find the best way to add the newly framed photos to those already hung. She started using the savings she'd had before they were married to buy more lenses and instruction books. And she suggested they go places to use different settings. She threw together a picnic lunch and they went to a lake but she hardly ate anything. She took pictures of Grant feeding the ducks, sharing his sandwich unintentionally with a goose, slipping on the mud near the water, laughing at his own wet behind. But Maureen didn't laugh. She had to concentrate on holding the camera still.

Then she moped when he wouldn't sit for portraits anymore. "Honey, c'mon," he said. "Don't you have enough pictures yet?"

"None of these seem good enough."

"Gee, sorry, maybe you need a new model."

"No, Grant, it's not your fault! It must be mine. I don't seem to be getting the exact right moment, these pictures just don't do anything for me. I'm losing things!"

"You're not losing anything. I'm still here." "You still don't understand, do you."

In the second year Grant's group, a dance band called "The King's Gentlemen," got an agent and started booking steady jobs for higher pay. Grant and Maureen moved to a larger house with an extra bedroom. "This is your photography room, okay, honey?"

He suggested she could go find some tables or a desk at the thrift shops, and she said she probably would, but many of the cartons of photographs and albums were never unpacked. She did hang most of the framed pictures, and spent several weeks rearranging them. The band was rehearsing more, so Grant was out afternoons and nights. When he was home they still played games and sometimes made love, and he often saw her lenses on the kitchen table lying on soft cloth with a bottle of cleaning solution nearby. Then one night he came home from playing at a nightclub and found her packing the lenses in styrofoam bits and sealing the boxes.

It was Maureen's idea for them to buy their first television, and while they were shopping he decided to get a video tape machine also. Maureen taped a few shows while Grant was at work, and they watched them together after midnight. He liked to make popcorn when he got home, and they became involved in a few serial-dramas, but during the summer the reruns came on and she stopped taping shows, then never went back to them when the fall season began again. The band was heavily booked and even had a tour coming up in the spring. Grant realized Maureen hadn't done much of anything for over a year. He couldn't imagine how she filled her days.

II

When Grant came home from tour, she apologized for the mess, but he just said, "I'm the kind of guy who may be standing up to his ears in horseshit, but thinks: there must be a pretty little pony around here somewhere." It was something he said fairly often lately.

He came in and leaned his bass in the corner as Maureen turned the television off, then he hugged her. She stayed for a moment, but squirmed and said, "I'm being choked." When he released her, she started picking up newspapers and dirty dishes, throwing pillows back onto the couch, straightening slip-covers.

He cleared his throat. "Well . . . you had some time to be alone and think. Feeling any better?"

She touched a pimple on her forehead. "I'm twenty-nine and still breaking out."

He smiled.

"Everything's the same," she said. She looked around. "Just messier."

"I like it, it's home." He tried to continue smiling. "So what'd you do all week?"

"I already told you, nothing, not a damn thing. You have a right to be mad. I'm a lazy slob, I guess."

"No, honey, maybe you just needed a rest." He went into the bedroom and threw his jacket on the bed. The bed wasn't made, but it seldom was. He usually slept until at least noon and she'd gotten into the habit of going to bed early at night. Why make the bed just a few hours before you tear it apart to get in it again?

She was still standing in the living room, hugging one of the sofa pillows against her belly. He went to her to hold her again, and bent to kiss her, but she started talking against his mouth. He said, "What?"

She sat suddenly on the couch, still holding the pillow. "I'm sorry about your cashew nuts. I ate them all."

"They weren't just mine. I'm glad you enjoyed them."

"You bought them."

He noticed an empty packing carton on the floor and the photo albums stacked on the coffee table. The top album was open, but a section of newspaper had been dropped over the page of photos. Also on the table were two magnifying glasses of different sizes propped upright in an empty juice glass. He picked up a paperback book that was halfway under the sofa. It was a pulp romance, printed on recycled newsprint. She reached for it so he handed it to her while he said, "Really, I'm glad you ate them. I was getting tired of them and wanted to finish them so we could get something else. Look, I've got a check here; what treat shall we get for ourselves?"

"I'll get fat and you'll hate me."

He laughed and sat beside her, pulling her close. He kissed her cheek and her neck. "Impossible," he murmured.

"Which, that I'll get fat or you'll hate me?"

"Both." He kissed her ear and she shivered. He laughed again. "Tickle?"

She sighed and leaned against him for a moment, then sprang up to remove a dirty coffee cup from the window sill. "How'd you get home? I thought you were going to call from the depot."

"I called from Riverside last night but couldn't get you, so Dave dropped me off."

Maureen parted the curtain to look out the window. "I was going to wash the car and didn't," she said. "That's another thing I didn't do. I'm terrible."

"No you're not." He leaned back, stretched both arms along the back of the sofa and crossed his legs. "It's okay anyway because you do a lousy job on the car."

"That's a nice thing to say." She glared at him.

"I was kidding, honey, come on!" he laughed, then sighed and closed his eyes. "Come here, Maureen."

"Just a second." She went into the bedroom and came back holding some envelopes. "I opened your mail. I'm sorry. Are you mad?"

Grant stood, went to her, took the envelopes and tossed them aside. "I missed you," he said, "how can I be mad at you?" She had her face down against his chest, so he kissed the top of her head. "Especially for such silly things. There's nothing private in my mail; was there anything interesting?"

"A letter from your sister."

"Good. Did you enjoy it?"

She looked up, hitting his chin with her head, then she backed away. "Don't patronize me, Grant. After all, *you* went off and had a great time on tour and I had to stay home alone waiting faithfully while you're out doing God-knows-what."

He didn't say anything for a moment, then took her hand. "Yes, I had a pretty good time on tour, but right now I want to have a *better* time."

They walked together into the bedroom and kissed for a while on the bed, then she turned her head so he kissed her neck while he unbuttoned her shirt. "I'm cold, Grant," she said. She pulled the sheet over herself. He undressed and got in bed beside her. She still had her pants on. "It's good to be home," he said, his mouth on her shoulder. "I missed you and thought about you all the time." She was looking at the ceiling. A thin cobweb floated from the light fixture. "It's all right, Mo, I understand. I'll help with the housework and stuff you need to do, whatever will make you happy again."

"Ha!" She rolled to her belly. He sat beside her and began massaging her back.

"Relax, honey." They were both trembling. "What's the matter?"

"Nothing."

"Do you want me to quit the band and get a job with regular hours?"

"No." He could hardly hear her.

"What can I do for you, Mo? You're all I think about."

"Stop it!" she shouted. She sat up, kneeling, but kept her back to him. "Okay, I'll *tell* you. I thought you wouldn't want to know; yes, I met someone, but nothing happened . . . isn't that *good*? You should be happy!"

He closed his eyes. He felt foolish sitting there naked, and he started to get dizzy. When he opened his eyes he saw her slowly lean forward, lay her forehead on her knees and sob. He stared at her for a long time.

III

She left four days later. She didn't even take a suitcase, but she put a bar of soap and her toothbrush in her purse. And she took the first apartment she found, which wasn't far away since she'd left on foot, but Grant wouldn't know that. It was a studio down on Adams Avenue. One of the walls was right on the sidewalk; people could look into her window as they walked by, if they wanted to. There was no heat nor electricty, no furniture and no phone installed.

She sat on the floor and held her head and thought about the jumbo bottle of aspirin on the bathroom shelf at home. Grant had taken it down every morning, the past three mornings, swallowed a few tablets, washed his face, and come back to the bedroom smiling. He wanted her to get up, get her camera and go to the zoo; get up, grab a coat and her camera and go sailing; get up, find her boots and her camera and go for a hike in the mountains. He had a week vacation before the band started a long booking at a local club. But Maureen wanted to stay in bed. She wanted Grant to sit beside her, instead of pacing back and forth at the foot of the bed, pinching her toes, laughing, fully dressed, sunglasses in his pocket, keys in his hand, saying, "C'mon, where do you want to go for breakfast?"

"Let's just talk, Grant."

"We can do that at the zoo or the beach, anywhere we go."

"I want to talk *here*. Grant, we *have* to talk about it."

He'd only stopped smiling for a second. "There's nothing to talk about."

"How can you say that!"

He was grinning again. "Come on, what do you want to do that's *fun* for you? That's all you need."

She didn't know how to tell him all she needed was an adrenalin rush, a sudden one, like her guts were exploding. Every time she thought about what had happened while Grant was on tour, she felt it again, a reminder, a taste. "I want to explain it to you, Grant," she begged.

At first leaving Grant was out of the question; it never entered her mind. The first night he was home from tour, he held her all night like a stuffed bear, and sighed just before going to sleep, but continued to hold her after he slept, just as tightly, while she lay there and thought about what had happened with Paul in the park, or what had *almost* happened or what had seemed to be something happening while it happened, but if she told anyone, she knew, it would immediately become *nothing* as she told it, because, after all, what *had* happened? If anyone filmed it and showed it to an audience, they would all say, "Nothing happened." That's what people thought nothing was, and she would've agreed, a week ago, but now how could it be nothing when all she could do was think about it?

When Grant was away on tour, Maureen had tried to be more energetic: at least she got up early, read, took deep afternoon naps and stayed up late playing solitaire and watching television. But she had thought a lot about Grant and how she was going to really try to make him happier, first of all by not being in such a funk all the time. Wednesday she decided maybe she should go out and do something, like take a bus to the park, but she didn't actually do it until Thursday afternoon. She hadn't taken her camera and didn't miss it as she wandered among fountains and museums and jugglers and goldfish pools, botanical gardens, lawn bowling, rose gardens planted in miniature mazes (which were too simple to become lost in), replica rain forests and deserts, and tourists. It was noisy, but not like crowd sounds at the racetrack or a ballpark. She could hear individual words and individual laughter. It was warm, early spring, and she sat on a bench letting the sun melt her limbs into rubber. She was only half interested in the mime act going on in a small quad in front of her, but a crowd of tourists had gathered, and Paul was in that crowd. She didn't notice him until he had already come out of the gathering and sat beside her on the bench. Even then she hardly glanced at him. Not until he asked her how she could be at the park on such a beautiful day, watching such a good show, and seem so unhappy.

Then when she turned and looked at him, his eyes were surprisingly close to her, and that first silent meeting was nearly violent. After that, he talked for a few minutes, unplanned, rambling, but fluent words: His first and last name . . . he wondered why she was sad . . . she must be a local because she didn't look like a person on a holiday . . . being 300 miles from home and on his last day of vacation made him feel uninhibited about coming to meet her and hear her story . . . maybe he could cheer her up . . . she probably didn't know how pretty she was all alone on this bench as though it was raining and the park empty.

But she hardly heard anything, just sat staring at him. Her left hand was a rigid fist held tight against her body, burying her wedding ring against her stomach. When he asked if she wasn't feeling well, she abruptly said, "No, I'm not well," and it was the truth: her stomach burned. He took her fist away from her body and loosened her fingers so her hand lay flat in his, but she immediately lifted her hand closer to his eyes and pointed to the ring. She didn't stop there. She told him how Grant didn't care what kind of *wife* she was, never complained if he got a cheese sandwich for dinner five nights in a row because she didn't feel like cooking or cleaning up; and he usually did the dishes so she didn't mind when he broke a glass about once a week; and they played games and even had designed one together once but never bothered to try to sell it; and she'd taught him chess and he taught her backgammon but he'd gotten better than her at chess while she still had to count the lines in backgammon; and sometimes she was a poor sport, sulked and wouldn't finish a game when it was obvious she would lose, so it almost seemed he was happier when she won; he didn't bump her single gammon pieces and warned her about her undefended chessmen. A few times Paul said, "You don't have to tell me this, I understand," but she couldn't stop because none of it sounded like much of an excuse to be unhappy. She even tried to boast about the band and took out a photo from her wallet, but Paul wouldn't look at it.

They walked together all over the park trying to figure out what was happening to them, periodically interrupted by moments of frantic silence, staring at each other, and how many times did they say, "What are we going to do?" Then they kept walking, and he gripped her arm as though she might run away. They walked and talked, then groaned aloud in the silences, and laughed because they groaned, but groaned again, and stared at each other in the lengthening shadows. They were in an undeveloped part of the park, beside a construction site where a new theatre was being built, surrounded by a fence with metal signs fastened to the chain links: Keep Out, Construction Area, Danger! Paul kept handing her his business cards. He said she might lose it if he just gave her one. She had a stack of them in her pocket, in her fist. He grabbed her shoulders clumsily and pulled her to him. She tried to avoid it, but only turned her head slightly, and he kissed the corner of her mouth, gently, but she remembered it as hysterical, stormy, brutal, because afterwards, when they looked at each other, they were actually afraid. Simultaneously they turned and walked away in opposite directions. Maureen took just a few steps then turned around. It was almost dark. Paul stopped at the corner of the fence just long enough to make a fist and hit the metal sign. Maureen's knees almost buckled, the whole fence rattled, sending the vibration all the way down to where she was still standing, shivering, her own fist in her pocket holding the business cards.

Grant had to move the photo albums so he could put his coffee and cereal bowl on the table in the living room. It was the morning after he'd come home from tour. She watched him open one of the albums, glance at the page, take a sip of coffee and turn two more pages, looking at each quickly. Then she suddenly picked up the whole armload of albums and started to take them back to the extra room. Grant said, "You were really getting good at your photography. How would you like to do some publicity photos for the band? We'll pay you. And it'll give you something to do."

Later he said, "How about if we save all the money from the weddings I've been playing and buy you some darkroom equipment so you could freelance."

And during a silent meal at a restaurant, he said suddenly, "I thought you used to want to be a photographer." She stared at her plate. She didn't need a photograph to remember the cold spring twilight at the park, the distant sounds of traffic and laughter, the force of the kiss which she'd almost avoided or almost *missed* and his urgent eyes. She tried to imagine herself lifting a camera and looking through it at Paul during the moments they'd faced each other in crazed silence. She certainly would've had a picture of him to keep: a picture of his face shocked, insulted, turning away, a picture of something else entirely rather than her animated memory of what it *was*.

She looked up at Grant across the linguini with clam sauce that she hadn't touched, and he smiled the same daring, toothy smile he'd given her when they met at the racetrack and shared hunches, before she'd ever taken a photograph of it, when she was never listless. If they weren't heatedly discussing horses and jockeys, they talked about themselves, as though they had to say everything that day or it would never be said. Then they'd come home together, hot, out of money, and lie on the floor of her apartment without turning on the lights where they explored each other happily. The first knot of adrenalin in her stomach had been so bright, she almost vomited . . . and now there was no adrenalin that night in the dimly lit restaurant with expensive food on the table. "This is fun," Grant said, and she ran sobbing to the restroom.

Later they took a walk in a tourist development of shops and clubs, and Grant showed her where the band had its next engagement. She took his hand and listened again to him talk about his plans for the band and the records they would make someday, and all the titles for the albums they'd already decided on. She wondered if any of the titles would change if she left him; that's when she first thought about it and what kind of songs would he write.

At home that night he took her in his arms and kissed her face and neck, opened her blouse and kissed her breast, slid his hands up her back, his fingertips callused from his bass strings, yet still gentle. But she was tired and weak; she felt as though she'd been crying for a long time, red eyes and sore stomach and she lay limp in his arms after he'd undressed her, watching him admire her with his dark eyes, his full mouth, his hands.

It was useless anyway. He turned away from her and lay still, then whispered, "I'm sorry."

"No, I am," she said, whispering too. And they hadn't said anything more.

She dozed a little on the floor of her new apartment, then woke stiff and sweaty. But she didn't go back to the house until after she went to the corner liquor store and bought some cola, a bottle of rum, and a package of paper cups. It was the only drink she knew the ingredients for.

Standing across the street from the house, she checked to make sure Grant was still out getting a haircut and getting the car tuned up, which was where he said he was going when he woke her that morning. Then she ran across the street, into the alley, and went in the back door, changed her clothes and wrote a note for Grant on the back of an empty envelope: I'll contact you when I know what I'm going to do. She thought a while, then added, Don't worry.

On the fourth drink, the cola was getting low, so she just used more rum. She wished she'd stuffed some extra pairs of underwear into her purse. How could leaving be so complicated. She hoped she wouldn't have to keep going back and getting things. She could wash out her clothes in the sink, but where could she hide while they were drying? People on the sidewalk might look through her curtainless windows and see her naked in a bare room, a woman obviously waiting for a clandestine meeting with her lover; even though she'd told Paul, "I won't leave my husband," the word had seemed plump and middle-aged, and the sentence incredible because she never even imagined leaving him, and even more incredible now because she had. She'd left Grant and Paul didn't even know it; he was 300 miles away and she was alone in a bare room. That meant she *hadn't* left Grant for another man. That's when she first started picturing them side-by-side, trying to put them in the same room or sit them on the same couch or at the same side of a table across from her. But she couldn't do it. She finished the drink quickly and crumpled the cup, now lying on the floor staring at the ceiling, as though pictures could hang there and look down without falling on her. It was still easy to see Paul's squinting pale green eyes, his tourist's sunburned nose, the scattered freckles, laugh lines visible even when he wasn't smiling, chapped lips, slightly messy, curly hair. She could even smell his sunscreen and his cottony new shirt and feel the dampness of his palms. And especially she could still hear the desperate or hysterical silences that just remembering made her pull her knees to her chest and roll to her side, a delirious agony. She vomited the rum-and-cola, panting; she couldn't wait for it to end, she couldn't wait until it started again. Wasn't it, after all, the adrenal gland that loved, and not the heart?

When she pictured Grant, it was the photographs. A few times when they used to have guests, someone would say, "What a great picture of Grant."

"But it doesn't even really look like him," she remembered answering. She'd thought more about those photographs in the past week than in the past year. Through untrained technique and fear of losing details in a blur, she had made him hold up a finger or pencil or his bow so she could focus on a vertical line. Clarity was all she asked of her photography, because how could memory ever be as exact or permanent? But she never used to doubt that each of the photographs *was* Grant, looking not at her but at the camera, smiling or serious, amused or pensive, all the Grants she had ever known except the first one. Where *was* the first Grant, the one who'd looked at *her,* what was he doing, perhaps looking at a photograph of her (if he even had one, she didn't know). Suddenly she couldn't remember what he looked like, looking at her, or was it really sudden? The elusive Grant, that deer alive in the thicket before being stuffed and mounted, before the bottomless liquid eyes were turned into polished glass. It wasn't the same animal up on the wall. Isn't that why hunters continued to go back into the woods with their rifles reloaded?

Paul sounded delighted when she called collect from the drug store. "Maureen, I just can't believe it's you."

"Well, it is."

"I know and it's great. I want to see you."

"When can you get here?"

"As soon as possible. Saturday."

"Not soon enough," she said.

He chuckled. "You know, I kept trying to explain to myself what happened to us."

"I know. Me too. It's hard."

"I know. We have to see each other again."

"The sooner the better." Maureen took a deep breath. "Tomorrow. Can you arrange it?"

"Of course, honey, don't worry."

"Don't call me that."

"Honey? Why?"

"Just don't . . . please. Tomorrow? What time should I meet you?"

"God, Maureen, I'm glad you called. I kept wondering if you would ever call or if you lost all the cards or threw them away."

"I didn't. Call me back when you get a time and flight number. As soon as you can. I'm at a pay phone."

"You sound sort of upset, what's wrong?"

"Nothing. Everything'll be okay when you get here."

"That's right. This is great. Okay, okay, I'll call right back, don't go anywhere. God, I don't want to hang up, I'm afraid I'll lose you!"

"Oh Paul," she groaned.

Once again she stood across the street to see if Grant was home. It was hours later, so he couldn't still be having the same haircut, but the car wasn't in the driveway. She hurried as she unpacked all her lenses and loaded them into her camera bag, but again she didn't take any extra underwear.

She waited at the airport in the back row of plastic seats, in the far right-hand corner of the room. Her camera bag was beside her feet, the camera inside loaded. It was Friday at 4, so the airport was crowded, but not noisy. The other people sitting in the plastic chairs rustled newspapers or talked softly to each other. When the announcement of Paul's jet arrival came, she got up quickly and walked to the rear of the room before any of the passengers came through the doors. She had found a place between a trash receptacle and a plastic potted tree. Several people stared at her as she took her camera out and replaced the regular lens with a more powerful one. Then she focused on the door and watched the passengers file past in her viewfinder. She picked up Paul and stayed with him. He was carrying a small overnight bag and had a light jacket over his arm. He was smiling the whole time, his chin lifted and eyes alert as he searched the waiting room for her. His smile never faded, but the jostling crowd kept momentarily blocking her view as his head bobbed among other people who were already finding each other, hugging or shaking hands or kissing while they still clutched their bags. He looked young and clean and excited and stood on one of the plastic chairs, still smiling he had dimples and his eyes crinkled searching for her, thinking of her, wanting her. He panned the room slowly and as his face came around toward her, she closed her eyes, squeezed the camera and felt the deep satisfying click. She left before he gave up looking for her.

She didn't bother stopping at the apartment to pick up what was left of the rum or the package of paper cups. The business cards were there still, too; she'd taken them out and left them in a strewn pile while she was rechecking her lenses the night before.

Grant's car was parked in the driveway, slightly askew, and the lights were on inside the house. She watched him through a window for a while. He was reading, sitting in the big reclining chair, but for a long time he didn't turn a page. Finally he turned back a few pages and read a paragraph over, tracing the lines with his index finger, nodded and flipped forward again. She stepped softly onto the porch, opened the door and slipped inside. Grant snapped the recliner upright and came flying toward her, but stopped short a few feet away. "Mo! Are you alright?"

"I've been missing something," she said, "and I want it back, and I came here to see if I could find it."

She dropped the camera bag and looked around. The couch and coffee table were piled with newspapers, with dirty dishes on top of that. Clothes, both his and hers, were slung over the backs of chairs. The houseplants were dry and drooping, a few dead leaves had fallen on the tabletops. And there were shoes everywhere, all over the floor, some with socks stuffed inside. Grant was barefoot.

"God, look at all this shit!" She kicked a shoe under the sofa. "And I don't want to hear about ponies. I don't know which I hate more, the ponies or the manure." She lifted her camera bag, unzipped it and emptied the contents on the floor between their feet. Grant had to jump backwards as a heavy lens hit his toes. Then he bent and picked it up. The domed blue eye of the lens had been smashed in. He picked up the other lenses, one by one. They were all shattered, and the camera itself had been bashed open. As Maureen looked down at the equipment, a few tears fell directly from her eyes to the junk without running down her cheeks. But when she looked up again, at him, at least she could see better. He was holding a lens, smiling at her another of his smiles she'd never gotten on film and thought she'd lost forever.

Silver Bullets

Diane Lefer

Bobby drives with just a couple of fingers resting on the bottom rim of the steering wheel. He's a good driver except for a tendency to tailgate which I forgive because it's part of what I love about his character—a belief in fellowship, a need to be close. When I was a kid, I used to imagine myself sealed inside an automobile behind a one-way windshield. I could see out and no one could see in. I tried to navigate my way through life, separate and safe, while Bobby—I'm sure—even as a boy, never saw the individual cars, just the shared highway headed out to a shared sky.

Thanksgiving morning, we left San Francisco before dawn and drove north, speeding through forests where the wind smelled of spruce and pine and blew away the backseat aroma of wet dog. We'd left Plato behind in the care of friends. Fine with me. It was Bobby who loved dogs. We stopped for chowder and loganberry pie, for cups of hot coffee, in joints where the jukebox played lumberjack songs. Bobby left generous tips. My last paycheck was going fast, but I didn't mind. It was Thanksgiving, I was with Bobby, we were going to spend the holidays with his best friend in Eugene. It was 1980, I was over thirty and my life was finally settled. I finally had some stuff to be thankful for.

We drove through little Oregon towns with their tended lawns and American flags, yards full of hazelnut trees and manzanita shrubs and grass that was still green in patches in the strange mild November air. Latticework at the foundations of the houses, sloping cellar doors, and station wagons parked in driveways. It was really not so very different from Maple Hill, where I grew up, three thousand miles away. Except, of course, the Oregon houses were dwarfed and low; west of the Rockies, decent people don't climb stairs. The dogs out West were different, too: the retrievers and setters that lay on their Oregon doorsteps, unleashed, looked at us with mellow eyes and never tried to chase the car. Back home in Maple Hill the canines tended to be highstrung. I used to throw snowballs at the collie at the corner of Annandale Drive just to see it fling itself, hard, against the white picket fence. Hysteria, that was the

East, along with the maples and elms, all those green and thickly leafed boughs overhanging the boulevards.

Really, Maple Hill hadn't been so bad. I had run away because I had been bad. Bobby would have been happy in Maple Hill. He fit in everywhere and he always had friends.

When we met, I could tell I shocked him a little, so I told him a lot of stories about myself to shock him a lot. My checkered past only seemed to increase the value he put on my soul. "You're a cynic because you're a romantic who's too easily hurt," Bobby told me. It wasn't terribly original or profound, but no one else had ever bothered to say it, not even as a line or a come-on. Bobby didn't come on at all. He never wanted to come upstairs with me at night. "Don't rush it," he said. "I want this to be the normal adolescence you never had."

When we finally spent the night together, he was very reserved. It wasn't very good, so I was surprised in the morning when he held me close and said, "Stay with me, Joanie. This is your home." Maybe that was how decent people did it, I thought. But I was sure it would get better and so I stayed. Now, after a year and a half, we were good friends, if not much else, and I didn't want to lose him.

In Eugene, Oregon, Larry met us on his front porch, naked except for a black bow tie. It was going to be a formal Thanksgiving. He opened his arms wide for Bobby's hug.

"Hey man, what's new?"

"Nothing, man, nothing," said Larry, with a beatific smile.

Bobby laughed silently. A lot of blond men do that. They just open their mouths enough to show their teeth. No sound, just a little expulsion of air, like a belching lion. I had only recently started to notice that Bobby touched his beard a lot with his fingers and watched himself in the mirror while talking on the phone.

"Well, come on in and take your clothes off," said Larry. Bobby gave me his "Now-don't-start-getting-Eastern-on-us" look. Easterners were violent because they ate red meat. Coffee made them sarcastic and mean. "Getting Eastern on us" meant I would have preferred a real gobbler with stuffing rather than mock turkey made of tofu. It also meant I associated nakedness with sex, that I couldn't see Bobby's body without wanting him. We hadn't made love in months.

Bobby said I'd had too many men and he wanted me to learn that love went beyond desire. I could see his point, but how much longer would we have to live this way, never touching at night anymore, naked in bed? Sometimes I suspected it was not really a matter of philosophy or for my own good. On a ranch in Texas once with one of those too many men, I had learned that among physically perfect bulls, 15% show absolutely no interest in sex. And that's without complexes, religious upbringing or fear of commitment. Those bulls end up as shoes and leather bags since they're not good for anything else; sometimes at night, I admit I imagined Bobby facing the butcher.

And I hadn't had too many men. You didn't *have* someone just because he jammed you. Before I met Bobby, I'd been in love twice and had sworn never again. Love was tyranny. It was like religion, a great subject for art but the cause of nothing on earth but misery and war. Like religion, some people couldn't seem to do without it, but from the time I was nineteen years old I had decided you could count Joanie Fein out of all that. Till Bobby.

Anyway, it wasn't men I'd known before him, but ceilings. By the time I moved into his house, I couldn't remember the others, not their bodies and not their names, only the falling plaster, the water stain in the shape of a frog, mirrors and cherubs, a nipple where a chandelier used to hang, Peter Max posters, paper lanterns, signs of the zodiac painted in day-glo. I'd looked up at ornamental moldings, grapes, ventilation ducts, paper stars pasted against discolored spackling, dome lights of automobiles, rain spattering on filthy skylights, the night sky.

"Love is different from all that," Bobby said, and of course he was right, but no one knew it better than I did.

I washed up in the bathroom. The soap was homemade. I undressed and joined the others.

The kids were all outside running around. They'd already been fed and had been sent out to play. I watched from the window while the boys sprayed each other with streams of piss and the girls sat on the sidelines with nothing to do.

There were handmade candles on the table. I helped Larry's girlfriend Terry set places for twelve. Terry had made all the plates and wine goblets on her potter's wheel and painted them by hand. The napkins were embroidered; the napkin rings were macramé. No wonder none of Bobby's friends had time for jobs.

I was out of a job again myself. I'd been working for an agency that sent people around in vans to visit elderly shut-ins and give them rubdowns.

"I get it," said Terry. "Feels on Wheels."

I laughed along with her, but funding had run out and the program was being closed down, so it wasn't very funny.

Terry was fat, which made me less self-conscious about my own body. The first thing men notice about me are my breasts, which are big and which, I hope, distract attention from the fact that I have no hips and no ass. Someday, some engineer will explain to me how I walk without tipping over on my face. There was nothing to be self-conscious about anyway. The men were in the kitchen, talking and laughing. No one was looking at me. Maybe they'd prefer Terry anyway. Some guys like fat women, and Terry carried herself with style, flaunting her size instead of shrinking inside her flesh. She looked soft, ample, but at the same time pretty firm. She could be a real turn-on to a certain kind of guy. When the naked men finished their kitchen caucus and joined us in the diningroom I took a quick look. The small penises hung like red little babies' fists; the long ones flapped, out of use but not forgotten.

All these naked people, the men in black ties, the women—or "ladies," as they say out West—in nothing but their silver and turquoise, rings on all their fingers and Indian jewelry circling their bare arms. All these bodies, and no one seemed to notice them but me. Men with tanned buttocks, West Coast men who'd never had a skin rash. Women who didn't need to shave their legs. I kept staring at their laid-back legs, downy blond hairs below the knee and a few wisps and curls at the thigh. Nakedness was natural. But so was sex, I thought.

But the main thing about these people was, they were all so nice. And nice people, really nice people, don't have to hide inside their clothes. I suspected I still was not reformed. It wasn't their nudity that bothered me; I just still find nice people very hard to take.

As we went to the table I reached for Bobby's hand. His fingers brushed mine lightly and then I saw him jiggling his head around on his shoulders. It always irritated me when he did that, and anger—Eastern anger—made my guts get tight. Don't get excited, I told myself. He's just doing an exercise. It's just to relax his neck. What are you making such a big deal of it for? Because what the hell was he so tense about? He was nervous as a man who's not telling the truth.

We all joined hands for a blessing and then Larry carved the beancurd. Bobby poured me some wine, which fortunately was the real thing.

"Joanie's originally from New York," he informed the crowd.

"Really? City?" asked a blonde, smiling at me like an angel from outer space. Her freckled face dissolved into the ether. Her voice was a breathy whisper. "Are there really eight million people there?"

"Just about."

"Wow. New Yorkers must be really smart," she said, "to remember all those names."

Bobby stroked his beard. "She's not from the city. She's from Maple Hill. You know—Westchester County. Scarsdale. New Rochelle. Doctors. Lawyers. White picket fences."

"A real live JAP!" said Larry, pouring me some more wine. "I've never met one before."

"Hey, I've never been in Bloomingdale's," I protested. "Even to shoplift."

"Hey hey hey," said Larry.

Doctors. Lawyers. Bloomingdale's. I thought of my father, working behind the counter at Hi-Tops Discount House. The manager would get on the PA system and turn up the volume, Jimi Hendrix-style. "Attention All Shoppers! For the next ten minutes and ten minutes only, all Hamilton Beach electric blenders will be on sale at the small appliance department in Wing B." My father would take a deep breath—heroic, the way I imagined a fireman would do before running into a burning building. "And are you ready for this, shoppers? An additional 10% off to the first five customers! Now, on your mark, get set, GO!" and then I'd lose sight of Dad behind the stampede of bargain hunters from the Bronx.

The space angel smiled at me. "Michael takes me to the sauna when I get busted shoplifting. So I can feel clean again."

Which one was Michael? Did it matter? I just wanted to like Bobby's friends.

"The problem with you New Yorkers," said someone, "is that you're too touchy."

"And you always want to discuss everything," said Terry.

Larry turned up the radio so we wouldn't have to talk.

After dinner, we got dressed and drove downtown to the co-ed sauna and got undressed again. I couldn't take my eyes off Bobby's body, glowing in the mist. The steam was heavier on my chest than a man. I watched Bobby scrub the space angel's back and I tried to see if he was getting hard. I couldn't breathe. The others, they all lay on the benches, sweating. They had to come here, I thought, because none of them would ever work hard enough or love hard enough to work up a sweat on their own. They seemed happy. I watched the little boys strut around.

"Hotter," Larry demanded. "More heat."

When we got back to the house it was dark and the stars were out and the air was still warm. We stretched out our sleeping bags in the backyard and Terri hooked up the outdoor speakers. The radio blared an upbeat instrumental version of "Raindrops Keep Falling on My Head." The Fuller Brush Man stopped by and delivered some loose joints. He looked nice too—the kind of drug dealer who sends Christmas cards. I wanted Bobby. I wanted to hold him and I wanted him inside of me so bad.

I was going to be 32 and couldn't waste time. I saw old bodies all day, old skin that I rubbed with lotion to keep it from tearing, skin that didn't adhere to its flesh, that made me think of the way Bobby used to pull back the skin on a chicken breast to stuff it with shallots and sausage, back in the days when I first met him and he still ate meat. Time was running out. The first time I massaged Mrs. Hernandez, she started to shake. "Do you know how long it's been since someone touched me?" she asked.

When I tried to explain it to Bobby, he froze and jiggled his head. "You want to have a baby," he said.

"No, that's not what I mean about time."

"You don't want a baby?"

"No."

"Well, I do," he said, and he started to cry.

Bobby didn't really want a baby. He couldn't even take care of himself, but he started to call our lovemaking sterile and obscene. Now, in Larry and

Terry's backyard, I watched him tossing someone else's baby in the air and cooing at it. Larry sat nearby, his lotus position gone into a slump as he talked about his sorrow. After winning the custody fight against his ex-wife, he'd left his kids in Iowa with some friends.

So his love hadn't been sterile. Just careless. I sat there, critical and apart.

I went inside the bathroom, to get away from these people and to throw cold water on my face. The water helped, but what really revived me was the idea that I didn't have to go back outside. In the kitchen, I poured myself some more wine. Someone's child was wandering around the living room, half-dressed. He'd managed his jeans OK, but was having trouble with his denim shirt.

"Hey, I'll help you with the buttons," I said. He reminded me of myself when I was a kid—very sure of himself, but confused at everyone else. He didn't belong with the people outside either.

"C'mere," I said.

He glared at me. "I'm looking for something to destroy."

He stalked off and I laughed. Yeah, he was just like me. For years, whenever I *did* anything, it seemed to be destructive, till I finally scared myself and stopped doing it. These days, I was trying to go with the flow. It wasn't easy. Right now, for example, I wanted to wring Bobby's neck.

I stumbled into someone's bedroom, but how could I sleep? It was just like I'd always known. Love was the old shell game, and Bobby was making me reach for a prize that wasn't there. I'd been better off when I could still take sex like whiskey, when it went down so warm and easy and made me feel so good and it didn't matter what bottle it came from.

Outside the house, he was howling at the moon, the joker. He was a fool, but I loved him. I lay on someone's bed and my body convulsed with pain. Everybody loved everybody here. It was in the environment, it was bullshit. It had me, all that toxic love, building up without mercy in all my cells.

In the morning, Larry found me in the bedroom. "I could do a lot for you," he said, and I thought it would serve Bobby right if we did. "For your financial planning."

"That's not what I need," I told him.

"You'd be surprised. I only charge $25 for the initial consultation. Do you know the advantages of an IRA or a Keogh plan? Do you even know if you qualify for foodstamps?"

Bobby and Terry woke up. Everyone else was gone, and Larry decided we should drive into the Coastal Range. I wanted to stay behind. I'd had enough driving and I'd had enough of their company. Maybe with no one else around I could get some sleep.

Terry took me by the arm and gave me two aspirin and some Maalox. "Come on, you'll feel better."

I could have used a beer, a shot of whiskey to clear my head, but there was nothing but Yago Sangría, six-packs of the stuff, sweet enough to make you sick. We passed the bottles around in the car and I drank some anyway.

We entered the rainforest, ground snow melting in the sun and rising into mist. Clouds brushed and parted on the windshield and it was beautiful, it was so beautiful, but now, for me, beauty was just not going to be enough. Bobby was singing songs, telling jokes, making his friends' eyes glow. For a Westerner, he had energy, a limitless supply of funny stories. He'd never grown up and everyone always loved him, even someone like me who was supposed to be immune.

What are you going to do? What are you going to do? It was an old question. I'd thought Bobby had supplied the answer, but now the question was back. It started in '68, senior year at McKinley High. I graduated, and what was I going to do? I got a job at the StopNShop and lived at home, paying my parents room and board and letting boys in leather jackets take turns with me in the backseats of their cars. What are you going to do? My parents badgered me about going to secretarial school, and I said no, and hung around waiting for my life to change. Then I threw some clothes into a drawstring laundry bag, left a note for my parents, and got on the Greyhound bus alone. That was a long time ago—ten, twelve years. What are you going to do? How are you going to change your life? The ringing in my ears didn't stop until I met Bobby.

Bobby believed his life was his work and he watched himself unfold with fascination. "You can express yourself just by living," he said, and I wondered if that was what I'd been doing all along. Other people created real art. Terry made raku pottery, the surface covered with cracks. The flaws didn't threaten to destroy the pot, she explained, they created the design. "A good description of Bobby's character," she added. Then she put an arm around me. "Hey, he's a wonderful man," she said, "but don't pin any expectations on him."

"Hey," I repeated, squeezing her shoulder, "all I ever expect is trouble."

Bobby had been good to me. He had tried to reform me, to teach me self-discipline and how to care about other people. He tried to make me clean, but now that he'd made me value love, I wanted it. He'd made me start to value myself, and so the old ringing in the ears was back. What was I going to do?

Spruce trees closed around us and spears of sunlight dazzled my eyes, sparking off the melting snow and glinting in the rocky shallows of creeks. On the curve we passed a red VW, a blonde driving, her long hair tied back beneath a red bandana.

"Pussy!" hollered Bobby. "I need some pussy!"

His friends laughed.

"Aooooow! I need to get laid!"

My pain moved higher, all the way to my heart. Why was he doing this to me? Why was he such a clown? Out in the backyard the evening before, he had stretched in his bag next to Larry and I could hear him talking, in a revery about some old girlfriend, her marble breasts and her satin twat.

If he didn't want me, why not let me go? But no, he'd hold me and we'd rock back and forth in each other's arms. When I worked at the State Hospital, the patients rocked too, the poor lunatics finding it a comfort, an empty comfort, but one you couldn't let go. Bobby would never let go. "I can't live without you," he said. "I've never been so close to a woman before."

Larry parked in a ditch and we climbed out of the car, Larry, Terry, and Bobby with their arms around each other. I lagged behind, watching a muskrat splash over the bank, watching the snow melt and drop like rain from the vines and moss. Then I trotted behind the others, over a wooden plank bridge and out to a clearing where the sun had already dried the grass and the bright light made my head throb. We passed around a joint. I don't smoke much anymore, but I took a few tokes. Bobby was whispering something to Terry and she was laughing. He hadn't so much as looked at me.

I wandered off. They didn't even see me go. They didn't like me anyway, his friends. I was an Easterner, stubborn, wrapped up in my own alienation, refusing to join the communal life and relinquish my ego to the stars. I climbed a hill, following elk tracks. Looking back, I saw Bobby and his friends, Bobby in his plaid jacket, the other two in matching parkas. They were so happy, sitting crosslegged and at ease while a chipmunk ate from Bobby's hand. There were wild birds stepping so close around him, it seemed they might brush up against his legs, sleek as cats. The sun wove its gold in his hair. My own hair still smelled of hemp and, down in the clearing, smoke still rose like incense. I watched the three of them pass the joint around their circle. They looked so young. I wanted to rub my hand against Bobby's cheek. I wanted to lie down with him by the creek and make love. He held up his hand and a bird landed on his wrist. I, alone, had been kicked out of Paradise. I watched them and I wanted to die.

They were eating sandwiches when I returned to join them—tuna salad on homemade whole grain bread, sloppy with mayonnaise and heavy as stone. My stomach couldn't handle it so I settled for more wine. After a year and a half with Bobby, I just wasn't tough anymore.

"You were gone a long time," said Larry, but it wasn't the accusation I expected. He spoke with respect. OK, I get it: I'd gone off like Thoreau, the only Easterner worth his salt, to commune with nature, solitary and alone. What did these people really know? I'd communed with the only nature I knew well, lying on a flat rock and fingering myself, proving that I didn't need Bobby—or anyone, damn it. But I did. I worked up a desperate little orgasm, like retching on an empty stomach. It had all been so easy once.

When the food was gone, Terry started blowing into the top of her sangría bottle, making it toot, and Larry opened up his backpack and took out the wooden case. He opened the latch. There was his .45, and an ivory-handled pistol, and a .44 Magnum—Dirty Harry's gun, he said. Back when I was a teenager, I used to imagine getting my hands on a gun with silver bullets, a magical gun that let you kill anyone you wanted without getting caught. I used to think about having that gun and make lists of the people I would kill. Back then, I played a lot of violent games. Some of them weren't hypothetical, and that was all a part of what Bobby was supposed to save me from, what I was trying to leave behind.

Larry caught the look on my face. "Easterner," he said.

He was right. Back east, everyone was so uptight. They were all busy drawing lines, defining categories, putting people in pigeonholes. In high school, you got a label: collegiate or hippie or greaser. If you drank vodka, you couldn't smoke dope. If you ate beancurd, you couldn't own guns. I had carried all that with me—Maple Hill's logic and rules. Larry was free.

"You've got to respect firearms," he was telling me. "As long as you have no violent impulse towards your fellow man, as long as you know what you're doing, no one gets hurt."

"Look, man," I said, "we're all high."

"Inexperience is the killer," he said. "These family picnics where Mary Lou picks up a gun for the first time and it goes off and Uncle Aloysius drops dead. When you're raised knowing how to handle a gun . . ."

"I don't think we ought to . . ."

Larry loaded up. He kept Dirty Harry's gun, Terry took the pistol and he gave Bobby the .45. It was my job to put the empties back in the cartons and carry them along. I didn't want to be part of this, but I followed Larry up the hill. He set up the empties on the rock where I'd been lying, thrashing about, touching myself and wanting to die. Then we stepped back. Larry took aim, both arms held out rigid before him. He fired and the first bottle shattered.

"Someone could be hiking up behind the rock," I said. It was an effort to speak, with my head pounding and my throat so tight and dry. "We'd never see him in time."

No one seemed to hear. Terry took the next shot and missed. "Motherfucker," she said. "Anyone got a joint?"

Bobby let out a warwhoop and fired in the air. I loved him for that, refusing to take aim, refusing to take the chance of hitting anything. Bobby couldn't pluck the petals off a daisy. He wouldn't swat a mosquito sucking happily at his arm. That's why I loved him, but why couldn't he be a man?

It was Larry's turn again. He sighted carefully. He had no violent impulse towards his fellow man. I wondered if that made him normal and made me bad, that I had impulses I fought to control. It seemed strange that no one here had guessed about me.

The explosions rocked the hills. Even the dripping moss and the melting snow couldn't absorb all the sound. I had refused to wear the earplugs Larry offered me. It was too much complicity. I really didn't want to be part of this at all. There seemed to be water, water melting and rushing everywhere, and bang bang bang echoing in my stomach. It must have sounded like this when the Titanic hit the ice, I thought, and there was nothing I could do to stop it. Disaster ahead, but let it crash. I wouldn't mind sinking. There was nowhere else to go. I didn't want any part of my old life anymore, but I was tired of Bobby's world, of holding everything inside, being half-dead, holding back to please him. I couldn't please him anyway. He'd torn me open to put a heart inside my empty chest. He'd made me whole only to withdraw and leave me more worthless than ever. He made me let him in, to fill me and become the center of my life, and now he didn't want me. If only the earth would open up and let me plunge to my death. Such things did happen. Why not here? Or some bough, some bough might drop its snow over us, or an avalanche. I wanted to die. And why? Why should I die? It wasn't my fault. I was miserable, but it was all because of Bobby. Why did he have friends like this and why did he treat me this way? Why didn't he love me? Why couldn't he be a man?

They were all looking at me. Larry reloaded his gun.

"How about it, Easterner? Want to try?"

"No."

They were staring at me, Terry and Larry. Not Bobby. He was making clicking sounds, trying to call a squirrel. He loved the Universe. He loved everyone but me.

"The people who talk gun control don't even know what it's about," said Larry.

How could I let him give me the gun now when I wanted to die? I wasn't sure what I might do with a loaded gun. But why should I be the one to die? I didn't know anything about guns, I was drunk and stoned and unhappy and I hadn't slept and it was all Bobby's fault. Larry was forcing it into my hands, but it was Bobby who was forcing me. He wouldn't let me go. He held me and rocked me and said I was wrong to want more and then he jiggled his head. He told me how to live my life and then he climbed on top of me and said, "Lie still, Joanie, don't move." Everything had been so good, and then he changed. He was wrong. He had to be. It couldn't be right, how I felt him shrink inside me when I moaned. And still I didn't know how to leave him. But with Dirty Harry's gun I could get away. And get away with it. The Oregon police were used to this sort of thing, an accident at a family picnic. Larry and Terry didn't believe in accidents, only designs in the cosmic web. It wouldn't be murder. It would just be one of those things. Larry put the gun with silver bullets into my hands.

Bobby was beside me and I could hear him through the ringing in my ears. *Stop me*, I thought. *Please stop me.* "All right, Joanie," he said. "Let's see what you can do." The object in my hands was heavy and the metal cold. I could pull the trigger and send someone I loved to a far-off place, out of reach and then he wouldn't be able to hold me and rock me and ask me to stay. He wouldn't be able to turn away from me anymore. I turned to look at Bobby. He would stop me. He really did love me and so he would have to stop me. But he was already distracted. I was already forgotten. He was craning his neck, looking at the sky, maybe trying to spot a hawk. I could look straight up into the blue, and the tops of the spruce formed the bottom fringe of the world, and lower, even lower, was Bobby, who'd never really wanted to be of this earth.

I fired, seized from outside, one shot after another. The gun was a living thing in my hands, an extension of myself that I had to try and control, but it bucked up, hot and alive, with a will of its own. So this was why they loved their guns and their cocks, the bastards, and I squeezed six times while the gun jerked, shooting fire, and Larry was slamming me on the back because the remaining bottles were gone.

Where was Bobby? We should be throwing our arms around each other in triumph. He'd set me up for the final test, and I'd passed. I'd really believed I was ready to kill him, but I wasn't capable of it after all.

We climbed to the rock and examined the shattered glass. It would be a long time till someone used the place again as a bed. I picked up some bullet fragments, sharp, twisted bits of copper, and dropped them in my pocket—solid proof that I could trust myself. I wasn't really bad.

On the ride back to Larry and Terry's, Bobby dozed off in the car and fell towards me. I cradled his head and let him lie in my lap, but he woke abruptly and jerked himself away, pressed up against the door like a dog. What the hell was the matter with him anyway? I reached into my pocket to jab my finger and remind myself that I could never really hurt him.

The next day we left Oregon. We had just crossed the California line when I realized how lucky we'd been. I reached out and touched Bobby's arm. He kept staring straight ahead, at the van less than a car length away.

I said, "I'd better go home to New York."

He didn't answer at first, trying to think of the right thing to say, and I knew he was right to be careful.

I had to go home, because I couldn't be trusted after all. I had to get away before something happened. It had been a toss-up in the woods, I could see that now, because I was angry again already. I was fuming mad. It had been close. If Bobby had said the wrong thing, if he'd dared say one word about pussy, one single word about love, I would have killed him. I would have blown his beautiful head into the high blue sky.

Taking Care

Louise A. Blum

Vivian tells me that she's sworn off men. She makes them sound like cigarettes. "I'm into women now," she says. "I mean, like totally." She leans toward me across the table. The light glints off her glasses, makes them look like gun barrels. "I mean, like you, Marion," she says.

I take a sip of my coffee. The light in the restaurant is too bright; we are lit up as if we are on stage. Vivian's cheekbones glow like a fever. "I thought you were straight," I say.

She leans still closer to me. "I'm reformed," she says, and smiles.

Other people have reformed themselves on me, usually in the other direction. Usually people go straight, all of a sudden, like giving up drugs, or getting religion. Like it came to them in their sleep, or as the result of a vision quest or something. You think you know a person, and then one morning you wake up and they've shape shifted into someone else, and they kiss you politely on the forehead and let themselves out the door, go on to their new life. And you lie there in your bed alone and worry that it might happen to you too, wonder why it is that you're the same person all the time, a woman loving women, a girl who digs girls, like the title of a porno movie I've seen in the back room of our little local video store but never had the nerve to rent, why it is that events and people don't really sway you, the real thing is there all the time, like a part of your skin, a thing that other people put on and take off like winter jackets. You lie there in your bed hearing the door shut on your blessed privacy and pull the blankets up to your chin and lie as still as you can, awaiting transformation, a new configuration, some sign that you too might change, that the one thing that you have always counted on, the one gift you thought you had, might dissolve and slip through your fingers like sand. You lie there, bleeding, and wait to heal.

The day had started out simple and grey, just like any other day, an ordinary day moving toward fall. I'd had my three cups of coffee, walked the dog and put him on his run in the back yard, fed the cats, even though they didn't need it; they sit there like those roly toys that you can poke with a finger and they come right back up, I got my jacket and took my last cup of coffee out to my car with me and drove to work. The neighborhood I live in is a quiet one, lined with trees and, this morning, bags of garbage, an occasional old chair. My neighbors keep to themselves, nod hello to me, but save their real warmth for Grady, my dog, whom they greet as if he'd just had them over for dinner. On my way to work I passed the usual little kids, going to school, dragging book bags and bad attitudes, one or two of them waving when they saw me. They, too, know me for my dog. They calculate his age in people years and determine it's near theirs; they come out of their houses even if they're eating dinner when they see me walking by, ask if they can pet the dog. I watch them pat his head, stroke his ears, touch his whiskers with tentative fingers still pudgy with baby fat. I stand there and watch them and think sometimes of how different my life would be if I had one of them, instead of just my dog and my cats, if I had a child to shape and to raise, to suffer and rejoice with. About that time, I usually pull Grady away and say good-bye.

Some things are better left alone.

But there was nothing unusual about this particular morning—I drove to work on the usual streets, took the usual detours, saw the usual people, got to the place where I work, a small and less than enterprising ad agency, a few minutes after nine. My coffee was still warm. I breezed in in a short skirt, said hello to the secretary, headed to my desk, sorted through my mail, my various lists of things to do. The boss tramped through my space on his way to his office, looking like his stomach was off. There was nothing to suggest that it would be anything other than an ordinary day. There was nothing to indicate that my life might change, earthquake fashion, to something unrecognizable to anyone. Nothing at all, that is, until Vivian called, to invite me to lunch—her treat.

I meet her in a restaurant on Main Street. It is just a diner; there is nothing about it to tempt you to call it anything else, like a cafe, or a bistro, or a bar. It is even stretching it to call it a restaurant, since it closes every day at 3:00 p.m. Vivian has ordered a second breakfast, scrambled eggs and home fries, a bagel and cream cheese, coffee that she doses liberally with half and half. I can't imagine what her cholesterol level is. She's got a booth in the back; she flirts with the waitresses, who keep her coffee coming. She is a tall woman with short wavy hair and well-defined upper arms. She works out at the gym; she goes there every day. She's wearing a sleeveless black turtleneck; her wrists are heavy with bracelets. I can see her muscles ripple when she dips her knife into the cream cheese and spreads it on the bagel. When she looks at me she smiles;

she has this space between her front teeth that's big enough to slide a quarter in. She's full of little imperfections like that, glasses, freckles, moles, a tiny raspberry birthmark on her forehead. Her shoulders are bony, pure enviable bone plainly visible inside the collars of her blouses, and her legs are muscular. She wears hip-hugging straight skirts and pantyhose, high heels that never impede her step. Today she looks like she couldn't sweat if she tried, but I know she plays basketball every Saturday with the high school age boys on her block. She teaches them English during the week, grades their compositions with her cheeks sucked in, then muscles them out of her space on the court on the weekends. She does everything flawlessly, dresses impeccably, and has always been, without question, absolutely, irrevocably straight.

Until today.

I take another sip of my diet soda, pick at my salad. I try to eat healthily, watch my fat intake. God knows why. Vivian across the table just sits and waits. "So, what brought this on?" I say, brightly. I could be talking about a bout of the flu.

Vivian sighs, brushes her hair back from her face with fingers as long and fine as pencil leads. "I don't know," she says. "I just can't stop looking at women."

I push my salad around my plate with my fork. "Most people can't," I say. "It's in our culture." I do, after all, work in advertising.

Vivian leans forward, locks me with her big, dark eyes so that I can't look away. "I'm serious," she says. "It's you," she says. "I can't stop looking at you."

I can feel myself start to sweat. No way, I think. I like my life. I like my apartment. I like opening the door at night and being greeted only by small animals who love me with exuberance and the only thing I have to do is feed them. Her face is only a few inches from mine. Her lips look like fruit, like deep red plums, ripe in their skins, aching to be bitten. I am wondering what I should do when she leans forward and kisses me, right out of the blue, right there in the restaurant, in full view of the waitresses, then gets up and grabs her purse and the check. "Come over tonight for a drink," she calls back over her shoulder. Her hips sway when she walks. "Around eight," she says.

I go back to work and am useless until 5:00, when the boss walks back through my cubicle on his way out, his step heavy as death, his shoulders slumped, shaking his head. I grab my coffee cup, ringed with the morning's crud, and my jacket, snap off my computer and race for the door. My job means nothing to me, and I like it that way. I turn it on at 9:00 and turn it off at 5:00, same as my computer. I never take it home. I don't, after all, have any aspirations to be the world's best advertising agent. And in a town this size there wouldn't be much room for it anyway.

Vivian sends off every alarm bell in my body. Don't fall for it, I think. She's only playing around, I think. She thinks it's a game, like sexuality is something you can switch on and off like a light bulb. Not like me. I've been a lesbian since the second grade, when I first saw Jennie Anderson walk down the hallway and bend over the water fountain for a drink, catching up her long blonde hair first with one hand and holding it back from her face so that her cheek and neck were exposed, her lips pursed, her tongue drawing the stream of water into her mouth. It never occurred to me that there might be a problem with that. Jennie Anderson didn't seem to mind either, when we were playing doctor together later that week, and she lost some of her virginity to my littlest finger, greased with vaseline. I've never slept with a man, never even gone out with one. I knew from day one that it was girls who turned me on.

I always watched girls. I was the last kid in the neighborhood to give up playing doctor. I watched them all the time, the same way they watched boys. I took stock of their haircuts, their breast development, their ventures into makeup. I watched them move. They had grace in their wrists, energy in their steps. I loved them all. And some of them loved me back.

I drive back home, stopping for each of the three traffic lights that adorn our streets, turn down Maple, past the high school where Vivian teaches composition in her horn-rimmed glasses and her bright painted nails. Vivian. Who does she think she is, anyway? She's into women now? Now? She's talking about my life. She's talking about the reasons why I buried myself in this town, wrapped my solitary life around my shoulders like a shawl and slammed my door shut with one foot, surrounding myself with cats.

She's into women.

Of course, when was the last time I was into one?

I get home at 5:05; the stoplights slowed me down. Usually I have them timed. I could walk to work, but I never seem to have the energy. I'd have to wear more sensible shoes. Like Vivian, who hikes to work in her running shoes and then changes in the teacher's lounge to arch-crushing pumps that make her legs look long as phone poles. But I'm trying not to think about Vivian. I've been doing fine on my own, ever since Renee left.

Renee and I were together for three years. She had long, straight hair and bangs that nearly hid her eyes, which were such a pale blue they were nearly white. She was a nurse at the hospital—I met her one day when I was helping them do a PR campaign. She walked by me quickly in the hall, carrying a clipboard, her head down and her eyes straight ahead. I watched her walk all the way down the hall—she had a step like an angel's. For a moment I forgot where I was, just lost myself in her walk, the bend of her rubber-soled shoes as they hit the floor and lifted off, the movement of her hips in her tight, white uniform. When I came back to the present, the head nurse was watching me, her eyes as hard as pavement.

Renee was a couple years younger than I was. I kept finding excuses to go back to the hospital and check on the project till I finally hit her on her break.

I fit the key into the lock and push open the door, shove it shut behind me with a shoulder. My home is dark as a cave, silent as the night. The cats ring round me like a fan club. They ask nothing more of me than I can safely give, a half a cup of food two times a day, and in return they'll curl themselves around my head and knead my neck for hours.

Not a bad trade.

Grady bounds into the front room with all the grace of a bulldozer, his tail knocking a lamp to one side. From the blanket fuzz on the side of his face, he was probably sleeping on my bed. He knows he's not supposed to do that. I feed the cats, pull off my clothes and slip on my sweatpants and an old sweatshirt, tennis shoes. I catch a glimpse of my body in the mirror. It's not bad. A little short, but thin. My breasts are full and my stomach is flat. There is a line of hair that runs from my navel down to my crotch. Renee called it an arrow pointing home. I wonder what Vivian would say about it.

I slam the bathroom door shut, hiding the mirror.

I get Grady's leash and take him for a walk. We stretch it out for as long as possible, but there's only so many streets in this town. I walk fast; Grady pants along beside me, foolishly pleased. He doesn't know yet that he's going to spend the evening alone with the cats while I go out. I pat his head. He looks up at me as if he had forgotten I was there. He's a very independent dog. Sometimes I think that if I were replaced with someone else he wouldn't notice. As long as the food kept coming and the walks kept happening. I pull on his choke collar when we get to the curb and we wait for the light to change.

Grady was a present from Renee, just before she broke up with me. You'd think I would have seen it coming—a tiny, fluffy, black and white dog with no more form than a crumpled handkerchief, lying helpless in a wicker basket, making my heart melt on the first sight of him. I'd lifted him up and had him in my arms before I knew what was happening. His head fit naturally into the curve of my throat. I'd looked up at Renee, my eyes misting, and then I saw her face. I knew it before she even said a word; I could see it in her eyes—it was like she'd slammed a steel gate between us, locked it shut and slipped the key into her mouth, swallowed it down before I could stop her.

"Marion," she said. "I've met someone else."

I kept Grady up against my chest like a shield across my heart, held him tight as if I thought that that might ward the pain off, tried to make my voice light, but the words came out as hard as hammer blows. "Do I know her?" I asked.

"Marion," she said, "it's a man." It was the pity in her voice I couldn't take; I had no defenses against it. I had no defenses against anything. It was spring outside; the streets were damp with rain, glistening in the sun. Flowers were pushing through the soil. New life was everywhere, right down to the puppy who lay in my arms as if he'd never leave me, as if he'd live his life by my side until he had nothing left to live with. She'd already packed her things. She turned and waved before she shut the garden gate, an unsteady wave, as if she were afraid to leave me.

I shut the door after she left, put some water down for the puppy, got some food out for the cats. I turned off the porch light, locked the door, put on some music, Bonnie Raitt, or something. Who am I kidding? I know it was Bonnie Raitt. I remember exactly. I remember every moment of that night. I remember locking the door and turning around and the kitchen counter coming at me in a rush, I remember grabbing hold of it like a football, squeezing it with my hands as if I could wring my anguish from it. I remember cupping my face in my hands and thinking I would never let it go again.

It was Grady who brought me back to life, licking my hands in earnest concern, then pissing on the floor beside me.

When I take Grady back to the house he looks at me expectantly, as if to tell me he's looking forward to an evening on the couch with me, watching a video and sharing some popcorn. The cats rub against my ankles, reminding me how much they love me, how deeply hungry they've become in my absence. My house hums around me, familiar as a favorite shirt. I love my house; I love its tiny windows that give me so much privacy, I love its front porch with all my hanging fuchsia and the flower garden that covers most of my back yard. I love its carpeted floors and its ivory walls and its dark, stained wood trim. This is my house; it is clean, neat and absolutely mine.

When Renee moved out, I filled every room with incense, burned it round the clock. I vacuumed every rug, washed all the sheets and blankets and even the mattress pad. I turned the mattress, swept under the bed. I took the room she'd used as her study and painted it a rose so bright it nearly made me wince, moved the litter box into it, and Grady's bed, which he disdains, preferring to sleep as close to my bed as possible, on the off chance that I might sometime invite him up. I filled it full of pictures, vaginal-looking Georgia O'Keefe flowers, posters of Picasso nudes, vulnerable Degas shoulders that appeal to no one but me. I made a shrine out of it, a place of absolute perfection, then gave it to my cats to piss in. It was more my room than any other room in the house.

There was nothing of her left in it.

I had thought she was the last when she was with me; when she left I was sure of it. I had thought I'd spend the rest of my life with her, rubbing her feet after work, combing her hair before bed, slipping off her clothes and kissing her shoulders, lifting her long straight hair off her neck and kissing her throat, her chest, her breasts. Her nipples in my mouth tasted like berries, felt like salvation. Her ribs, the convex curve of her stomach, her belly button taking my tongue like a hungry mouth, the hair that curled between her legs. I loved the touch of her clitoris against my lips, I loved the taste of it beneath my tongue. I loved to put my mouth on her until she shuddered with it, then plunge my tongue inside her till she writhed with my touch, slip my fingers deep inside her and rock her to another life, till her moans lifted the room, lifted both of us, spinning us through time till there was nothing left but a glistening pool of come, dampening the sheets.

"You treated me like an icon," she said before she left. "Mark treats me like a woman."

I would have given her anything she asked for, if she'd only stayed in my life, stayed in my house. I would have found out from men how they treat a woman and done it for her. I would have done anything.

I would have changed my style. I would have treated her differently, just to touch her clitoris with my tongue and feel her whole body respond like I'd pushed a secret button.

"It's so much work," she said, "this taking turns. It takes all the spontaneity out of it."

I would have forfeited my turn, to give her hers.

Grady nuzzles my hand with his nose, pushes his body against my leg. Touch me, he begs, silently, hold me. I'll stay with you. I kneel on the kitchen floor, put my arms around him. I want nothing more than never to leave this house again; I want to stay here forever, secure with my cats, growing old with my dog. I like my life. I like my world. Oh, god, I want nothing less than to change it, nothing less than to say good-bye to my animals and to go out that door and lock it behind me, brave the changing wind that heralds the fall. I do not want a single thing to change around me. I do not want to lose track of it, this temple I have built around me. I do not want to fuck it up.

I arrive at Vivian's door promptly at 8:00. She has it open before I can even knock; she must have been watching through the eye-hole. She doesn't even ask me what I want, just hands me a glass of scotch on the rocks. Michelle Shocked plays in the background. I can see that we aren't going to waste any time. She opens the doors to the balcony, a warm fall breeze floats into the room, the curtains shift in the breeze. She arranges herself on her couch, suggestively. She is wearing a T-shirt and sweatpants; she could be wearing an evening dress, her body seems so exposed. Her feet are bare; they are so long they seem to go on forever. She has a runner's feet, thin and highly arched, propped up on the pillow at one end of her couch like a trophy. She clears her throat.

"So," she says. "How was your day?"

Oh, god. Her voice is harsh and compelling as Harvey Firestein's. I take a sip of scotch and remind myself again that I am single and proud of it. "Great," I say. "And yours?"

"I was distracted," she says, and looks at me. Her eyes are dark as rainclouds. Michelle's wail is a sanctuary into which I allow myself to sink, depthlessly, alone. "I was thinking about you," she says.

I set my glass down on the end table. "Look, Vivian," I say.

She interrupts me. "Come on, Marion," she says. "You're not with anyone now." She lifts her glass to her mouth and takes a sip. I swear I can see the scotch, traveling down her throat, mixing in her bloodstream, catapulting on a whim to her head and heart and stomach simultaneously. "How long has it been?" she says. Her eyes work witchcraft with my soul. I pick up my glass again, stiffly, play with the ice with one finger till I feel her eyes on it, then I fold my hands in my lap.

"That's immaterial," I say, politely. At least I try for courtesy. She only laughs at me.

"Is it?" she asks, and settles back into her pillows like a monarch, biding her time.

It has, in fact, been four years since Renee left me for Mark, a history teacher at the high school, a colleague of Vivian's. I'm not trying to break any records—I'm just taking care of myself. It is not so bad to be alone. I've bricked my life back up, mortared it down. It's a solid construction. I have left no cracks.

I have lived in this town all my life. Everyone probably knows about me, but they think I'm reformed—undergone that magical conversion that seems to come so easily to other people, like confirmation, or baptism. You say a few words, wave some incense and sprinkle some water and presto: a new order.

Renee and her husband have a baby now; they live in a house on the other side of town with two maple trees in the front yard. The trees keep it private. I still run into her sometimes in the grocery store, the baby gurgling in the cart. She always looks stricken when she sees me, as if I have some disease of which I can't be cured. "Marion," she always says, whispering, as if we just wouldn't want anyone to hear it, placing a hand on my arm, gently, as if I might break in her grasp. "How are you?" she always says. The worry in it kills me.

Oh, fine, I want to say. I didn't slit my throat when you left me so I'm not likely to now. But if you don't get away from me right now, I want to say, I might take this five-pound chicken out of the freezer and club you to death with it.

But I always smile, so tight I think my lips will crack, they're so unwilling to give it up, and nod, tersely, and push my cart on down the aisle.

"Let's get together sometime," she'll say, calling after me. "Mark and I will have you to dinner."

In your dreams, I think. I haven't been that close to a nuclear family since I left my own.

I have known Vivian since grade school, when her family moved in next door to mine. She was always straight. We never played those dark and secret games in the privacy of our rooms. We played catch together though, always by her request. I would have preferred something more intimate, a game of dolls in a bedroom somewhere, even a game of rummy on the floor in some corner. But Vivian preferred her spaces wide open, preferred to be outside, with a mitt in her hand, breaking world records, or at least pretending to. Her dad used to hit us balls in the evenings after supper. She always got them, throwing her long and angled body through the air right to the spot where they would land. I just watched her, standing there with my glove hanging impotently at my side, mesmerized by the poetry of her, sliding through the dirt, bruising with the contact. "Good going, Vivian," her dad always said, winking at me, the awkward one with the knees of her jeans still intact. "Hang in there, Marion," he'd say to me. "You'll catch up with her yet."

My father didn't play with me. He died of alcohol poisoning my sophomore year of high school. He'd never been around much. I got a job at the drugstore on the corner, stopped playing ball with Vivian, who seemed to have grown up anyway, all of a sudden; her straight lines transforming into curves that turned all the heads in town.

Not mine, though. I was too smart for that.

I was always too smart, to fall for things beyond my reach. At least, that was what I told myself.

Vivian looks at me, her eyes as deep and even as ocean waves, her body pulls me to her like a tide. "Come on," she says. "What are you afraid of?"

What am I afraid of? Good God, isn't it clear?

Vivian touches my hair, smoothes the wrinkles on my forehead with her fingers. "Marion," she says.

I look at her, feel my heart swelling up in my chest, feel a shaking deep inside like the tremors before a quake. "No," I say. "I can't," I say. I can barely hear the words myself.

"Marion," Vivian says. She reaches for my hands where I am twisting the hem of my sweater back and forth, closes her fingers around them and holds them in my lap, squeezes them tight. "I'm not kidding around," she says.

I look at her. I can barely see her through the fear. I don't want to get hurt. That is what I am thinking. I do not know if I say it aloud or not. There is such a roaring in my ears it is like there is an ocean in the room, sucking me down, threatening to hold me forever, drown me in my fear.

"Marion," Vivian says, holding my hands. "Even your cats are going to die sometime," she says.

I laugh despite myself, and she laughs with me, and then she is kissing me, kissing the tears from my cheeks, kissing my eyes, kissing my nose, kissing my lips, kissing me so deep I think that she is kissing my heart, mending it with her tongue, drawing the tremors right out through my skin, slipping her hand beneath my sweater and touching my breasts. I tense; I do not want to be her proving ground, her experiment, but her fingers on my nipples are soft and gentle, and she is still kissing me, and has been, for what must have been hours, and then I am just not thinking at all, and she is making love to me, as if she has known how to do it, all along.

When I wake she is holding me against her, her arms around my body, hugging me to her, her hands on my breasts. She holds me as if I were a child, her body curved around mine, her mouth against my hair, her breath soft and even against the back of my neck. It is like being in a fortress. Nothing can reach me—her body shields mine like a womb.

When I push back the covers, she reaches for me sleepily. "Where are you going?" she asks, mumbling into the pillow. Her hands pull at me, pull me back into the bed. I bend and kiss her, pull her tongue into my mouth and hold it there with mine, close my eyes and inhale her scent, memorize it.

"I have to feed the animals," I say. "Call me later."

I let myself out of her apartment, close the door behind me as softly as I can, slip down her stairs to the street where I'd parked my car the night before and it is like I'm walking on air. Everything looks different; the leaves seem to have changed overnight. The entire street is red and gold, a few people are up early, raking the leaves into piles on their lawns. I pull open the door of my car and throw my purse inside and it is like I am on fire. The air is growing colder and there is this snap in it that fills my lungs and clears them out, is drawn through my body like a cord, holding me tight. When I inhale, the air goes so deep inside my lungs it seems to lift me in my seat. I drive home with my window down and one arm hanging out and the radio on, and it is like I am dancing inside, to the music that I hear.

When I open the door to my house the cats curse me like sailors. Grady has controlled himself, but he throws me a stricken look as he hurls past me out the door to relieve himself in the yard. The cats follow me into the kitchen, swearing at me till I fill their bowls and then they fall silent, falling to their food. I kneel beside them, stroking their ears. I can still feel Vivian's fingers in my cunt. Every pore of my body feels alive, my breasts throb with the memory of her tongue. Exhilaration fills me. I put Rickie Lee Jones in the tape player and turn the volume up loud. The cats do not pause in their eating, do not notice me at all. I open the refrigerator and get out the coffee, make myself a pot and lean back against the kitchen counter, thinking of Vivian's eyes, closed, her throat arched, her mouth open in a wild scream that burst from her like a geyser, her pelvis raised and the hair of her cunt glistening like dew. I think of Vivian, holding me through the night, coating my hair with her breath.

The cats finish eating, rub against my ankles in forgiveness. Grady scratches at the door, still looking injured through the screen. I lean back against the counter, look around my house. The rooms are small, the ceilings low. The light is bad; the plants are drooping in their pots. The whole place could use a fresh coat of paint.

The phone rings and I pick it up in my hands and hold it to my face like flowers, like a baby, like one of my cats. I know it will be Vivian, and I think that I am ready for it, whatever happens next. Grady sighs through the door, settles himself on the step. The cats stretch out on the kitchen floor, close their eyes in harmony. All along the street the neighbors stir, throw back their bedsheets and stretch their bodies and pull on their robes to make their coffee, bring the paper into the house. Radios turn on and showers run and car engines start up. Everyone is rising, starting their day. Vivian's voice on the phone is clear as sunlight. "What are you doing today?" she asks, uncertainly.

"Spending it with you," I say. "Come over." When I hang up the phone, I get Grady's leash, open the front door and snap it to his collar, and together we move down the street, ushering in the day. I'll give this thing a shot, just to see what happens.

Jackie Boy

Jodi Varon

Her threads were all over the house, strands separated and skeins of unmatched colors, needles stuck into the arms on the sofa and in her reading chair, the floor near the footrest a web of colored strands. She had slides everywhere, of calypsos and prairie smoke, orchids and Indian pipe. The real worktable in the den was piled with needlepoint grids, and stacks of cushionless footstools, sanded, stained, some cracked and in need of repair, lined up against one wall of the den. In front of them the edges of her splattered canvas caught flecks of paint from the armoire she was stripping for one of Danny's customers.

We hadn't seen Danny since he hauled the armoire to our house for Penny to work on, the autumn afternoon the last alpenglow shone on a whole herd of grazing mule deer. We waited for him at Windy Boy Point, Penny, my mother, smoothing down my hair in the absent way she did when she was waiting for something to happen. It had been Danny's idea that we live there, in the crazy house high above the Blackfoot River, so he could hunt, I suppose, and have his place in the woods when he wanted to go there, though after a year most of our nights were filled with stillness in the house as Penny rocked while the wind bombarded the flue pipe outside. Up there every human thing was diminished and we stood eye to eye with the hawks hunting in the updrafts the cliff made.

Penny had said she loved the wild things, that they held no menace for her, the deer and hawks, the elk and her calf on the wash across the highway on Bonner Mountain. So she said yes when Danny asked if she'd move up on the ridge away from town, away from him, no rent, all the space she needed to do her work, away above the last long curve out of the canyon.

When I close my eyes, I can still feel my way along the suspension bridge across the river, the metal cables on the guardrail rough and cold, icing over with the sweat from my palms, the bridge rising and falling as Danny jumped up and down on it to demonstrate its strength. Penny put her hand on my back and pushed me forward, whispering, "cats on ice in summer," as she laughed at my fear.

The house itself was sunny and grand, open rooms and three fireplaces, but the trail up was a talus slide or three miles through the woods on a roughed-out road. We got used to the slide, the seven switchbacks and the leap over a ledge where the trail had washed away, and I could have done it blind, I think, certainly in the dark.

In November when the chill began to stick, even during the sunniest part of late morning, the river began to freeze. When we stood on the bridge the coiled wire raised its pitch and the current which had lathered in swales underneath slushed over, the froth caught in foam bubbles along the bank. A scum of ice formed over our swimming cove, and right before Thanksgiving the main channel turned white with ice. Ice floes and the current itself made intrusions along the surface, so the river jagged and scraped and jutted up along the brown cutbank above it.

I was twelve then, and in my mind odd things associate, breast pains and hawks, colored thread and snow. At Thanksgiving it snowed, and Penny urged me into the car and drove it off the mountain, along the logging road they sometimes ploughed and sometimes didn't, down to the cutout across from the Blackfoot Tavern. It took us two hours to walk back up the road after she'd stopped in the tavern, the snow seeping into our jeans and up our legs, me moaning, Penny slapping me, stings enhanced by frost and dark and the woods covering over for winter.

"Our Thanksgiving," she repeated, "Thanksgiving, thanks for always giving." She picked up Danny's place setting and put it back in the cupboard. Then she laughed, flat, not lilting, and I didn't want to be near her, like a foreign noise in the woods you try to run away from, a noise outside your catalog of sound—a cone falling, a deer snapping a twig, an animal caught in a trap. We had Cornish game hens for supper. Penny thrust her fork deep into the breast of the bird and raised it into the air. "I am an English lord," she sang, "and this is my domain." She looked at me and chucked me under the chin, put the bird back on the company plates, then left the table. I watched the honey and butter floating in my orange squash boat and I dipped my finger in the center of the pool and licked the sweet. I knew how to eat alone. I tore the tiny drumsticks off the hen and ate those, then the scant meat off the rest of the bird. Everything was honey and browned, white breasts.

Penny came back into the dining room with a clear tumbler of ice and opened the liquor cupboard. She swallowed hard and wet her lips as she filled the glass, sniffing the thin fumy odor as she swirled the ice in the tumbler. She put her glass down and moved behind me, placing her hands on my shoulders. "Baby," she said, then she squeezed me so hard I had to drop my forkful of supper, and the clatter of my fork on the company plates startled her and she let go. "Just leave everything when you're done," she said, "I'll get it in the morning." She stoked the wood stove, picked up the tumbler and walked upstairs, so softly I wondered if she floated.

My room was cold so I left the door opened to catch the heat from the stove as it rose over the banister to my room as I tried to sleep, the ceiling fan slicing the heat and dust as I lie awake listening to the house breathing and my mother moving in her room.

I could see the stairwell leading down to the living room from the safe barrier of my pillow. Penny held on to the wall, the muscles in her back tense before she jumped down the steps. Her body made a terrible thud, and I struggled with the angel that prevented me from jumping out of bed. She stood and walked back up the stairs, then jumped a second time, this time leaping higher, throwing her arms back, then forward. Her body crashed on the landing and I heard the bang of her head on the hardwood floor. She rolled her tongue against the soft skin at her gum-line, dabbing at her bloody lip while she raised herself up, her veins popped out where the skin was stretched to counter the weight of her torso. She took a long time to stand up, and I could feel the muscles crimping in my middle.

Her legs began to shake as she wobbled up the steps to her bedroom, rubbing her hand along the sharp slabs of white plaster in the hallway. "Jackie boy," she sang, "Master? Fare thee well? Very well. Hay ho, hay ho . . ." The notes crescendoed into wails, until the house was filled with shouts. At the top of the stairs she paused to look around at all her needlepoint work and laughed, her eerie notes drifting to the corners of the room, waiting for the right moment to spread, to smother me.

Penny closed her bedroom door behind her. I got out of bed and went to my window, slowly rocking back and forth from the balls of my feet to my heels. The glass was cold when I put my forehead against it, the cloud of my breath dimming the view of deer grazing in the yard. The canvas awning suspended from the eaves had come free from its clasps outside, and the wind banged it against the window, slapping fabric and cord until the deer drinking at the spring startled up and ran away.

I could see the yellow line of light eking out the curtains of her bedroom window, a line I watched for on those sleepless nights when I counted the days we had lived on the mountain as a way to pass darktime. I could tell from the triangle of light in the snow that she was standing at the window looking out, and from my dark spot I tried to see what she was seeing, the deer running off, the empty clothesline strung between two lodgepole pines, the edge of the cliff. That odd shape of light became my momentary comfort; it meant my mother was up, standing, thinking and breathing, not lying in a pool of blood.

When light came into the house I knocked on her door and when I knocked again and heard no answer I went in. She was lying down with her knees propped up, all the covers thrown on the floor in a pile like snow around her. Her hair was tangled on her pillow, and strands stuck to her wet forehead.

She stared at the ceiling above her bed, her hands playing with the shoelace tie of her bathrobe at her throat. The bottom part of her bathrobe was stained with blood.

An ugly, gurgling noise came out of my throat, and my mother turned her head. "Cloudy," she said, "could you get someone for me?" She started to hum again the song we shouted all over the house on long winter nights, "Jackie boy?" she asked.

I knew my part, but couldn't answer. She turned her head away from me. Her back moved slowly up and down, and I imagined my hand resting there where the blood had come up. I thought funny things, about brushing her hair and twisting it into a knot, offering her my new set of barettes or the snail shell I found on top of the snow, anything to make her better.

"Cloudy, you'd better call," she said again, her voice low and unembellished in the light-filled room.

"Who shall I call?"

"Call Danny, if you can find him," she said, then twisted her body around to face me. She pressed her lips tight and looked at me with those cold blue eyes, flaming and radiating ice. She moaned and made a fist with her left hand then bit her finger, so that I could see the teeth marks in her skin when she let her hand fall. I looked at her too closely, and saw the smoke around her eyes, the uneven rage smouldering behind that, an occasional spark leaping the nerves that connected the world outside of her body directly with her heart.

Danny was smaller than Penny, so limber and quick he could move almost without detection, and his grasp was like a lock, his handshake a torture of western etiquette. He only ate dark meat. He watched everyone's plates, mine, Penny's and said he liked the lungs the best, and his small thumbs would dig underneath the ribs of chicken until he retrieved whatever particles weren't scraped away by the cook before she plunged the piece into the deep fryer.

Penny skipped lunch with us that Saturday before Christmas. I saw her once across the street looking at a bamboo fishing rod in the window of the sporting goods store, then she moved on, shopping for other Christmas gifts. Danny had gone downstairs to the bar and left me at the table to finish my lunch, both of them always descending steps or the trail to leave me watching for their return, and by a sign on their faces, I learned to recognize how the rest of my day might go. When he came back his face looked yellow like beeswax and the smile he always pretended when he was with customers was gone.

The two of us walked around the block and up the street to Danny's antique store. A blast of snow and wind came out of the canyon east of town, a bitter frozen wind that made the glass in all the storefront panes shiver and rattle. The roundhouse in the railyard pit squealed in the conductive air, the whole town throttled by winter.

Danny hurried into the store and down the steps to the basement. He left me to wander past all the jewelry display cases and the guns mounted high in racks along the wall behind the counter, shelves of stereo equipment. I tripped the buzzer by the door too much, and Danny yelled up to me to cut it out. I moved deeper in; I liked the warehouse best, the big room the shop opened into, and wandered past armoires Penny had refinished, wondered what clothes had been hung in them, past oak dining room tables that an entire family graced on Thanksgiving, wishing them dinners of stuffed goose from Choteau or antelope or elk steaks. There were hat stands and ugly brass beds that looked like the hospital bed Penny had lain in after her miscarriage, the entire bar from Paradise, Montana, its maple front dadoed and carved with grape vines wrapped around the edge of the counter.

I opened and closed all the little drawers in the sewing machines, tried on thimbles and wiped my fingers on the stained and waxy pincushions, tired of pumping the treadle with my foot. I tried to avoid the glassy gaze of the trophies: elk, Rocky Mountain bighorn sheep, a shellacked rainbow trout endlessly arcing.

When I'd touched and refolded all the stained linen in the maple buffets, I followed the sound of Danny down the stairwell to the basement underneath the warehouse. The banister was rotting and splintered and each step announced my coming.

My parka was wet, rivulets of water along the quilted seams where snow had melted. I was uncomfortable. I could smell the fumes of paint remover and varnish curling up from the refinishing room, and the whir of a fan that spread the fumes thin, but never dissipated them.

I stood on the last step and let my eyes adjust to the dark. The basement was half-full of cardboard crates scattered throughout, the silver poles of ceiling jacks scattered like a forest on sagging floor joists. Danny stood in the center of the room, frowning, cuffing the cement floor with his shoe tip. He held a long, black dart in his hand, and he cocked his arm behind his right ear for a shot. The dart flew over the top of the target and struck a floor beam. He wrote something down on a slip of cash register tape, then twirled a dart around on his palm. "Go back upstairs and wait for your mother," he said to me as the buzzer rang upstairs.

Penny was sitting in an old rocking chair, her eyes closed, head tilted back a little as she rocked. A big brown bag lay at her feet, and the rung of the rocker when it hit the edge made the sound of paper being wadded up.

I sat down near her, in a ring of doll cradles and highchairs with thick brown trays. She opened her eyes and asked, "Danny downstairs playing darts again?" and when I nodded, she closed her eyes again. "Good thing he doesn't do any business on Saturday or somebody'd rob him blind." She kept her eyes closed, "I bought a vise to tie those little flies he's always losing."

Her face was very red as the blood rushed back to warm the cold surface of her skin. "I don't know what else to get him. Your father always said that was a bad sign, when you couldn't pick out a Christmas present. He was very wise."

The zipper on my parka stuck as I tried to get out of my hot coat. I fiddled with it, jiggling the zipper handle, then panicked, sweating, locked into my parka. Penny opened her eyes and stretched out her arms to help me. "You ready for your lump of coal?" She smiled as she unstuck the zipper.

I saw a dark smudge move across the floor near a glassed-in buffet, then tangled black fur disappearing underneath it. "Did you see that?" I asked Penny, who was shifting her package so that the rung wouldn't crush the tip anymore.

It appeared again, hissing and sputtering like the boiling kettle Danny kept on top of the wood stove in the store. The cat arched its back and extended its front claws, eyeteeth showing as it hissed again.

Penny got out of her chair and walked backwards away from the cat. "Mr. Lily," she whispered. She took a step towards it, but the cat curved into a perfect "c," its matted fur clumped in stiff spikes along its chewed-on spine. "Danny? Danny!" she called down the stairwell. "Mr. Lily's in the store."

Danny came up, skipping every other step. "You and that damn cat. Where'd you see it?" he asked. "I knew it would come inside, the way you kept feeding it." He moved to the register and took out a pistol from a shelf underneath.

"You can't shoot Mr. Lily," Penny said. "Get me a stick, I'll try to chase it out of here." Penny grabbed for a sauerkraut masher in the row of crocks. "You can't do nothin' with that cat. Can't you see it's wild? Take Cloudy out of here," Danny said. While he spoke, the cat began a drum-roll growl, a serious sound that made the hairs on my arms stand as my skin tightened. We all stood so still, Danny with his silver pistol pointed at the sound. Penny grabbed me by the shoulders and pulled me backwards toward the jewelry displays. Danny stomped his foot and the cat moved farther underneath the buffet. The cat darted, and Danny fired his pistol, nicking the rocking chair where Penny had been sitting. The cat turned and he fired again; the impact of the shot sent the cat up into the air, its chest heaving, blood seeping from its haunch. It looked around in mid-air and focused on the pistol, its claws ready, soumersaulting twice. Danny fired again. He missed the cat and the bullet shattered the beautiful beveled glass on the mirrored door of the armoire. Before the cat landed he fired two more times, but the cat sprang at him anyway, lunging at Danny's extended arm. Danny danced backwards and Penny swung the masher, the follow-through caught the cat mid-air, and sent it across the room past the over-stuffed loveseats. It landed in the middle of a maroon mohair sofa, and Danny fired again.

He missed the cat. The bullet tore through the fabric of the sofa and stuck somewhere in the gummy center of springs and wadded cotton. He held the pistol out at arm's length, but when he fired again the trigger went click, click, the cat shredding the cushion in frantic undulations, twisting its body and howling a hiss so high, it sounded like the scream of the first dying thing.

"Finish it off, you trigger-happy ass," Penny shouted at Danny. He looked at her as he walked backwards to the counter for more bullets, and she grabbed my arm, her fingers stiff and strong. She pressed me close to her, so I could feel the softness of her breasts against my shoulder blades, the heaving of her chest. There was so much tension in her body that against it I felt like a rubber band stretching, arms that I always wished were extended to me pushing and pulling against something invisible.

She pulled me backwards toward the door. The sudden jerk in her arms made my ankle turn, one part of my body moving while the lower park buckled under. I fell backwards and Penny caught the impact of my fall against her middle. She groaned loud as she stumbled, her hands letting go of my shoulders. When I turned around, her eyes were wide and glazed with tears, but I couldn't tell if they were for the fall, the pain, or Mr. Lily. Hand on the front door knob, she tugged at me and pulled me outside into the cold air. As the door slammed shut, I heard Danny fire three more shots, then I remembered that she'd left his Christmas gift on the floor near the rocking chair.

I saw Danny's green truck first, its tires spinning at the turn-out along Windy Boy Point. Penny was in the woodshed at the back of the house chopping kindling for the morning fire. The house was still and shadows hung low across the walls, the sun occluded by the peak of Bonner Mountain across the road.

Penny was in her housecoat and her blue furry slippers had wood shavings peppered near the toes. She dropped the armload of kindling into the woodbox and told me not to answer the door until she was dressed. There was a knock, then another, and I stood as drawers crashed in the bedroom upstairs. I heard crunchy footsteps in the snow, then Danny's face was pressed to the glass of the picture window, his hands a cupped visor on his forehead. Danny looked surprised when Penny opened the door and I was sitting at the kitchen table wrapping the Christmas tree ornaments in tissue paper. Penny came to the doorway and stopped, her arms crossed tight over her chest.

"You missing anything, then send me a list; I'll mail it," Penny said.

Danny looked over at me. I was wrapping a little wooden figure on a red bicycle. He watched me take out a fresh sheet of tissue paper and fold the corner around the figurine. His parka had a fine layer of blown snow which spread all the way up to his moustache and eyebrows. His skin looked waxy and sad, his face more puffy than usual. He dug in his coat pocket then held out three silver thimbles for me to take. They seemed so out of place in his rough hands, the metal caps uneven in the ridges of skin in his palm.

Penny pushed my arm quickly down to my side. "You can't take those," she snapped. "It's nothing to him. He lifts them out of old sewing machines at the auctions he bids."

"But I almost have a set," I said.

"Give them back. I let you keep those others before I understood his generosity."

"But he gave them to me!" Penny grabbed my wrists and began to shake, whipping my body back and forth.

"Penny, Penny!" Danny said, "leave the kid alone!"

Penny let go of my sore wrists and pushed me down into my chair. "Get out of here," she said to Danny. "I don't care if you drive off Windy Boy Point in this storm, just get out of here."

Danny put his hand on his forehead to wipe away the snow drops which had begun to melt in his hair. He wiped the moisture on his jeans. "Could I tell you why I came?"

"What's to believe? You want to help me make some money, you like my work, you know a quiet place? It all came with quite a price tag." Penny closed her eyes, as if we were all very far away from her. She put her hands over her ears, letting out breath until her face flushed so red I thought the veins in her temples must be empty.

"Your mother's flipped," Danny said.

Penny stood there with her eyes closed, and Danny slipped the thimbles into my hand. I wrapped my fingers around them, cold, nubby metallic where the design was stamped.

She stood like that too long, Danny fidgeting, her eyes still closed, until she started to hum. At first it was only notes out of sequence, then a kind of melody. I really don't know the name of the tune.

Danny took the gate key off his keyring and put it in the nest of tinsel on the kitchen table. He zipped up his parka and when he put out his arm to tousle my hair I grabbed his hand and touched the soft part of his palm. It didn't feel right.

Danny shook his head. "Everybody wants a little piece of you in this town." He looked out our picture window at the snow flying in the canyon below the house. "I think I'd rather face the weather."

Even in the way he said goodbye, you could tell there wasn't any laughter in his voice, not like there was in Penny's, when she looked out the window and watched his truck hit the curve at Windy Boy Point, blind to ice and snow.

I heard the closet door open and the sound of something heavy being dragged across the floor. When Penny came back downstairs, she held a huge feathered barrette that hid her hand: hawk, osprey, and eagle feathers in a starburst more magnificent than sunrise.

"Here's my prom corsage," she shouted to the house. She put her hand on the handle to the wood stove door. "This dance is yours, Daddy," she said, as she pushed down the handle.

I ran to the stove and tried to shove her away. "No! Danny said I could have that!" and when she flung the barrette into the stove, I pushed her and without thinking put my hand into the stove box. The heat was like a wall and

I pulled my hand back, but before I could get it out of the stove my sleeve caught fire. I screamed, and started to stand, but Penny was on top of me beating my sleeve with her bare hand. She sat on my back and I heard the clang of the woodstove door slamming shut, felt the twist of her torso.

She beat my sleeve a long time after the flame was out. The room stank with the smell of burned hair. I tried to get up, but when I tensed my muscles she pushed my head against the floor. "Let me up," I screamed again. She was breathing fast, and I could hear her gasps of choking air above my own. I felt her gather my hair into one big bunch, and then she pulled, until I thought my scalp would tear. "Stop," I said, "Stop!" I tried to twist away, but she held me there.

"If you didn't have all this hair," she breathed, "you wouldn't need any Blood barrettes."

I turned my face and bit her hand as hard as I could. I felt the hair tearing out of my scalp, and the pain. She slapped my cheek, and the strike banged my head against the floor. She raised her hand to strike again, the wisps of my blonde hair still in her clenched fist. "Let go, let go," she said before I felt the rest of the sentence on my face.

Even now, her needlepoint flowers hide everything in their still beauty. I can remember how I used to like it when my mother combed my hair. She would comb the knots out first, the soft bristles making my hair fly and shimmer with electricity. She would gather it over and over, letting her hands fall to my shoulders, when she'd start again. She used to call me Indian Pipe, because the flowers' silvery stalks were the same color as my hair, and it grew right by my bedroom window. "Indian Pipe," she'd say, "if your braid were a stairway we could walk to the clouds." And that's how I'd imagine hair and braids and walking in the sky, on a rope of coiled hair that came out of my own scalp, my mother leading me by the hand.

Monsters, His Monsters

Terry Ehret

She went on swallowing monsters, his monsters
because he couldn't tell her that he didn't,
and because he couldn't tell her that
she waited. For his phone calls. For his letter.

Because he couldn't tell her that he didn't
(from the bottom of the stairs he couldn't)
she waited for his phone calls, for his letter.
Because he didn't, he couldn't tell her not to,

from the bottom of the stairs he couldn't.
She told him about the red blood and the hemorrhaging.
Because he didn't, he couldn't tell her not to.
She was swallowing monsters, she said,

she told him about the red blood and the hemorrhaging.
He could stand halfway down the stairs and look up at her.
She was swallowing monsters, she said.
He could watch the space between his feet.

He could stand halfway down the stairs and look up at her;
he couldn't tell her that he didn't want to;
he could watch the space between his feet;
he could leave. He would close the door behind him.

He couldn't tell her that. He didn't want to.
She went to live in his home town.
He could leave. He would close the door behind him.
She went on swallowing monsters, his monsters.

We Visit a Poet & Ponder Life

Alta

We visit Mitsuye, she's been married to Yosh for 34 years. As we drive away, Marty notices my silence & asks, "Regretting your past again?"

"You know, I've always maintained that my husbands pulled unforgivable stunts, but perhaps, it could be my own restlessness that killed those relationships."

"Well, you know what happened to me & Robin."

"I forget."

"She was really important to me. But spring came, & my hormones went on a rampage."

"Ah."

"& she was really special. It wasn't just sex with her."

"Yeah. Scoff was the greatest lover, but when I turned 40, I just went after everyone that was still alive." We drive along the freeway, staring silently at the cars ahead, & at our unloving past behavior.

"You know what it is?" I start thinking out loud, "I've swallowed the poet's religion of GO FOR IT! The religion of experience. But it's not the only way to go, plus which, it's exhausting. Plus, it ignores all the pain that living like that causes other people: all the women who spend a month crying because you've run off with their husband for an unforgettable week in Carmel except in about ten years, you can hardly remember the dude's face!

"& these self-vindicating poets don't tell you how to survive this lifestyle. 'Go for the peaks," they give you that part of the map, but they don't warn you about the long slide down, & some of them die, because they don't know, any better than the rest of us, how to cope with sorrow & pain."

"You do go for the peaks & valleys," he agrees. "As if the only other choice were the plains. But hey, Altie, there's also the foothills!"

"On the other hand, Mart."
"Yo."
"My first husband drank, & a couple of times he socked me."
"Yeah?"
"So l was right to get out of that."
"Of course you were! Who said you weren't?"
"Mom said I caused his alcoholism."
"Hardly."
"& then the next one dislocated my jaw."
"Not that nice guy from New York?"
"Right. & you know the one I just divorced."
"O, yeah. l hope not all men are like your husbands, Alta."
"Well, so, restless or not, I think I was right to get out of those relationships. I have met women who stick it out through all those situations, though; I guess I could have tried that."
"Not your style."
"I had to drag the kids through those divorces, go on welfare, go hungry, but by God, l walked away from those men."
Marty nods, "It was historically the first time possible. When ever before in the world have women been able to leave their personal oppressors & survive?"

Irreversible Seasons

Anita Santiago

The classroom smelled like ripe bananas, an odor offensive to Alma so early in the morning. This was her first day of college, and she felt a strange combination of excitement and sleepiness. Students shuffled at their desks, adjusting themselves to the hard wooden seats. The sun came in at an angle, journeying millions of miles to land at the floor near Alma's feet. Cumulus clouds were twisting themselves into a knot high in the sky. She was distracted, longing for someone to love her.

Professor Alcazar stepped into the classroom, the crisp scent of pipe smoke on his wool coat. He looked thick and feral, like a bull hunched over by too many New York winters. He tapped his pipe gently on the edge of the desk. The gesture made Alma think of a blind man with a cane. She noticed he wore a wedding ring.

As the Professor wrote on the blackboard, Alma traced his flowery handwriting with her finger, moving it imperceptibly on the desk. She followed the way the loops on the S's turned inward in a heavy curve like a woman's hips. He stopped to add serifs to his letters, making the T's overhang like protective arms and the M's flatten out as if they were wearing shoes. He wrote about the songs of whales off an island in the Caribbean, about sunsets in wheat fields, when tiny particles fly in the golden rays just before another day is lost.

When class was over, Alma looked around to see if the other students were as moved as she was, but they just picked up their books and walked out placidly. She had just seen a man point to an ordinary object and, like an alchemist, make it shine. Three weeks later Professor Alcazar followed her out of class.

"Coffee?" he asked, sucking on his pipe. It took a moment to realize he was inviting her to the cafeteria. She was confused and not sure whether she had the option to say no.

"I walked all the way up from Chile, through rivers without bridges, through barren flats, through kilometers of humanity," he said over his cup of black coffee, as if the thought weighed on him. She imagined him packing his hopes into beaten suitcases which he carried the whole length of the continent through colonial cities with broken light bulbs and dirty towns with hungry dogs. She saw him arriving in California, contemplating his first American sunset in an artichoke field, his suitcases at his side. Alma stared into her cup and pictured him and his wife waking up to the flat silver light of the winter sun.

"It was a Friday night, the night I became a citizen. The judge who swore us in, forty of us in all, smelled of whiskey." Professor Alcazar told her these things as if he were in a confessional.

"I haven't seen my father in fifteen years," he said. "He may be dead." His father was an Arab who owned a hacienda in Chile. "My last memory of him was hearing him call for the servant girls to bring more wine. There was a full moon on the night I walked out, with just the clothes I was wearing." His mother had died, years before, of grief or madness, he did not know which.

"Look at these," he said, handing Alma letters addressed to him from Cortazar, Llosa, Marquez. She touched them delicately, wondering about the famous hands that had touched them. "Dear Carlos," she read, "I thank the angels for men like you who cherish our savage words carved out in stone." She looked at Professor Alcazar. He looked pleased, puffing on his pipe, watching her. He explained he was editing a series on Latin American authors, the first of its kind.

Alma ran into him several more times during the following weeks. She sat outside, propped against her books in the quadrangle of grass and trees near the building where his class was held. She had never met anyone who spoke to famous authors and received letters from them. She daydreamed about what his wife looked like, what she said when he got home.

"Ah, the jaguar soaks up the last feeble rays of sun. How will she survive the winter?" Professor Alcazar said, smiling. She was startled by the comment. She sat up quickly, wondering if he could tell she had been thinking about him. He seemed awkward outside, at odds with the fresh air and trees.

"I think I'll survive. I have a coat," she said. She stood up, brushing the grass off her jeans, for something to do.

"Well, winters here make you want to cry. So enjoy what's left of the sun," he said.

"You make it sound like doomsday, Professor," she said. He laughed.

"Call me Carlos," he said. There was an easy familiarity on his part. But she could never call him Carlos. She was only seventeen and he was old enough to be her father. She suddenly felt shy, as if she had been thinking dirty thoughts.

"I have to go on an errand. Want to come?" he asked. It was a strange invitation. She was bored and not in the mood to study.

"My journal arrives after Christmas. It's like waiting for a baby. And on a more practical level, it will also help me get tenure, I hope." He smiled. She had the fleeting sensation that he should not be confiding his professional strategies to her, but she was honored. She had always felt smarter than her masculine peers, who tediously explored their manhood in rough talk and beer.

They drove to a jewelry store, and she waited in the car, looking around inside it, curious about the details of his life. There were books in the back seat. When Carlos came out, he showed her a gold ring inlaid with the profile of a man carved out of tiger's eye.

"This was my father's lucky ring," he said. He handed it to her. It felt old, as if many people had previously worn it.

"I had it adjusted for you," he said.

"Oh, no," she exclaimed, extending it back to him, "I can't accept this."

"I won't take it back," he said. "It was meant for you." He started the car.

"Fine. Then I'll just borrow it for a while," she said, slipping the ring on her finger. It felt hot and she had the sensation that she was burning down a house with it.

"Do you like Chinese food?" he asked. They both acted as if what had just happened was perfectly reasonable, and that now it was okay for a professor and his student to have dinner together. Maybe it would be acceptable if they discussed semantics or linguistic theories. And besides, she really did want something hot and spicy after months of bland cafeteria food. They sat at a table near the window with a large red lamp that hung like a harvest moon over them.

"Your face is like sculpture," Carlos said. "The slope of your lips, the way your eyelashes reach down towards your cheeks. You could have been a model for a Renaissance master." Alma blushed.

"There were none in Caracas last time I was there," she said. The waiter had just brought the tea and left them again when Carlos stared at her across the wide expanse of white tablecloth.

"Alma, I love you." It almost sounded like a complaint. She felt a wave of apprehension and excitement sweep down on her. She fought off the discomfort by pretending that the table between them was a wide savanna of snow, and she was a Mongol riding away on a horse, through a sparse forest made of salt and pepper shakers, soy sauce bottles. The horse's hooves kicked up snow and she could hear it huffing with exertion. I'm getting away, she thought. But Carlos reached over and took her hand, bringing her back to the Chinese restaurant, to the table, to him.

Alma propped her chin on her hand, suddenly tired, and said, "I'm sorry."

"I'm sorry too. But I know enough not to fight love when it finally comes for me," said Carlos.

"You make it sound like death," Alma said. He shook his head sadly. "I didn't think this could happen to me," he said. "I had planned my life. Found a wonderful woman. I thought I could love her, given time. But it's been ten years and there is no passion. The magic is either there or it isn't. You can't force it or will it into being."

And when magic happens, it's not right, thought Alma. She was shot through with sadness. Professor Alcazar was so much older and married. They didn't have a chance. And yet she felt that turning him away was like throwing a diamond into the sea. Maybe this was the only time she would ever be loved. How do I know he's not the love of my life? she thought. On the way home, the green light from the dashboard lit up his face. A pawn shop, with dented trumpets and old silverware and outdated cameras, the dregs of someone else's life, looked desolate. They drove past a dusty bridal shop, with faded dresses in the window.

"Everything reminds me of you," he said. "I dream about you. I think of you when I wake up, every second of the day." He parked outside her door. They sat in silence, contemplating the quietness of the street. The neighborhood had an orderly quality to it, as if in the houses there were only families at peace, families started by men and women who had no problems, who were the same age, who were legal. She was envious. Then suddenly his mouth was on hers and she was engulfed by a sensation of urgency. It's madness, she thought, but she couldn't stop. He kissed her until she lost all sense of time and geography.

The following day, Alma was astounded by the blue fluorescence of a bird's feather on the sidewalk, the crisp taste of an apple, the clarity of a note struck on a piano. She avoided him at the university. She was embarrassed by the heated kiss. There was no one she could turn to. She thought of his wife, and felt a sorry kinship with her. She was ashamed to have become the catalyst of a betrayal. It bothered Alma that she had willingly become his accomplice, plotting to be at the right place, staying just a bit later after each class, trying to make it seem casual. Maybe she could still pretend it was an intellectual friendship. No one else had to know that she looked at the way his hands cupped his pipe and imagined them cupping her breasts. Several days passed and she did not see him.

It was a cold black Orion night when she heard a tap on her window. He was standing in the chilled air, breathing fog, like a drowning man surfacing at her window. She felt a sense of horror when she realized his bags were packed and loaded onto the top of his station wagon.

"I'm leaving her," he said. His eyes shone with victory and despair. Alma stared at him, overwhelmed by the irreversibility of this action. She thought of his wife, dissolving his absence in her mouth like a communion wafer. Life was moving forward too quickly.

"Are you crazy?" she whispered through the window.

"Yes," he said. "I can't live without you. Come here to me." She hesitated, and then went outside into the frosty air. He took her to an apartment, empty except for a kitchen table and a bed. In the kitchen, they danced to a slow Latin

American song about heartbreak, their feet shuffling loudly on the white linoleum floor. Alma had the sensation that they were breaking all the rules. That they would be prosecuted. That it would mean life or death. But it didn't matter because it was love. He held her tightly, he kissed the top of her head. Then he stopped dancing and leading her by the hand, took her into the bedroom.

The moonlight was blue and intrusive, bouncing off the snow and illuminating them through the curtainless window. He lay down next to her, the full length of his body pressed against hers. He ran his hand through her long dark hair and in the shadows she saw a waterfall in Africa. His hand glided over her stomach, spreading warmth. She felt the bulk of his body on her and she was in space, looking at the green and blue earth from above. The earth they inhabited was silent, primitive, as it must have been before humans. We are round and complete, she thought, holding onto each other as the planet spins. Red rivers of thought ran underground. I am selfish. This is suicide. This is love. This is the end of the world.

Everything they did was cloaked in guilt. They felt like outlaws or refugees, meeting in distant parking lots, entering movie theaters separately to find each other in the dark. They spent late afternoons together in cafeterias that smelled of grease and Pinesol, where they pretended to care about the lukewarm cups of coffee in their hands, while the feeble Long Island sun sank in the city smog. She was captivated by his stories: his sinking ships and sharks, his prayers and coffee beans. She was enchanted by the way he traveled through literature, stopping to admire paragraphs polished like stone, putting his arm around characters he loved.

Then at night, they went to stores. He was good at pretending that they were just a couple out shopping. Carlos let her choose the curtains, the chairs, the plates. She wanted bright colors: the reds of the butterflies that lived in Amazon trees, the blues and purples of oceans full of turtles.

Winter was streaked a dirty pink, and the days were short and muted. Carlos filed for divorce. He sat at the edge of the bed, on the white cauliflower bedspread. His eyes were red. Alma held his hand, and it felt as if she were holding the word betrayal for him.

"There is always pain in everything," he said.

"Go back," she said. He shook his head.

"There's no going back. It's not that. It's the pain of a newborn breathing oxygen for the first time." he said. "You give me life."

Alma was scared. She wanted to go home for Christmas, back to the warm blue light of Venezuela. She wanted to see if she could think of him in the hot green fields of Caracas, when the orchids released their fragrance into the humid evening air. Carlos drove her to the airport. There were tufts of snow on the ground, and in the distance, stacks of desolate brick buildings stood condemned to death.

In Venezuela, the balmy air rolled down from the folds of the mountain every afternoon. Alma dreamed of gigantic giraffes who craned their necks into the windows of her seven-story apartment, and large black birds that blocked out the sun.

Francisco, her high school boyfriend, picked her up at dawn in his jeep. He brought her a gardenia for her hair. He was young and healthy, a Viking with a copper-streaked beard. He had somehow acquired more manliness in the few months she had been gone. She was tired of the burden, the responsibility of love.

"Kiss me," she commanded. Francisco braked suddenly in the middle of the road. He lunged at her, kissing her nose, her lips and pulling at her bathing suit top. She screamed in laughter, batting him off, as startled iguanas darted back and forth in the bushes near the side of the road.

Francisco flew them to an island. The plane was like a sheet of paper, shivering at each cloudy draft. They headed out into nothingness. Then the island, a green fleck embedded in the water. There was no airport, only a sandy strip cutting across the island.

The water was melted aquamarine. They took their bags and walked up the beach. The sand was white and soft as sifted flour. As the day wore on, the water got warmer, and they took their bathing suits off, reveling in their nakedness like children. Francisco held her as she floated, running his hands up and down her back. Then he bent over and kissed her, a long salty kiss, pulling her closer. Their bodies slipped against each other in a delicious, muscled, soft and hard way. There were no promises, only a sense of abandon, and she was grateful.

They flew back that evening. The lights of the city appeared along the coast like a citrine necklace. Alma thought about Carlos. She pictured him sitting at his kitchen table in New York, with a sink full of rust and dirty dishes, reading a book, surrounded by silence. He was waiting for her. She regretted her fickleness, her indecision, her confusion.

The next day, she went to a woman who could tell the future. There was something severe about her, something thin and Caribbean. She gave Alma a cigar to hold, showing her how to wrap her fingers around it, in order to instill it with her essence. After a while, the woman took the cigar from Alma and lit it, staring at the ashes, making clicking sounds with her mouth while she turned the cigar around.

"You come from a white country. A land full of snow." Alma nodded. She felt a cold draft in the air, though the day was sunny. The woman closed her eyes and Alma sensed she could see Carlos in his house.

"There's a man there. He's much older than you," she said. "And he loves you more than his own life." The woman opened her eyes. "There is fire," she said, staring at Alma. "You are playing with love." Alma felt the weight of the accusation and remained silent. The woman gave her the name of someone to see in New York.

When she returned, Carlos met her at the airport. She saw his dark curly hair in the crowd and for an instant thought of taking another exit, getting in a taxi, escaping. Then he saw her and came over and picked up her suitcases. He did not kiss her in public. He wrapped her in his pipe-scented coat, even though she had her own coat, and they stepped outside into the winter. She was again surrounded by gray pigeons and steel.

In the car, Carlos did not say much. His coat felt oppressive, like a heavy hand claiming her again, as they joined the stream of slow-moving cars.

"So how's the journal?" said Alma. She wondered if he could tell she had been unfaithful. She felt loathing for her inability to control herself.

"It's extraordinary. I have a copy in the back seat for you."

They stopped at a traffic light. There was some heaviness between them as he lit his pipe.

"What's the matter?" asked Alma.

He paused. "I didn't get tenure."

"But why not?" she said.

"Apparently the dean has heard rumors about you and me. But it's really professional envy. All my colleagues voted against me," he said. Alma sat in silence. She felt guilty, as if she had caused the problems in his life. If only he knew that she had been thinking of leaving him, of returning to Venezuela. If only he knew she had been disloyal.

"I've heard about a man who can help you. His name is Don Raimundo," said Alma. "Why don't we go see him?" Carlos gave a short, bitter snort.

"Nobody can help me," he said.

"Please?" said Alma. She told him about the woman in Caracas. She convinced him to try, one time only. Carlos drove faster than usual, clanking over bolted metal bridges. Don Raimundo's apartment was filled with plastic statuettes of saints, crosses, palm leaves, rosaries and candles.

"There are white nuns flying around your head," Don Raimundo said to Alma, "and they don't like my cigar." He crushed it in an ashtray. "They can get pretty nasty", he added with a smile. Alma smiled and thought, this man must be a Santero. Immediately Don Raimundo turned to look at her, slightly offended.

"No, you're wrong," he said. "I'm not a Santero." Alma felt as if he had stepped right into the red cave of her head, helping himself to her thoughts. She tried not to fight it.

"My job on earth is to bring guidance to troubled souls." At least he believes in miracles, she thought spontaneously.

"What can I do about my tenure?" Carlos asked.

"Accept what life has in store." Carlos began to object, but Don Raimundo raised his hand. In her mind Alma screamed, how can I know if I love him?

"Stop analyzing. The answer will come some day soon."

"I'm not sure," said Alma, knowing he would understand. Outside, the city flowed into the smoggy orange sunset, the slanted light in the room was rusty. Alma looked at Carlos. It felt like a dream.

Don Raimundo frowned. He took Carlos' hand in his and said, "Trouble will come soon. And there is nothing you can do about it. Here, let me cleanse you both of bad spirits." Alma felt foolish standing in the middle of the living room, as Don Raimundo blew candle smoke on a leafy twig. Then he blew the air around Alma's head and shoulders. She began to relax. The air in the room was pure, blue oxygen. She closed her eyes and thought she felt the thin wisp of a nun's wing glance against her hair.

The following week, they went back to Don Raimundo. He said that the spirits of four African horsemen were causing chaos in Carlos' life, and it was important to signal that they were not welcome. He told Carlos to place glasses of water with knives crossed over the top in each room in his home. He was to walk down the hallways of the university, particularly near the offices of those colleagues who had voted against his tenure, and saturate the air with the smoke of his pipe. He was to pray, and have faith. Don Raimundo lit candles for him.

One night, Carlos fell asleep on the couch. He heard his ancestors speaking languages that he could suddenly understand. He woke up at dawn pronouncing Arabic words he had not spoken since childhood.

"Alma," he exclaimed, "I know the word for father! I know the word for house!" He had seen angels in his dreams.

"The spirits are here! I can see things," he laughed, reckless with new powers. After that, he looked into bodies and saw what was hurting, which bone was weak, which heart needed care.

"Please don't drink any more," he told a colleague. "I am seeing black silhouettes."

And every day Carlos went to Don Raimundo. Alma stopped going. On those nights, she sometimes felt Carlos' presence near her, when she was alone reading. The house would creak and moan with winter sounds, the snow-filled winds spitting cold on her windows, and she missed being in his arms, missed the way he was before Don Raimundo.

"Faith," the old man repeated to Carlos. "I see you teaching somewhere upstate, in a big university."

"Will Alma be there with me?" asked Carlos. But Don Raimundo could not answer. So Carlos went on interviews, taking his books and journals with him. But he was sidetracked by his vision.

"I have a special power," he told stunned interviewers. He was innocent, almost childlike. Out of politeness, the interviewers would murmur what he took for admiration.

"In fact, you will soon see major changes," he continued. "Your mother will come live with you," he said to a smallish dark-haired woman. "And you will have another son, your third," he said to a man with glasses.

"How did you know I have two sons?" the man asked. Carlos smiled. He never heard from them again.

"Stop it," said Alma. "You're scaring people. They think you're crazy."

But Carlos didn't care. His complex linguistic and analytic theories had evaporated, and in their place was an absolute credence in the invisible. It was his goal to harness the mischievous spirits Don Raimundo saw around him. They were responsible for his difficulties. Following Don Raimundo's mandate, he made himself a gold tunic with a large red cross on the back. Alma hated it. It made her fear the meanings behind everything he brought home: medals of saints, candles with prayers printed on them that burned all night, masks made of shells. There were too many instructions from Don Raimundo.

"Please stop seeing Don Raimundo for a while," she pleaded.

"He's the one who stood by me," said Carlos. "All those so-called friends, whom I helped publish, don't even talk to me any more." He reached for her hand.

"Don't worry. Something will come up," he said.

But nothing seemed to make a difference. Alma was becoming restless. She longed for fun, for the firm flesh and smooth skin of boys her own age.

"Marry me," said Carlos. But Alma would just smile. She lay in bed hearing him snore and thought that she had no business trying to be the life companion of someone from another generation. She feared her hunger for other men, and pictured herself still young but beginning to gray, pushing a wheelchair. Carlos sensed a change in her, and became suspicious.

One evening, Carlos saw her at the library with another student, a boy who sometimes studied with her. He stormed up to them and said to Alma, "May I have my ring back, please?" The boy stared at him, and then at her, wondering what was going on. Alma was stunned. If word got out about this, it would not help his cause. There was a tense silence. She was not wearing his ring. Carlos looked at her with intensity and then walked away, leaning into the astringent wind. Alma shrugged, fighting a burning sensation in her eyes as she said laughingly to the boy, "He's nuts." Instantly she regretted it, feeling disloyal, but also as if she had just inadvertently spoken an undeniable truth. That night Alma did not go to his home. He called and called until she picked up. He pleaded with her to come back, saying he had been foolish and had reacted out of love.

"I'm not sure I love you." said Alma.

"You do," he said. "This was meant to be."

"You shouldn't have left your wife, even for love, even for me," she told him.

"I'll always look after her. But I can't sacrifice my soul," he said. "You're the one I love." She stayed away for several days. But then a longing started in the pit of her stomach, as she thought about the endless hours they had spent talking, creating their own striated worlds. The longing grew, filling her like a vine, until she felt that leaves would come out of her mouth, like green tongues of backed up words. So she went back. He was solicitous, taking her out at night, buying her trinkets, unable to hide his joy.

But soon the burden of his love was again too much and she ran from him, telling him she was visiting relatives. Instead, she would lose herself in the anonymous city with young men. He followed her to the train station, hiding behind oak trees. In her absence she was sure he opened her class notebooks, looking for betrayal. He reached into her purses and stole letters from Venezuela. Carlos and Alma fell into an unspoken agreement, a conspiracy of silence, a condition she imposed in return for staying with him. He didn't ask, she didn't answer.

One Saturday, Carlos and Alma were reading on the bed. Alma touched his shoulder, feeling genuine affection for him. Carlos took the book out of her hand, and kissed her gently on the lips. She tasted the tobacco, the yellowness of it, the decay. Then he rolled over onto her, and above his shoulder she felt presences, as if Santa Barbara had stopped her white horse mid-air, and with her ruby-tipped staff in hand, was watching them. Alma looked to the side. San Isidro, with his white beard overflowing, was sitting in the armchair, softly shaking his head. Carlos kissed Alma's neck, as Santa Rita, the saint of impossible miracles, stood in another corner of the room. Even love can't conquer these illusions he wants to follow, she thought. Alma heard the wind chime, made of white translucent shells, clink softly. She knew instantly that something precious was gone forever.

That evening, Alma saw Carlos kneeling in the living room, wearing his gold tunic as he prayed at an altar he had constructed.

"Carlos, I've asked you to stop seeing Don Raimundo."

Carlos said nothing. He continued to kneel. The sound of a bus pulling away from the curb outside seemed to punctuate the silence.

"Well, then I think we should not see each other for a while," said Alma, digging her nails into the palm of her hand. She wasn't sure about anything any more. Carlos turned and stared at her.

"But I love you," he said. The way he said it made her feel ungrateful.

"I think it's best," she said.

"I need you," he said. He touched his heart.

"I've made up my mind," she said softly. The image of this moment burned into her mind: Carlos wearing his tunic with the big cross, kneeling in the middle of the living room on the green rug, his hand on his heart. Just outside was the sound of traffic, of people going home to dinner.

Alma went back to the small house she had shared with another student. Several months passed. She avoided the quadrangle of grass at the university, the library, the cafeteria. Every now and then, she thought she saw him out of the corner of her eye, but she was wrong. She was almost surprised that he didn't make more of an effort to find her. She missed the afternoons together, the dinners, the discussions. She wondered what was happening with Don Raimundo. She wondered if his wife knew she had left him. She felt relieved that she was no longer standing in their way, in case their relationship could somehow be fixed.

One night Carlos ran outside his home holding a gun, threatening to put a bullet through his brain. A neighbor called the police, and they came and surrounded him, talking to him for hours. Alma did not know about it for several days, until she saw an article in the newspaper. She could not believe what she was reading, and had to read it several times. "University professor in asylum after suicide attempt." How did he get a gun? Was this another command from the spirits? she wondered.

Alma went to see Carlos at the hospital. The windows were covered with green wire. He was in his room, looking small and wasted. He smiled happily when he saw her.

"You cut your hair," he said. She sat down on a chair, just far enough to be out of reach. Carlos ran his hand across the white bed.

"I like it here. They bring me my food and the doctors want to hear about my visions." Alma nodded.

"What do you tell them?" she asked.

"That I can see my dead father now. Soon I will get a job. You will come back to me." He smiled. "I can wait." Alma looked out the window. A car moved slowly down the street. There were red buildings surrounding an island of sand, an empty playground. She looked at Carlos and saw that his eyes looked as if he were a hundred years old. Was he always like this, she thought, and I just didn't notice? Or had love aged them both?

"The doctors ask me questions all the time. They know I understand the meaning of life."

Alma said, "Carlos, they don't believe you. They are just trying to find out what is wrong with you."

"No," he said. "Some of us see more than others, glimmers of truth in the universe." Why, she wondered, why did you want to kill yourself? Because of me?

"There is only one man on earth who knows the meaning of life, and he has written it down in an obscure book," he said. "I'll share it with you."

"Tell me," she said, still curious as to what he would say.

"First, tell me that you love me," he said. Alma lowered her head. She regretted getting into this, she knew it would lead nowhere.

"Wait," he said, looking at the space above her head. "You used to have an aunt named Ursula. I see her, right now," he smiled. "She's old, frail. She wears her hair in a bun. She is now your guardian angel." She could almost believe him.

"It's getting late," she said, "I have to go now." Alma got up to leave. Carlos stood up, too. He reached for her hand and kissed it.

"You smell like lilacs, my lady. Remember the ones that grew by our window?" he said. She looked at him, wondering if she was about to throw her life away.

"I will die for you," he said.

Alma turned to leave. Maybe this was it, this had been her experience with love. Maybe she would never know love again. She walked away from him, his touch still warm on her hand. She walked down the empty halls of the hospital, to the exit.

Once outside, her vision became blurred by tears from the sensation of abandoning him to a place with caged windows, and her thoughts of what could have been. In the distance, a small gust of wind was lifting the sand off the playground, creating a whirlwind. She stopped and watched the rapid movement of the spinning funnel. For a moment she could see the silhouette of Santa Isabel, the saint of forbidden love, her golden hair and her robes fluttering in the wind, and she heard the sweet music of a single clarinet. But it was only a car horn in the distance, and the soft, shimmering sand settling down after its sudden flight.

Wet Paint

Christina Sunley

I wasn't dying to get released from the hospital—it had been a gloriously numbing experience—but after three weeks they evicted me and I found myself alone in my apartment in the midst of a blistering hot, around-the-clock heat wave. Gone were the tender nurses who had brought me cracked ice and TV Guides, the high-tech bed I could crank into the one position that allowed me sleep, the air conditioning. No longer a heroic accident victim, I became simply a lonely, sweaty, broken-armed, cracked-ribbed, jilted skeleton of my former self. And so I went about creating the most comfortable habitat a skeleton could ask for.

My aim was to simulate a nice quiet tomb in the middle of New York City. I pulled down the shades, took the phone off the hook, and rationed out my remaining stash of codeine. Mostly I lay in bed with my eyes closed, listening to the fan and concentrating on the dull bone pain in my arm, but occasionally I sat up and composed another left-handed letter to the driver of the truck that hit me. *Dear Sir, you'll never believe this but that accident was an act of divine intervention. You see I was speeding breakneck on my bike toward the East River and for all I know if you hadn't run me over I might have gone ahead and taken the big plunge. And now I'm in so much pain I can hardly think at all about how I looked into my lover's window that night. Saw her with her. Looked in and saw the end. Thank you. Sincerely.*

But after a few days the pain and the pain killers began running out, and the real, underlying pain began seeping through: *Della. Della left. Della left me. Della left me for . . .*

Only in my dreams was I vindicated; I slept twelve hours a day, fourteen when I was lucky. Sometimes I dreamt Della was at my side, changing my bandages, stroking my brow; sometimes I dreamt I was watching her at my funeral, staggering toward my open grave; but mostly I dreamt of her new lover, mugged on the F train and left handcuffed to a pillar at the Houston Street Station, or slowly sinking into place alongside those other cement-footed criminals preserved in the sludge of the Hudson. Every day Della's new lover died a thousand deaths, but the dreams were a cheap thrill because at the back of my mind I knew I didn't even deserve to be jealous: the whole time Della and I were together, I'd resisted her. I'd insisted I didn't love her, right up until the moment I looked in her window and saw her kissing somebody else. It was that sight, the back of her neck shimmying like a snake in heat, that made me realize all at once that I loved her and that it was too late to love her. If I'd been honest I would have been going out of my mind with regret, but jealousy was simpler and much more satisfying. It became my sole source of sustenance, aside from an occasional swipe of peanut butter from the open jar by my bed. I forsook my life, my friends, my painting. I had been Betrayed. I would never love again.

I might have remained entombed indefinitely but on the morning of the eighth day, in the middle of a particularly gratifying dream (in which Della maintained a twenty-four hour vigil on my front stoop, repairing my battered bike and begging me to take her back), the honeymooners upstairs launched their first Really Big Fight, estimated 8.2 on the Richter scale. By this time I was fairly delirious. When the man yelled *Give up, bitch!* I was sure he was talking to me. When the woman screamed *You don't know how to love!* I wondered how she knew so much about me. I'd met them once, when the tin cans were still banging off the bumper of their car, warning, warning.

I tried drowning them out with my TV but the louder I turned it up the higher they hiked their own volume. All day they fought, through the morning game shows and into the afternoon soaps, until finally the woman let loose a scream so high-pitched and call-of-the-wild it tricked all the mutts in our building into howling like a pack of urban coyotes. That's what it took to rouse me from my cozy bed of self-pity, down the stinking hallway reeking of grease and out into the blasting heat of the street.

Lower East Side August. Mothers with dozing babies sweating on stoops, cynically fanning themselves with flaps of cardboard. Men pressed against walls, drinking beer under thin ledges of shade. Everyone moving slowly if at all. The glare singed my eyes and I had to use my good hand like a visor, blocking out everything but the small circle of cement spinning around my feet.

I don't remember walking into Cafe Yip, I don't remember passing out at my table. What I can't forget is waking up gazing into a pair of eyes blue as swimming pools. In the dim room Francie's bleached hair seemed the only source of light, rising straight up from the top of her head, then planed abruptly flat across the top. A great blonde mesa. And maraschino cherry red lips murmuring *How can I help you?*

I was too weak to answer. She propped me against the wall so her manager wouldn't kick me out, then served me a protein shake laced with espresso. I stayed all afternoon, mesmerized by her balancing acts with plates and glasses and the swing of her bare arms as she loped into the kitchen to pick up her orders. During her shift break she brought another shake, then listened while I poured out the whole sordid nightmare leading up to my accident.

"Poor baby," she said when I finished. "That Della was a fool." She lifted my limp hand into hers, stroking the palm with her cool dry fingers and leaving me with a strange tingling sensation. Pleasure. It took me a moment to remember its name.

By the time she collected me at the end of her shift I was too exhausted to speak, but I remember how her body became a walking drama of geometries as she guided me back to her apartment: feet triangled in black leather sandals, the straps weaving diamonds of bare skin up her calves; short trapezoid skirt; square shoulders; perfect ovoid face. Someday, I decided, as she eased my broken body onto her lumpy futon, someday I'll paint her.

It's not as if Francie was a total stranger. I'd seen her waitressing at other East Village cafes (they come and go faster than you can say gentrification) and we're even distant lesbian relations (she's the ex-lover of one of my ex-lover's ex-lovers), but I'd have gone home with her anyway, cousin or not. I didn't have a will of my own anymore. That desperate two-wheeled death ride was my last self-determined act, and when the truck smacked into me it jolted my will clear to Brooklyn. Maybe it needed a vacation. Meanwhile, I was Francie's. After that first day we returned to my apartment to pick up some clothes and then I never bothered going back.

Determined to keep me from drifting back over to the Other Side, Francie came straight from work in the afternoons, smelling of steamed milk and cigarettes, and fed me plates of food snuck from Cafe Yip: baba ganouj, hummous, kalamatta olives, washed down with tamarind soda sipped from glass straws. We ate avocados like melons, sucked mango pits, fried plantains. Sometimes she dragged the futon onto her fire escape and we'd lie there all evening, drinking Rolling Rock beer, flipping through her musty Spiderman comic books and watching live street sit-coms unfold on the street below. If it was hot she ran me a cool bath, and after she helped me undress I'd lower myself into the freestanding tub that was the centerpiece of her living room, a dainty-footed, salmon-bellied wonder as large as a small pool. Then she'd strip. Slowly. And join me. Slicking my body with her huge soft bar of French beeswax soap. Afterwards she'd lay me across the chartreuse chaise lounge and lick me like quickly melting ice cream. I still thought about Della but the pain was less original, more like the way a scar occasionally twinges, a remembered pain.

Everything Francie did had one end: my pleasure. After a few weeks I was eager to rejoin the living. I started taking walks, seeing friends again. Usually I'd be home before Francie in the afternoon, but one day I went out to dinner with my art school pal Robbie, after we'd done the gallery tours.

"That's nice," Francie said, when I told her where I'd been. "But don't you think you should be taking it easy?"

She seemed suspicious of my friends. "They're too much for you right now. You're still recuperating."

I felt my will return from Brooklyn. "I had a life, you know, before I met you."

"And now you've got me," she said, wrapping me in her arms.

Things started to change. I got sick of leftover cafe food and began cooking my own meals, things I knew Francie disapproved of: grilled American cheese sandwiches, spaghetti and meatballs from the can. I stopped letting her bathe me and one night I stayed out late on purpose, coming back after I knew she'd gone to bed. The next day, she brought home Rage.

"Just for one night," she promised as she arranged a sleeping bag in the bathtub. Rage was a runaway who'd had the great fortune of sitting at one of Francie's tables. Although she did look kind of scary, with her pierced nose and perpetual sneer, Rage was actually very shy and afraid to leave the apartment; she spent the whole day there, getting on my nerves in her quiet, punky way, waiting for Francie to come home.

After the third day of Rage I decided to move back to my apartment. The cast had just come off, and my arm, though pale and flabby, was capable of wielding a brush again. I could feel the old painting urge nipping at my fingers. When Francie got home from work I was packing my things.

"Why?" she asked, pulling a chocolate croissant out of her purse. Her hands shook when she offered it to me.

"I have a painting I want to start."

"Start it here."

"I just want to sleep in my own bed again." I tried to hold her but her body stiffened against mine. "It's OK," I told her. "We'll still be together. Besides, it's you I want to paint."

She relaxed then, slowly turning to face me. "I'll be a very good model," she murmured. "I'll stay perfectly still."

For a moment I saw her as I had that first day, when I was null and void and she was dazzle, and she almost succeeded in sucking me back in. But I summoned my will and explained that I paint from memory, that I'd call her soon. I knew she was angry, but I figured she'd get over it. I hadn't realized that Francie considers herself the Big Answer, a one-woman rescue team. Why else do you fall for someone who's just been run over by a Mack truck?

Francie called me three times a day after I moved out.

"I have baba ganouj," she'd say. "I've got Rolling Rocks." I'd tell her I was working, that I couldn't be interrupted. Then the phone would ring an hour later.

"I want to see the painting," she'd say. "I want to see you."

I didn't want to see her. I kept telling myself it was because I was painting, that I needed distance from the real thing in order to create the rendition. But the truth was that she was beginning to seem like a hex. After each phone call I'd find myself starting all over again, and everywhere I tried to position her was wrong, threw the composition off. Finally, at three o'clock one morning, I stuck her into a far corner of the canvas, more out of frustration than anything else, and it looked right: Francie standing in the back doorway of the cafe, half in, half out, one arm flung against the door to hold it open as she stepped into the bright garden. The other arm balanced a silver tray loaded with cappuccinos and lean brown iced teas with lemons riding piggy back. Despite the fact that she seemed to have everything under perfect control—the door, the tray, herself—cups and glasses were toppling to the ground. But something wasn't right about her lips, and I couldn't decide what it was. I'd have to wait for them to dry. Red oil paint takes a long time drying, and I'd chosen for her an especially humid shade. I was lighting a cigarette on the fire escape when the phone rang.

"I want you to stop painting me."

I told her I was sorry but it was too late. It was something I needed to do. I'd started, I couldn't stop.

"You're violating my copyright." She drew in her breath. "I'm calling the police." She hung up.

I stared at the canvas, the light shining on her glistening red lips, and imagined the police storming in, Francie pointing me out. "I'm afraid we'll have to confiscate this," one of the cops would announce, and then they'd solemnly carry my painting out the door, red paint smearing onto their dark blue uniforms . . .

I didn't try to call her back. I gave up on the real Francie. I couldn't love her anymore, all I could do was paint her. I cleaned my brushes, unplugged the phone, and went to sleep. When I woke up, the painting was gone.

All I can think is maybe it's for the best. Maybe she'll learn something from it. There's nothing for me to do now but move on. It's time to start my Della series.

It's funny, but as soon as I painted her lips, I couldn't imagine ever kissing them again.

Losing Weight

Elizabeth Searle

In happy November she weighed one hundred and forty pounds, had a new noticeably softened surprised-looking face, a swelling white curve of stomach and big upward-tilting breasts that she paraded around the office, her back straight, her newly rounded-out thighs rubbing together as she moved. It was November. The Phoenix sky made a huge solid swoop of blue. The only thing that looked *real* in a city designed by Frederick's of Hollywood, Andrew once said. He used to make the two of them bulging salami and mayo and cream cheese submarine sandwiches, thick Black Forest chocolate cakes, heaping chunky plates of buttered spaghetti and sausage sauce. Their lips would gleam.

They'd eat nothing all day, meet for wine before work, after work race to her cluttered apartment, devour the meals and then fall into bed with that same abandon, Dorothy almost literally breathless the whole time, struggling like a swimmer to keep aware, to enjoy every second. Because she knew from the start how long this would last, liked knowing it.

"Hey you—" she'd said to him at first.

He had been standing halfway across the white and beige maze expanse of office that night, and even from a distance he didn't look at all like Arizona. He was pale, exactly as pale as his white shirt, the only pale man in the whole damn building. He looked to her something like Edgar Allen Poe: Poe's eyes and forehead, but long shaggy hair and an incongruous body, tough and stocky and big-shouldered, the body of a hood or a lightweight boxer. At work he never spoke. This was back when she was "Dottie": small and buxom, tightly packed, straining against hated fat, chatty in flashes, fast-moving, efficient, somewhat hard-looking. Andrew was the first man she ever took seriously, the first person really, aside from her mother. And her mother had been dead for five years. Dorothy had since become "Dottie"—a name she truly hated. She kept the long tan office people at a definite distance, made no close friends off duty. Her three-inch heels clicked past like heavy ping-pong balls; her hair and eyes were shiny snapping black, her blouses too tight and too bright and worn with an air of defiance that was not at all flirtatious. She slouched slightly no matter how fast she moved, dressed in overbright colors, electric green or red orange. She thought of her breasts then as personal weapons. Go on and look, she seemed to be saying. See if I care.

He was the first man she took seriously. They both worked the four to eleven shift, typing test results and sorting computer chips in a sealed glass building deep in downtown Phoenix. That first night she found him by the coffee machine, tragically Poe-eyed, his hands too shaky to hold the styrofoam cup because, he told her—"Hey you, anything wrong?" she'd asked loudly in her Dottie voice—because on his way to work he'd glanced out of the bus and into a car below and had seen a woman's face peering out the back window, her eyes enormous and, he thought, desperate, and then in a flash a man's hand had reached up and pulled her down, and then the lights had changed and the car disappeared and now he didn't know if he should call the police or what since he couldn't be sure *what* he'd really seen since he was, to tell the truth, a little drunk.

"That's funny, so am I," Dottie said. "Just can't get through this job any other way."

It was late October. They sat together on Dorothy's mother's overstuffed blue sofa, surrounded by the dark scrolly walnut tables and footstools that seemed out of place in Dorothy's small stucco tan-carpeted Arizona apartment, designed for lightweight aluminum furniture and lots of sun. The window was wall-sized, cut around the enormous sky that had opened up over Dorothy in the long U-Haul drive west. Trees had disappeared.

"So you're from Ohio?" he said.

Her old oversized furniture was making them both feel so small. They wound up moving close on the couch and talking about back east. The rain, the green, the heavy humid air. Dorothy thought that no man had ever stared so frankly at her breasts.

He used to work as a store detective at Zayre's in Newark, he told her three hours later, in bed. His voice was New Jersey hard, sounded that night like he was putting on a Jersey accent.

"All day I stood behind this two-way mirror thing," he said. "And I'd watch *women*, you know, stare them up and down any way I wanted. Just stare at legs and cleavage behind that mirror."

"Did you catch people?" she asked. She was lying against his chest.

"Sometimes."

"What'd you say? I mean when you caught someone . . . ?"

"Well I'd step out—"

"With a card or something?"

"Yeah. Yeah, and I'd flash my detective card thing and I'd say . . . Uh . . . Yeah. I'd say Excuse me Zayres Security Come with me please, No—not even *please*, just Come with me."

And somehow she had still been a virgin at age twenty-two. Incredible, but then her 8th grade breasts had been incredible too, taking everyone aback. If they'd voted, she'd have been chosen Girl Least Likely to be a Virgin. *Woman*, her whole bewildering body seemed to say. Her locker door brushed against her breasts whenever she opened it. Boys' arms just barely touched her in the hallways. Excuse me, sorry.

Please no, she told them on dates.

They thought she had an older man somewhere. It was 8th grade and she was the girl whose father had died. Car crash, she'd learned to say, because it was short. They felt awed, thought she was tough, somehow much older than they were.

Then, again incredibly, in her senior year, in this small Ohio town, incredibly, her Mother had cancer. For two years she was the girl whose mother was dying.

All through high school Dorothy had lived alone with Mother, and every evening Mother lay on the overstuffed sofa sipping red wine in the gentle blue-white T.V. light. She let Dorothy sip wine too. Both their lips would stain a dark cracked purple by the time they kissed goodnight.

Dorothy read a lot then, modern novels full of neurotic women. Her mother lay unconscious on the couch downstairs while Dorothy took notes til 2 A.M., writing down the things she, Dorothy, must never do.

If you feel yourself becoming obsessed with something/someone, she wrote at fourteen, *then RESIST*.

The main thing, she always thought, was not to let what happened to Mama happen to her. For Daddy's presence—his temper, his violent headaches, his disappearances—all had given her mother a definite purpose, that of keeping the family together in spite of him. Without him, Mother had lost her old drive. That Mother, Dorothy thought, was gone for good.

All through high school, Dorothy made their suppers, did the shopping, woke Mother up every morning, helped Mother prepare for her Bible study group. They were both quiet, both shared a nearly wordless alliance when Daddy was alive. Mother would give Dorothy a silent significant look as a door slammed behind her; the two of them would dry dishes together, rubbing plates tenderly, saying with their quiet, Isn't it better this way?

Then Daddy really was gone, and they had little to say to each other, still. What to have for supper, what was happening at the church.

Usually Dorothy slipped upstairs as soon as Mother's soft chin began to slacken, Mother's eyes drifting shut. But upstairs, lying in bed, Dorothy could feel Mother downstairs on the couch, then later across town in the hospital, could feel it in her stomach when Mother wasn't there anymore.

Dorothy was twenty-two. She talked herself through the months before and after the death like she was talking herself off a ledge. One step, one step.

At first the chemotherapy in Cleveland was working—Mother losing her hair, nauseous for hours afterwards—then not. Mother had her stiff blonde wig, and chemotherapy wasn't mentioned anymore, it was something they'd tried long ago. The hospital became home to both of them in the last months. When it was over, Dorothy called her Uncle Sid and told him she was staying with her Grandma, then called Grandma—who was, it turned out, only weeks from dying herself—and told her she'd gone to Sid. Then she took a motel room outside of town and stayed there a month, living off the beginnings of Mother's life insurance.

She read. Looking back two years later, the main thing she felt about this time was alarm over how unconscious she'd been. No plans, no ideas. Is There Life After Death? Beyond Life's Sunset. Essays on the Spirit World. She read avidly, not believing, not disbelieving. She ate little but her body remained heavy. She hated its heaviness. In early visits to the hospital, Mother's body always seemed to have undergone a shocking amount of change. Smaller and smaller.

And sometimes, Dorothy told Andrew in November, one of the few things she told him about her past, sometimes as she sat in the L & K restaurant across from the motel sipping coffee and watching the truck drivers, she'd feel that she herself had been *added to* in some way, that she was carrying around what she secretly thought of as a spirit, an aura, something coming from the skin.

Even months later, she said, when she had taken a job, when she was sitting in a beery restaurant booth full of people, even then she'd still feel it. Something more than just the sorrow, something glowing off her skin like a blue gas flame, setting her apart.

"I believe in it," Andrew told her. He was slightly drunk. "I never saw how anyone could, you know, *not* think there were spirits like that."

As they lay there, Dorothy halfway believed in it again herself.

But no. She thought it through plainly the next afternoon in the clear fluorescent blank of work. No—the spirit feeling itself simply had not lasted. It was something she wanted to believe but couldn't. Though she couldn't believe the other either, she thought just as plainly. That things completely disappear. No. No to both.

It was important to her then, in November, to keep a grip on the clear way of thinking that she'd worked out for herself, by herself, since Mother's death. At the dentist's, she'd always been determined to remain aware of what was happening to her, and even as she breathed the gas she struggled to think: Now he's got the needle, now he's inserting the needle cotton too some metal sound a needle? No it's over, now it's over.

In the motel, on Rt. 101 just outside of Clague, Ohio, she'd lost her virginity to a truck driver, a small-boned smooth-skinned red-haired man on his way to Idaho. He bought her a bag of peanuts from the vending machine down the hall, bit her ear as they began to make love because, he told her later, he'd read somewhere that this would distract a virgin, make it less painful. She liked him. She was proud of herself as she watched his truck pull away, proud that she'd separated things so neatly. Sex first, then love—how could anyone handle both at once?

And with Andrew, she decided from the first, it would be sex, pure sex. It would have to be. Andrew was twenty-one that fall, younger than Dorothy by three years. He'd lived alone since he was seventeen. When he talked at all on the job it was in tense teenage bursts. He hated the name "Andy" as much as she hated "Dottie," but used it too, in the same way, letting the men at the office dismiss him with it, letting the women enjoy their maternal crushes on him. He kept to himself. He and Dorothy would watch each other sometimes across the wide room, not meeting eyes. Dorothy often thought about how young he seemed, always, even from a distance. Too young, really.

And she knew what was going to happen, liked knowing, liked it that he told her the very first week about the older woman in high school, the one in Newark, in Philadelphia, in Kentucky, how he'd been equally in love with each of them, too much in love, every time. For when he was having these affairs—and he was always having affairs, intense, monogamous three to six month long affairs—he could do or think of nothing else, nothing important, it was very feminine in a way, did she know what he meant?

"Sure," she answered.

"Sure," he repeated, looking at her, intrigued and maybe a little disappointed by how calmly she'd taken it. He couldn't figure her out, she liked to think. And she liked to let him do the talking. Not so much to keep up a distance but because that fall she was usually happy when they were together, creature-comfort happy, and there was no point, she told herself, in messing that up with talk. They ate. They made love.

"Can't—" she told him in November, her mouth full of spaghetti or cake or sausage. "Can't hold all this—"

Before, one day a week, she'd cleaned out her system with cranberry juice, apple juice, lettuce and vinegar. She would lose one and a half pounds per day exactly. It was exhilarating, fun even. Now fun was wolfing down a double helping of Cookies 'n Cream: whole cakey-thick oreo cookies swirled into vanilla ice cream. Their own discovery, their favorite dessert.

"When I first saw you," Andrew told her one night after a huge meal, "you looked like you were sucking in your whole body the way some people suck in their stomachs."

It was late November, and she had gained ten pounds. She'd begun walking with slower, looser movements. It was a relief to be so round, fat really, and not to worry about it or flaunt it or particularly hate it. Or even think about it, about anything much at all that fall, early winter. The Phoenix weather was glorious—sun all day in an absolutely cloudless blue sky, cool air, light breezes. She began walking to work. She stopped wearing high heels, stopped clipping her black hair, let it grow long so it brushed her face and eyelashes, always fringing her sight.

What she loved most that November was watching Andrew cook. She'd let her hair fall over one eye and sit crosslegged and silent on the cool-tiled kitchen floor in her underwear watching him crack eggs with an elaborate one-handed wrist flip. He spattered sauce as he stirred, threw out wide orange arcs of oregano or paprika. He beat cake batters with exaggerated force, the bowl grasped between his knees, his shirt off, his thick forearms knotted. He always worked up a sweat when he cooked.

Once, he told Dorothy that he liked to smell his own sweat at the office. "Lets me know I'm still all there," he said.

At work Dorothy began to notice the smell of her own thick hair, the faint oyster trace of last night's contraceptive form. She noticed the fruity perfume and avocado sandwiches of the woman next to her.

Sometimes she'd lazily wonder what it would feel like to be pregnant. She'd try to imagine it after a meal, in bed, resting her hand on her tight strained stomach, or at work, pushing out her stomach muscles and holding them like that, forcing her stomach into as round a shape as possible. But it was too hard, hard to imagine at all. She'd let her muscles relax, sneak off her shoes under her desk, rub her feet idly back and forth on the nubby beige carpet.

She and Andrew made love long and slow, sometimes both at night and the next morning, sometimes eating both before and after.

Even the talking they did seemed to Dorothy primarily physical. What she would remember afterwards was how warm and cool at the same time the new silky sheets had been, how his voice had slurred and his breath, hers too, had smelled of wine. What had they talked about? Him. The woman in Kentucky he thought he still loved. Stories Dorothy took in sleepily, picking up on the details—strawberry blonde hair dyed orange to spite him, the jerk she finally slept with, one day by the river, said she'd considered suicide more than once, made him weep more than once.

"Ohh," Dorothy would say, drawing out the word. Tasting it. "Mmhmm."

Privately, almost as an exercise, she went over things he said, mimicking in her mind his tone of Romantic suffering, his theatrical use of those deep-set dark eyes. She'd think of his general lack of interest in her, in asking about her own past. Not that she'd have told him much. But often she became secretly annoyed with him. Meanwhile, their sex got better and better.

It was Christmas week, a peak period of sex for them, *the* peak as it turned out, that he told her one night about the month he'd spent in the mental ward of a Newark hospital when he was nineteen. In general, she didn't take seriously his occasional references to mental problems. And he didn't bring up such things often. But this, an actual certifiable breakdown, this felt different.

Even if it wasn't completely true, which she knew was possible, the idea of shock treatments still fascinated her—much more than she let him know.

"What was it like?" she asked, sleepy-sounding.

He couldn't remember, he said in an unusually flat voice. She was lying against his chest then, feeling his voice vibrate in there, inside her chest too. He remembered only the helpless sensation of lying down, rubber in his mouth, as they prepared the treatment. A touch of metal on either side of his head. Then the trouble remembering what people looked like, certain faces.

What faces, she wondered, but didn't ask. Are you telling the truth? she wanted to say, for the first time. Really?

Instead she got out of bed and drank a slow glass of water alone in the kitchen.

She didn't call him the next day, but thought about him, it, the rubber in his mouth and the touch of metal, the whole idea. It was unimaginable; it made her think of the time when the doctor first talked about removing one of Mother's large soft breasts, and Dorothy had been unable to believe it, up to the day it happened.

She wondered where exactly the electricity was channeled in a shock treatment, how it felt as it happened, even if the feeling couldn't be remembered afterwards.

She didn't call Andrew for a week.

It was late January. Things were winding down. The Phoenix weather was still gorgeous, but normal by now. Andrew had begun staying over three, two nights a week instead of five. On New Year's day, the woman from Kentucky phoned him drunkenly long distance, said she wanted him to fly out and visit, just visit.

"The thing about her," Andrew told Dorothy after a near-silent late-January meal, "the thing is you can never tell when she's serious because she never knows. What she feels one day has nothing to do with what she feels the next. I mean it—she changes completely. But she has this way of making each man she's with feel like the only one . . . and he *is*, see, for *her*, that moment."

"Mmm," Dorothy murmured, and she stood to begin clearing the table, embarrassed by his over-bright black eyes.

Often around this time she would give brief deliberately closed-off answers. She watched herself do this, faintly pleased, then, the times she noticed herself being pleased, faintly embarrassed. But she couldn't help admiring her own calm. And she kept inviting him over, at least twice a week, and he kept coming. She wanted to keep up the sex as long as possible.

By mid-February she was definitely losing her appetite. She noted her own gradual loss of weight, sporadic loss of sleep, the general dulling of her lately overcharged senses. At work she did not return to her former quick Dottie style. Instead she still moved slowly, still looked at him sometimes across the office.

Though he seemed more foolish to her now, more self-indulgent than ever when he talked, which was seldom. But the sex, when they had it, was still good, better even, sometimes.

"Listen, I mean how do you feel about it?" he asked the night he told her, gently, that he was leaving. He wanted some kind of scene, a tender scene, she could tell, and she wasn't going to give it to him.

She shrugged. He kept staring at her like the laid-back Phoenix people used to stare in the office as she clicked by so fast.

"But I just can't tell," he said finally in his flattest voice, sulking. "I never could tell what you were feeling, you know?"

She nodded. This gave her a lift, seemed a kind of triumph, almost, as she drove him to the airport the next week. It was mid-April. She wore green sunglasses and a short-sleeved cotton dress, pale yellow, and she drove without talking. He was nervous, she could tell, but she made no effort to figure out what else he might be.

"I bet she changed the locks," Andrew said out loud as the first TO AIRPORT signs flipped by.

"What locks?"

"Our apartment together, the one we still had when I left." He was speaking more to himself than to her.

In the past weeks she'd managed to hear little of his plans. Now, as the car was pulled into the winding maze of parking ramps and terminal signs, she felt curious.

"So you've still got the key?"

"Sure," he said. Then, after she'd backed the car into a slot, "God—I'm starving."

They ordered gin and tonics, chili, taco chips and guacamole dip at the cowboy airport bar. Dorothy's stomach had shrunken drastically in the past weeks. She picked at the chips, watched him eat. In the dim reddish brown leather booth he looked again, like the night she first saw him, as pale as his shirt. His black deep-socketed eyes were shadowed. He'd lost weight too, she noticed for the first time. She watched the bones of his jaw as he chewed. She touched his foot lightly with hers under the table. She wanted to move her foot slowly up against his leg, move over next to him so she could touch him under his white shirt. When had they last slept together? For a moment she couldn't remember. Certainly she hadn't known as it happened that it was the last time.

"Know what they oughta have in airport bars?" she asked, her voice too loud.

"What?" He was chewing chips, hunched over his gin and tonic, elbows on the table.

"Little closet rooms where people could go and screw for the last time before a flight. Or businessmen and strange girls, you know?"

"Yeah." He swallowed, just starting to look at her.

"Do you think that'd be a good line? To use on some man—I mean if I went up to some man and said 'You know what they oughta have in airport bars?' "

He was really looking at her now. She brushed her hair out of her eyes. "You're not gonna do that, are you?" he said. "After my plane goes?"

She shrugged. In the red-lit bar mirror, she caught a glimpse of herself as they stood up to leave. She looked, she thought, unfamiliar. Her hair was full and dark all around her face; her dress seemed baggy, her bare arms surprisingly thin.

Then they were walking down the vast canyon expanse of terminal and talking about back east. How thin his jacket and white cotton shirt might be as he stepped into a Kentucky spring rain. Would the woman meet him at the airport? Dorothy wanted to ask. Instead she found herself saying, "God, I *miss* Ohio, you know? It was so wet there and green—"

And she was standing in a Ladies Room booth, covering her face with her hands, overcome by an unexpected wave of longing for drizzly tree-darkened Ohio: the old white frame houses and mud and squirrels and her fourteen-year-old self, lying awake all night reading so she wouldn't make any mistakes, ever, in her life. Had she believed that? Dorothy stood there sniffling and not quite crying. Really? She couldn't remember.

A little girl was banging on the stall door, and outside a far-off loudspeaker voice announced a flight—his?—so Dorothy pushed out and wiped her face on a brown paper towel, disgusted with herself.

Her heels clicked across the bathroom tile in weak echoey imitation of her old walk. She ran down the long orange carpet to his bench, saw him from a distance looking paler than before, his traveling case clenched between his knees.

"Sorry," she said, out of breath as she sat down beside him. "It's just that I felt so dumb and sentimental all of a sudden. No, I mean—" She shot a glance at the terminal clock, late, less than ten minutes to go. "—I mean back in the bar I just felt so *horny*, watching you."

"Me too." He didn't look up. He took a long breath. "Something about us eating together, I guess. Does it every time."

She half nodded, not looking at him either. After a moment more, she stood. She had wanted to be the one to stand first. They held hands walking to the gun-detector machine.

"If the apartment was half my rent, even if it is in her name, I'd think they couldn't arrest me for breaking and entering, wouldn't you?" His voice as they approached the line was the same Jersey voice he'd used that first night. An accent he must, she realized, fall into when especially nervous. "See, I can imagine her changing her mind about me in the time it takes to fly out there and changing the apartment locks fast, the whole works. But it's half mine, still—"

He took his place in line and paused, breathless, seeming for once to be embarrassed by his own talk. When he spoke again, it was quietly, slowing down, leaning close to her. He was next.

"See," he said, "even if she does feel nothing for me anymore, I feel like she's still part mine, don't you think?"

At that moment, right in front of the gun-detector belt, this seemed an extremely complicated question, and Dorothy felt she was way back at the office coffee machine hearing the equally unanswerable story of the woman in the car. Andrew's face looked as strange as the airport faces all around him, his inky madman eyes a wholly unknown quantity.

"Hey you, let's go have a drink—" Dorothy said, almost shouted. For they were announcing his flight, now boarding.

She turns when he turns, starts off down the terminal moving fast, as if she too is hurrying to catch a plane—though she's conscious as she moves against the crowd that she carrries no suitcase or overnight bag, not even a purse. She swings her bare arms, walks faster. Towards what? The bar?

Maybe. When she reaches it she slows, hesitates, glancing into the open doorway at the reddish-shadowed men. She stops completely, thinking of the truck driver, her own secret triumph as she'd watched him roll away. She ducks her head, continues walking.

Her past month's half-conscious sense of victory feels silly and hollow now, feels childish. She moves faster, pushing through the first giant glass doors she sees, rushing outside into the noon sunshine and breeze and the enormous airport parking lot. Half hour parking. Out here, she can feel how loose her dress is, how her short cotton sleeves blow around her arms.

She drives straight home; once home, walks straight to the kitchen. She eats. Cheese from the package, standing in the open refrigerator door, milk in gulps from the carton, three slices of Wonder Bread with more chunks of cheese, more milk.

Her stomach stretches. Maybe it will never again be as flat as it's been these past weeks, or as round as it was last fall.

What had he said? That before they met she'd looked like she was sucking in her whole body. When had he said that? It's hard to remember exactly, near the beginning, she thinks. She pulls the last slice of cheese from the wrapper, the refrigerator door propped open against her back. In the bar, she'd felt such an unexpected and immediate desire for him. She still feels it, that urgency, though she knows it won't last. By next week, or next month, it may still be painful, but it will be something she remembers, gone as an actual live feeling.

Why don't you get rid of the pictures? she'd asked him early on, when she saw photos of the Kentucky woman in his bedroom drawer. Why don't you burn them or something? You'd like that.

"Hell no," he'd said, slurry drunk. "That's like burning up someone's *soul*. I mean it—African natives get scared out of their minds if you show them a photo of someone. They know. It's the *soul* in that little square."

He believed things like that, Dorothy thinks now. Or at least she guesses it must be true. He must really believe.

She doesn't. But still. As she stands in the kitchen holding the empty cheese wrapper, she wishes she had some photograph of him to prove he was here, that they were, and that they had something.

The sheets. She lets the wrapper drop to the floor and steps into the bedroom, pulls the silky bed sheets they bought together off the mattress, rushes into the living room trailing then, then rushes back empty-handed and pulls open her drawers, finds, immediately, one of his socks, then, moments later, on the closet floor, its mate.

Then she remembers the special no-stick frying pan he bought and she fetches that too, dumps all of it in the one clear space on her tan-carpeted living room floor.

It is a small pile, unimpressive, and her heart is still beating fast. She looks around the crowded room, all that old Ohio furniture, then looks down at herself.

Her body. The right place to look, certainly. Because if there was anything, it was that. She presses one hand against her stomach, her damp cotton skirt.

Maybe I'm pregnant, she says to herself quite clearly.

It's possible. Unlikely, but possible. Because, she thinks slowly, being pregnant is a purely physical phenomenon. A pinpoint hole in a diaphragm, a heart stopping. She presses her warm stomach even harder, tries to imagine it stretched out unrecognizably. Only this time she adds, tries to add, a baby. When my stomach gets that big, she thinks, it's not completely mine anymore. Not completely. She stands still, considering this.

Then she unbuttons her dress, fingers stiff. She slips it off over her head, smelling sweat as she raises her arms, then unhooks her bra, pulls down her thin pantyhose, her underpants. She walks naked into the kitchen, where it's light, and stands on her bare feet on the cool floor and looks down.

Her breasts are still large but not melon-shaped anymore, not sturdy-looking, heavy and loosely packed, almost hanging. And her stomach has lost its curve. It stretches down pale and flat, only slightly rounded from the bread and cheese. Her legs are looser versions of their former shape, the packing gone there too. Even her feet seem different, the bones showing more, or maybe not. She can't tell.

She sits on one of the cold wooden chairs, Mother's, and still looks down, trying to get used to it, this new body, still hers all right. She stares for a long while, and one thought keeps coming back and back.

Where did it go?

Where does solid living fat go when it disappears? There had been so much of it—heavy and soft as Mother's, an extra heaviness Dorothy had felt when she climbed stairs, her heart beating faster. Where had it all gone? Burned up into energy? What energy? Nothing she's done in these past weeks seems to have used any energy at all, not a single movement. She has not even really cried. She can't get over this. Her fat.

Where is it?

The Woman Who Thinks She's in Love with My Husband

Amber Coverdale Sumrall

She whispers
into the black
telephone,
her throat swollen
with sighs,
leaves breathless
messages
of longing,
invitation,
Sometimes
she hangs up
when I answer
and the hum of her
clings to wires,
resonates in the
dead air between
his body and mine.
The woman who thinks
she's in love
with my husband
makes me wonder
what I'm missing.

In the Box Called Pleasure

Kim Addonizio

My husband left me because he felt like he had no power. Now he has it; I call him up and beg him to come over and fuck me. I've just quit cigarettes and all I can think about is how good it would feel to take a deep drag of smoke into my lungs. He pushes his cock down my throat until I gag on it, makes me keep it there until I have to relax; if I don't I'll choke. I relax. Everything is fine between us.

I have papers on my desk that read Dissolution of Marriage. I call and ask my husband for his social security number so I can fill them out; then I scream at him; then I don't do anything. I am having a crisis of self-esteem because I am ugly and stupid, with a bad memory to boot. I forget names, including my own, and most of what happened in books I read. *Madame Bovary*, for example. I remember that Emma kills herself, but not how. *Sentimental Education*: someone named Frederic rides in a carriage and complains and is in love with a married woman. This is in the box called Flaubert. Also: origins of the modern novel. The Seine. Someone making love. A view of mist-covered pines from the apartment I rented one summer. End of box.

After I phone my husband he comes over and mashes me against the wall with his body. I love the feeling of being physically trapped. It's my worst fear, psychologically, why I ran from all my lovers before him. I realize I've lived by definitions; now there aren't any and it's impossible to function. Nature isn't friendly but it exhibits a profound order. I think that if I could somehow stir myself into it as one more ingredient, I would know how to get through this. He's silent on the other end of the phone and I wonder what he's thinking, if he gives a shit if I live or die. The only way I can get over him is if I die.

I don't die.

I live in a mansion with ghosts. At night the former lady of the house floats, transparent, over the lawn, calling each of her children by name. Sometimes they answer. It's that or cats. A frieze over my fireplace shows a naked man in a chariot, a horse, cherubs, women in filmy robes. I don't touch anything for fear I'll break it. I can't remember how I got here, but it's pleasant enough. The floor shines and there are windows all around, and a piece of furniture called a swooning couch. After a discreet knock, food appears on a tray outside my door; I never see the servants. Mostly I stay in my room, but sometimes I go down the wide red-carpeted staircase and into the drawing room, which is dark and filled with gloomy paintings of people I don't know in elaborate gold frames.

I masturbate constantly, imagining that my husband is ordering me to spread my legs. He slaps my thighs; if I try to close them he slaps them harder. He ties me to the brass bed and I can't get up to answer the servants' knock. After he fucks me he throws a fire ladder out the window, climbs down it and doesn't come back.

I call for help the first few days but nobody comes; nobody even knocks on the door anymore. After a few weeks I starve to death. I rise above my body and it looks so pathetic I can't believe I didn't get rid of it sooner; my mouth is open, my eyes have a scummy film over them, there's shit and piss everywhere, not to mention blood because I got my period. I'm glad my ugly, filthy body can't drag me down any longer; now I'm light as a feather, I spin around near the ceiling feeling like I've just chain-smoked an entire pack of cigarettes. At first it's fun but then I start to get bored with being dead and wonder what else there is to do. I decide to try masturbating and guess what, it's great: when I come I fly into a million pieces and it takes hours to collect myself from the corners of the room. I notice I can't go through walls, though, and that worries me. I don't want to be stuck here in this room with my body forever. It stinks, for one thing. A fly crawls over my cheek and into my mouth.

I'm lonely here, and I miss my husband. I write him a long letter, a letter full of questions about us. What is there between us, I ask him, besides our sex? Is there any point to staying married? What does that mean, anyway? We don't live together. We rarely see each other. I wear my wedding band on my right hand, if I wear it at all. His name is engraved on the inside so I won't forget it. Marriage is a) a capitalist institution for the subjugation of women and preservation of male power and authority; b) an anachronism; c) a way to get health insurance; d) a species of insect.

Dear, Darling, Sweetheart:

How I miss your hands on me, the smell of your skin, your tattoos, the harsh tobacco taste of your tongue. Though you should try not to smoke so much. I wish we could talk sometimes, instead of just fucking. You've become a total stranger to me except in bed, where I feel like we're the same person. I know it's the same for you. Marriage didn't kill our desire. Why can't we be friends? Don't you like me, just a little?

Love,
Your Wife

Every day I walk past the table in the hall where the servants leave the mail. There's nothing yet. Long-distance relationships suck. I wish there were someone here to fuck, but I'm too hung up on my husband to even consider it. Most men are lousy fucks anyway; that box is crammed full. Can't get it up, can't keep it up, won't eat pussy, comes in three seconds, holds me like I'm made of glass, can't find my clit, won't use a rubber, fucks in total silence, expects me to do all the work, thinks of it as work, as proof of his power, as pure release: I have to come, there's a hole, I'd like to come in that but shit there's a person attached to it. My husband is an incredible fuck. I'm not sure what we do should even be called fucking. How can I give that up?

My husband left me to punish me; I wasn't behaving like A Wife. Fuck that. We didn't know each other very well. I'm starting to enjoy my freedom, even though my heart is a crushed useless lump of tissue that gurgles constantly like bad plumbing. I blame him for everything. Then I blame myself. Then I blame my father, my brothers, and God. It's impossible to have a relationship, nothing lasts anyway, there are no models, men go into the woods and beat little drums and scream, gender is meaningless, or it's everything; I want a partner, I need to be strong alone since we live and die alone anyway. I want someone to love me. That's what everybody wants, right? Besides being stupid, ugly and amnesiac I am incapable of seeing beyond my own selfish ego. Until I do, I'll never get what I want.

Once we were happy.

Once he looked at me and I knew he loved and wanted me and I wasn't scared he would stop.

Once there was a queen who was the most beautiful woman in the land; everyone said so. Secretly, though, she knew she was a disgusting, hideous creature who had fooled everyone. Either that, or she was totally insane. She didn't know which would be worse, to find out she was really a monster or really a crazy nut, so she ordered her subjects to remove all the mirrors from the kingdom. Her husband the king humored her, but every year on her birthday he tried to give her a mirror as a present, figuring it was a phobia she would overcome in time. Every year the queen refused the present, and ordered the mirror taken out to the forest and smashed with a ball peen hammer.

One year the king found such a gorgeously exquisite mirror that the entire court urged the queen to accept it, but it was the same old story: smash the shit out of it. The woodsman whose job it was to do this took it out to the forest, but he couldn't bring himself to ruin a thing so beautiful. He went deep into the forest, and there he found a small house where he hid the mirror.

He broke a window in the house and brought the pieces back in a leather bag, to prove to the queen that he had done her bidding, and the queen put the bag in the bottom drawer of her dresser with all the other bags from previous years.

One afternoon when she was out jogging, the queen ran farther than she had ever run before, and came upon the little house hidden deep in the forest. Being extremely thirsty, she went inside to look for something to drink. As soon as she entered the house she saw the mirror, leaning against the wall under the broken window. She wanted to leave, but it was too late; as soon as she caught a glimpse of herself she stopped, transfixed, and couldn't look away.

I think all this has something to do with Lacan, whose theories I've forgotten.

Once we were fucking, I was on top, and between one thrust and the next I felt I didn't love him anymore. Suddenly I was just fucking a male body, not his body, and I felt a sense of freedom and power: now I could fuck anyone, do anything, create my own life. Then I was in love with him again and I thought maybe I'd imagined it; can love go in and out like breath?

I've got to find a way to get out of here and get to town. In town there's a store: nail polish. Tampax. Liquor. Cigarettes. Lipstick. I don't have to wait here passively for something to happen. Do you think she saw a monster in the mirror? Makeup, in the seventies, meant slavery to imposed definitions of beauty; now it's assertive, self-adornment, a hip feminist statement.

I hate it that everything changes.

Themes so far: loss of power; loss of memory; self-hatred; definitions. A large crow lands on the lawn. In the box called pleasure:

I'm riding my bike around the streets of our neighborhood. My mom, who happens to be queen of the kingdom, has given me a letter to mail. I'm proud of being chosen to do this, especially since my mom never speaks to me; she spends most of her time shut up in her room, she is beautiful but crazy as a loon. But this morning she called me in, handed me a letter. Her stunning black hair was loose around her shoulders. She used to jog and work out and play tennis, but now she just lies around watching TV all day and she's starting to get fat. I don't think she realizes this because there aren't any mirrors in the house; I have to go over to friends' houses to see what I look like. I'm blonde, I don't look a thing like my mother but I'm cute as hell. I'm six years old and I want to be on TV. My name is Buffie. I adore my mother. When she gives me the letter I feel warm and happy; she hands it to me and kisses me on my forehead.

"Don't tell your brothers," she whispers. "Or your father, either. This will be our little secret. All right, darling?"

When she calls me "darling" I think I'll pass out from being so thrilled. I tuck the letter into a pocket of my dress. She turns back to "One Life to Live," and I go out of her room and down the stairs.

On the second floor I run into one of my seven brothers.

"C'mere, Buffie," he says. "I've got something in my room for you."

My seven brothers are all older than I am. They take me for pizza and ice cream, or ignore me; sometimes they protect me from our violent father, the king, and sometimes they tie me up and torment me.

"What've you got?" I say, suspicious. "I have to go do something for mom."

"It will only take a sec," my brother says.

I follow him into his room. My brother's room is filled with rats: cages and cages of them, sleeping in wood chips or running on treadmills or staring out at me, their tiny hands clawing at the wire mesh. They give me the creeps, like my brother. I don't trust him.

"Sit down there," my brother says, pointing to his bed. He has a can of Pam—spray-on cooking oil—in his right hand. He takes a baggie, sprays the Pam into the baggie, and holds it over my nose and mouth.

"Breathe, Buffie," my brother says.

I take a breath. Immediately my ears start ringing, the room recedes, I know I'm still in it but I'm miles away, I can't find my body. I try to lift my hand, fall backwards on the bed; it takes hours to fall, I keep expecting to feel the bed but don't. I can hear my brother laughing somewhere. Then there's something hot between my legs and I feel like I have to pee, or maybe I am peeing; it's sticky, my underwear is wet, I try to move but I'm trapped under something I can't see. I'm blind. I start to scream; I open my mouth and something cold rushes into my lungs and I feel fantastic, I'm a big balloon, I start to giggle imagining myself as a balloon in a dress, my skin stretched tight over my enormous face I'm laughing so hard now I ache, more cold air filling me up I'm rocking back and forth in a rowboat in the middle of an ocean, rats are swimming by, their hairless tails whipping the water. The boat goes under.

I'm in my brother's room again. My head aches, I'm lying on his bed with my legs twisted open and my underwear off. He's standing over at the wall of cages, his back to me. He takes out a rat and brings it over to the bed.

"Ugh," I say. "Get it away from me." He knows I hate his rats.

"You'd better run," he says, smiling. He makes like he's going to toss the rat at me, but doesn't. I start crying. It hurts between my legs now. I jump up from his bed and run out, leaving my underwear.

I run downstairs to the garage and get on my bicycle. It's a pink five-speed Schwinn with streamers on the handles. As I ride, I feel more wetness come out of me. I press my crotch against the bike seat, rub it back and forth.

At the mailbox on the corner I jump off my bike, then throw myself onto the grass. I lie on my stomach and put my fist under my cunt, between it and the ground, and grind against it faster and faster. Cars drive by. I can't stop, I hope nobody pulls over. I keep fucking my fist, trying to open my cunt around it. Finally I come. I've never masturbated before this. I don't understand what's just happened.

I remember my mother's letter and find it in my pocket, all wrinkled and creased. I smooth it as well as I can, then open the mailbox and drop the letter into its mouth.

Dear Woodsman:

I hate my husband, the king. Unless you become my lover I'm going to kill myself. I can't divorce him because I'm terrified to live on my own, without money. If I could look forward to seeing you each week, death wouldn't exert such a powerful pull. I can't live for my children; they're on their own. Meet me at the house in the woods, and bring condoms.

Your Queen

Letters are a woman's form. And diaries. The domestic isn't historical; in most of history women don't exist. The self is constituted in memory, so I don't have a self, just a few ideas for one. I sit for hours in the room that used to be my mother's, looking out at the lawn and the enormous fountain; it's the size of an Olympic swimming pool. I'm dying for a cigarette. I drink too much coffee, chew gum, bite my fingernails; I'm not going to make it. I pull Dante's box out of the closet. Open it a crack, flames and shit and vomit spill out; I've only read the *Inferno*. My mom's in there. The Geryon flies past my window, or maybe it's an eagle; I should get a bird book. I wonder why birds sing, anyway. Is it necessary for their survival? There's one here that drives me crazy every morning, waking me at dawn. I'd like to sleep in, just once. All night it's ghosts, and then this fucking bird.

Dear Mom,

I don't know what the mail service is like down there but I hope you get this in time for your birthday. Even though you were a lousy mother I loved you; I couldn't help it. I was only ten when you died. Why did you leave me? Why didn't you protect me from my brothers, those shits? My childhood was one long molestation. It's all your fault. How am I supposed to get past this and stop being a victim? Happy Birthday. I'm sorry there's no present but you were always so hard to buy for.

Love,
Buffie

p.s. Would you please stop calling my brothers' names every night? They are all doing fine. They have wives and ex-wives and girlfriends and kids and cocaine habits and big-screen TV's. You're the one that's dead.

I'm so depressed. I try to live as though life has meaning, I know it doesn't mean anything. You get old and sexually undesirable and then you die, or you kill yourself before that. Before my husband left me I felt loved, attractive, sexy: he grabs me by my cunt in the kitchen, leads me to the hall and fucks me on the floor, we're two animals, I love that he never thinks during sex or at least never seems to; I love being the instrument of his pleasure; I love the tiny space on his left eyelid—I think it's his left—where a lash is missing. I can't remember now. I've been abandoned. Or I set things up so he would abandon me; I didn't love him enough, my ex-lovers came out of the woodwork to have lunch and flirt, my husband was jealous, I didn't reassure him. Now I'm suffering.

In that box:

A six-year old boy on his way to school in LA gets caught in the crossfire between two gangs and dies. A man with a Serbian mother and Croatian father gets drafted into both armies, runs away to America; in America he drives a taxi in New York City in summer, a lower circle of hell. In the Wood of Suicides my mother moans. A woman answers an ad for a maid, goes to the door, it's a Hell's Angels house, they pull her inside and rape her, later she escapes out a window and goes home to her alcoholic mother. She's seventeen when all this happens, then finds out she's pregnant and gets an abortion, but it turns out she's carrying twins and the doctor has only aborted one. That night at home she's feverish, delirious, the second fetus comes out, she's hallucinating, passing out; she wakes up, blood all over the sheets. Before this her father fucked her for years; she finally told her mother, who had her committed. She's my best friend.

It is, after all, the love of women that sustains me.

Another friend says, "Do you feel that sex saved your life?" She means boys. Actually I think art saved my life at the time it needed saving, when I was doing too much heroin and fucking junkies and living in roach-filled apartments with gunshots in the street every night and the guy upstairs beating the shit out of his girlfriend. Now art isn't enough; I have that, and friends who love me—they write me letters, even if my husband doesn't—and I'm miserable.

One day I'm whining about my life and a girlfriend looks at me and says, "Well, Buffie, the important thing is to feel bad." She's right, I'm complaining about nothing, I should be grateful.

I'm still miserable.

There's a knock on the door. It's my husband, finally; he's come all this way to see me, he says he's sorry for everything and it doesn't matter what happened between us, whatever it was—who knows what's true or real anyway—he says, "I feel the pain and love and desire in your words to me and you're right, darling, sometimes it seems so perfectly simple and natural and right between us, even out of bed on occasion," he pushes me down on the bed, begins to rip my clothes off, *rip* my troubles are over *rip* this is all complete fantasy; *rip* I hate academics, *rip* my underwear flies across the room, a bird goes up to heaven in a rush of wings and it starts raining, sheets of rain over the lawn and fountain, the roof of the house, the windows are streaming, *rip*, *rip*, *rip*, I can't stop remembering love.

The Lake

Susan Lewis

There was no need for words in this house surrounded by snow.

Until you came.

I have been here two months with nothing to remind me of the use of language except Barney, the caretaker for these lakefront houses. Barney trudges through the snow once a day with his ragged old Samoyed to see if I'm OK. He has lived through seven winters here. He knows how to be alone with the snow-covered woods and the frozen lake and no human being for miles.

Our love for the lake, our distance from things human, binds us, Barney and me.

I have never known anything like this lake. Its solid white expanse, uncrackable as granite. Beneath the frozen surface, the slumbering water moves in its slow currents. I sit naked on the floor gazing out the window at the white lake glowing in the moonlight. Its sharp reverberant groans echo with pleasure or pain, I cannot tell which. They sound so much alike. It is a huge living drum, a vast primordial creature, groaning with desire.

You cannot hear it. You are sleeping too deeply.

I exaggerate my isolation: there is the Lebanese shopkeeper whose groceries I buy, who talks of what people once bought (flour, baking powder, meat) and what they now buy (frozen dinners, liquor, glossy magazines) as proof of the disintegration of the family. And the pimply faced teenager who blushes when I pull up to have my tank filled, and calls me Ma'am. The one talks so much, and the other so little, I am barely called upon to speak.

My fear of losing touch with words surprises me. I am generally content to lose touch. Letting go comes easily to me. I have often wanted to describe the pleasure of it. The sense of freedom. Of limitless possibility. I have no need for the past, no need for memory. They are nothing but shackles, calculated to weigh me down. To cripple me.

I have cut away so much in these last months. In this blank white landscape, in this house lived in by no one, with no sign of myself but my paints and spattered clothes, I have eliminated all trace of the past. It is easy to convince myself I know no one but Barney and the Lebanese grocer and the gasoline attendant. That I never knew anyone else. Not even you.

Another thing I have in common with Barney: he shows no more interest in the past than I do.

At times I have worried about becoming addicted to the high of letting go, as others (like you) are addicted to the high of drugs, or alcohol. Addictions reveal the desire for high points. I know there is something wrong with this desire, with trying to build a life from solid walls of high points. Wishing to concentrate them too densely.

I understand the need for balance. For instance, when it comes to painting; how a heavy black brush stroke can lose its power if surrounded by too much darkness. There are those who fight this, painters prone to excess. You, of course, are one of them. I have seen gallery-goers pass your raging black canvases with a glance and a yawn. I have shaken my head at your failure to communicate the fire that consumes you. That drive for intensity stirs me. I wish I were not so sure of the necessity for lows and middles as well as highs.

Before I leave this house I will paint my own canvas of excess. Not in black but in white. I have become so intimate with white, here; every day I grow closer to it. It suits me: the color of emptiness. The color of solitude. The color of forgetting.

I did not expect to sleep tonight.

I watch you from my position beside the uncurtained window. Reflected off the white expanse of the lake, the moonlight gilds the room an icy silver.

Two days ago I went to the grocer for peroxide. With my new white hair I feel closer to the snowy landscape. I imagine myself crouched on the frozen surface of the lake, blending in as Peary, Barney's dog, blends in. I would like to wear a white snowsuit. I would like a photograph of myself crouched on the lake. Blending in. Invisible.

The beauty of the lake's white expanse, stretching to the peripheries of vision: the suggestion of infinity. The trees on the bank with their stark black trunks: a reminder of the finite. Of mortality.

I am struggling to evoke this expanse in my paintings. Positioning my subject in a smaller and smaller corner of the canvas, filling the center with a wider field of white. Exploring the outer boundaries of the frame. Challenging the expectations of the eye.

Painting is a language of immediacy, is it not? The image exists in space rather than time. It is self-contained. It needs no antecedent. Still (you would remind me), the viewer must be forced to accept this immediacy. Familiar conventions must be violated in order to jolt expectations based on memory, habit, what has been seen before. The viewer must be forced to experience the canvas on its own terms, without reference to what she has come to expect.

Barney has been posing for canvas number VII. I've used only his head and neck: he's too shy to pose nude.

Only the eyes remain unfinished. Their expression eludes me. They cannot know too much or too little. Until I can imagine them they will stare, blank and hollow as the sockets of ancient Greek statues.

Perhaps I will title this series "Self-Portrait I-X."

Your name is irrelevant. So are the details of our past together. It was long enough to seem all-important at the time. Short enough to be forgotten.

Today was, apparently, my birthday. Perhaps I should say yesterday. It is so close, now, to morning. So close to tomorrow.

I would never have noticed the date if Barney hadn't knocked on my door as I stepped from the shower. He hung back near the doorway, diffident as always, ragged cap in hand, looking almost sheepish as he wished me happy birthday. When I asked how he knew, he said, "There's a man here to see you."

I stared at him, my wet body dripping a puddle on the floor. "Somebody sent me a card?"

"No, there's a man here. He's waiting in my trailer. I wasn't sure you'd want visitors; I know you like to keep to yourself."

From pale puffy lids Barney's eyes gleamed. Did you notice them, as small and sharp as chips of glass, as clear as tropical seas? They sparkle like misplaced jewels from his coarse, pitted skin, gouged by a deep scar in the hollow of one cheek. His red nose swollen by cold or drink, I cannot tell which.

There were clouds, a threat of storm, in those sea-clear eyes. Was he hoping I'd send him back with a refusal? Could it be he was jealous? He seemed disappointed when I said I'd see you. As if I was betraying something we had together. Our commitment to solitude.

I asked where Peary was. The storm seemed to gather in his eyes. He said the dog had stayed behind with you. As if Peary remembered you from some other time, although that was impossible. I have often wondered why you are loved so readily by animals, without caring for them, particularly.

I wonder why you thrive on memory. Perhaps the power it offers, over other people's emotions? I prefer forgetting, the power it gives me, over my own.

There is a full length mirror in this bathroom. I am sure a woman uses this house in the summer. One whose body is the focal point of her vanity. I imagine her standing before this mirror after hot afternoons sunning on the green mesh lounge chair (tucked now in the back of the hall closet). Examining her tan lines. Checking the flesh at the back of her thighs.

I have always felt close to my body, secure in its compactness, its lack of surprise. Even in adolescence it changed only subtly, developing no curve that did not emerge organically from what had been before. Still, the body I saw in the mirror was something new, something different than the body I stood in ten years ago. This body was slimmer, stronger than that one. This skin was tougher, more weathered. Like an animal's skin. Like a shell. The woman standing before the mirror studying her naked body was less vulnerable than the woman you knew ten years ago. Less exposed.

I did not remember what you looked like until you walked in the door.

The features I recognized first were those which had changed with time. Once (the memory rushed in on me, sharp and sudden as a muscle cramp) you had been large, dwarfing me; I took pleasure in your generous supply of flesh. Now you seemed shrunken. Black eyes which had once winked from behind round cheeks had widened, staring from a face constructed of unfamiliar angles. Excess skin hung loose from your cheekbones, folded deeply around your mouth like an emptied sack.

How like me to get to memory backwards, from the perception of change.

Still, by whatever route, it came upon me. I did not know how to resist it.

Then I noticed the features that had not changed, as one suddenly takes notice of things seen every day, and so invisible. Your wide fingertips, with nails shaped like shovels. The metallic colors glinting from your beard. Your neck so long it seems bent at the adams' apple, as if at a joint.

I wondered how my own changes looked to you. If you noticed the ones I was aware of, or if your observations would reveal self-deception on my part, shattered illusions on yours.

I could not bring myself to ask.

It frightened me, the power you might have, from having known me before. A power I had not chosen to give away. Had no ability to withhold.

We stood in the doorway. Snow gusted in on a sudden draft. I said, "Come in. It's freezing!"

The situation struck me as funny. The way you inclined your head when you said, "What. What is it?" joining in my laughter even as you asked the question, was as suddenly familiar as it had been completely forgotten.

You said, "It's good to see you."

You embraced me. A light, friendly hug.

Instead of letting go you held me, pressing me to your chest.

At some point our embrace was no longer light and friendly. You were pressing my body against yours. I could feel your chin resting on the top of my head. Your breath tickled my ear as you murmured into my hair, "It's really good to see you."

Then you released me, passing your hand through the short ruff of my hair. The same gesture one might use with an adolescent boy, jumpy about physical intimacy. "You look great," you said. "Still a rebel."

I left the room to make tea and felt relieved when you asked for coffee instead. I did not remember you drinking coffee.

Eventually I asked you. We had been talking about this and that: my painting and yours, subsequent lovers, trips abroad. Small talk about big things. Conversation intended to reestablish intimacy, although it only emphasized the distance we had drifted apart. I swallowed my last gulp of tea, putting the mug on the floor before looking at you. It took a fair amount of courage to do.

"So what's this all about?" I asked. Waving at the room, at the two of us sitting in front of the fire, at the house, silent except for the hum of the refrigerator, at the darkening window (for night, soon to fall, was something that could no longer be ignored).

I liked the way you looked at me. A search for understanding, not a jockeying look at all. You laughed. I remembered then how much you'd always laughed at me, not a demeaning laugh but genuine amusement, a laugh I had liked for confessing how much wasn't understood rather than pretending to an understanding that wasn't real.

You said, "I couldn't imagine never seeing you again."

Perhaps you saw the panic on my face. You said, "Relax. I'm not asking you for anything."

I did relax then. I stopped being afraid to look at you. At the same time part of me was disappointed. I could see you were telling the truth.

I had not remembered your snuffling, puppyish snores.

When some small sound rouses you, the rustle of skin against skin as I shift my legs, you grunt inquiringly, muster words garbled by sleep. "Are you coming back to bed?" Or, "Are you OK?"

I murmur by way of assent, or laugh at you, and the snoring resumes.

This is the only night you will spend here.

The pleasure, being only for tonight, is the pleasure of the moment, as blank and pure as snow. It is for moments like this I have cultivated the art of letting go.

That is not quite the truth. The pleasure of the moment is not blank at all. Its brilliance is intensified by the shadow of its approaching end. That sweetness of a pleasure whose end approaches, second by second. That terrible necessity of contrast. Of balance.

You asked about the lake. You said, "It sounds alive."

At that moment I wondered if I needed to cut away as much as I have, in my life.

Then I looked at the backs of my canvases propped against the walls, and knew I did. I could never paint with you in my life. I could only turn away from you to the canvas once.

It is never painless, this process of making choices known as life.

I joined you at the window. The sky was washed in pinks and greys, the pale pastels of a winter sunset. You said, "Shall we have a picnic? I brought champagne."

I layered sweaters beneath my parka. You swathed yourself in blankets pulled from my bed, explored the cupboards for glasses. I felt them bulging in your pockets as we walked arm in arm through the snow. Their sharpness made me think of the weight you'd lost. A thyroid problem, you explained, with a wry shrug. Your bemused aknowledgment of the deterioration that is aging.

Walking towards the snow-covered lake, I imagined the sharpness of your hipbones pressing naked into mine. We have both lost our cushions of flesh over the years. The padding of youth, it seems, could not withstand the buffeting of experience. Our bodies' soft roundnesses, along with other kinds, have been whittled away.

As soon as we stepped onto the lake you stopped me, no more than a subtle pressure on my arm. How easily I recognized your physical signals, a knowledge stored in the unconscious and never lost, like kissing.

The sounds are startling, at first, as if a great creature is belching beneath one's feet. I laughed when you turned back towards the bank. I, too, felt insecure when I first stepped out on this lake, heard it rumble beneath my feet. I feared the sudden fissure of this frozen crust, dreaded drowning in those restless, frigid currents.

"It doesn't approve of you," I teased. Pulling you by the hand, dragging you towards the middle.

The sky was a deep rose. The only light glowed from the lake's white surface. You brushed the snow from a patch of ice. It shined as if wet, although it was too cold to melt.

That ice is strangely dark, more mysterious than black: the darkness of something colorless. I have spent hours tracing the cracks piercing the ice like webs spun one beneath another, into the depths. Hours, gazing at the bubbles frozen in the midst of rising, months ago, towards the surface. I have loved this lake for its vast expanse of emptiness. Its purity. Until I stood beside you and imagined what you saw, I was not aware that just beneath this wide white void the past is trapped, arrested, perfectly preserved.

You traced your finger above a bubble risen almost to the surface, frozen as it was about to burst. The lake rumbled, a deep satisfied groan, as if responding to your touch. You unwrapped a blanket from your shoulders and threw it down, then set the "table" with great ceremony: champagne, jelly jars for glasses, an apple I didn't know I had, a bar of Italian chocolate.

It was impossible to resist the impulse to kiss your neck. You pulled me to you, sinking onto the blanket, kissing my mouth ever so briefly before pulling away.

You said, "I had to see if I remembered your taste."

"Well?"

"Mm-hmh." You closed your eyes. "One of them, anyway."

We were lucky. There was no wind. The champagne and chocolate made it possible to ignore the cold. I kissed you the second time.

It was like kissing a stranger, at the same time realizing you have always known him. Like discovering you have led a life you had forgotten.

The moon will soon be setting. Dawn is not far off.

In a few hours I will wake you. We will drink coffee and say goodbye.

At some point I said, more of a statement than a question, "I loved you then, didn't I?"

"Like no one has, before or since," you said, and I felt I knew what you meant, and sat up suddenly to say, "it's never the same, is it? With any two people, I mean."

You laughed at me, at the way I had interrupted our embrace, but at that moment I knew I had loved you because I felt it. Not that I fell in love with you again but as if I was visiting, for the moment, my old feelings for you. They were waiting, intact. For the first time I could touch them, they had a size and shape my fingers remembered, as they remembered the swell of your shoulders beneath your coat, as, later, they would remember the hollow in the center of your chest, so vividly it would make me shudder. It was as if my love was a solid thing hidden away when I had no more use for it. I had not suspected its existence until your body pressed me there against the hard ice and I discovered it.

You said, "Are you freezing?"

I shook my head.

"Good," you said, and pressed me back onto the blanket. "Close your eyes."

You billowed the second blanket over me, letting it fall as soft as a whisper, tucking it under my feet. You have always been immune to heat and cold. As if your power of concentration enables you to remain at a distance from sensation, even as you seek to intensify it.

I had a bare moment to relax into the warmth of the blanket before the shock of cold air grabbed my throat. It was hard to breathe. You unbuttoned my sweater so carefully I did not feel the touch of your fingers. Only the light trace of your lips down my neck. Over my collarbone. Between my breasts.

My body craved the warmth of your touch. It arched up to your hands.

I felt the sharp sting of snow on my breast.

I said, "I can't believe you're doing this to me."

Sternly you said, "Keep your eyes closed."

I did. The snow felt hot and cold at the same time; soft as cotton. I imagined a fleecy blanket, nearly weightless, protecting me from the frigid night air. Even as my breasts burned and froze.

You packed it carefully, avoiding my nipples; focussing my attention there until I forgot the rest of my body, forgot everything but those two points of flesh, straining in dread and anticipation of the cold kiss of the snow.

Rivulets of melted snow trickled down my sides. Then there was something even softer than the snow. First warm, then hot. Moist. Unimaginably gentle. Capping my right breast.

Your mouth. Your tongue draped itself softly around my nipple. The snow-packed flesh was numb. Making the peak, enveloped by your mouth, all the warmer.

I imagine that was the closest I will come to feeling what a man must feel, inside a woman.

By the time you brushed away the snow and buttoned up my sweaters, I was too cold to move. My breasts, thawing beneath the sweaters, burned unbearably. I lay still and indifferent while you wedged the empty champagne bottle into your pocket and offered me your hand.

I could have lain gazing at the stars until I froze.

I did not doubt for a moment you caused me pain in order to heighten my pleasure.

You see how freedom can lead to trust? If there had been the possibility of a future between us, I would have had to cultivate doubt.

It was my body which remembered that talent of yours, that ability to treat each caress as an end in itself, a high point, a climax of its own rather than a step on a path towards some distant goal.

I had not realized you, too, were so dedicated to the fullness of the moment. I had thought you were one who held on to the past with stubborn grip. Yet I knew of your addictions. Your struggle to concentrate the high points. The compulsion of your painting and drinking and, yes, your lovemaking.

Perhaps I could not see myself in you, then, for fear of losing myself there.

Your face is glazed white by the light from the window. Your arm circles the bulk of my pillow, hugging it to your chest.

I wonder if you always reach to hold things in your sleep, or if there's something personal in the impulse.

I wonder. But not too much. I learned the danger long ago of believing the suggestion in your gestures.

Swaddled in my comforter, so close to the fire I could smell the smokiness of singed hairs, I expected you to continue the process you had begun on the lake. But you did not. You sat away from me, your knees folded in front of you. Staring into the fire. Not ignoring me, far worse: unaware of my presence.

Of course I recognized this withdrawal, an old familiar trick of yours. You give just enough to tantalize, then withhold.

I remembered then. I left you because I was angry. Angry at your concentration. That ability to focus on me so completely, one moment, and so thoroughly absent yourself, the next.

Perhaps, if I could have done the same, I would not have had to push you out of my life. Perhaps you would not have to leave in a few hours. But I am not like you. I can no more run hot and cold than the lake outside can freeze and thaw at once.

This time I had no need to resist the temptation of your withdrawal. No future to be concerned with. I cast off first the comforter and then my clothes. Crawling closer to you as I threw each piece to the floor. Your wider eyes twinkled as they once had, in my memory; stimulated and mischievous all at once. You remained in control, even as you sat without moving and watched me advance.

By the time I was beside you I was naked. You had unclasped your hands from your knees and were leaning back on them, watching me approach. Even when I was upon you, you didn't change your posture. I straddled you, careful not to touch your body while we kissed. You closed your eyes but still did not move.

I remembered this other feature of your lovemaking then; the way you challenged me, made me work, refused me that easy female posture of passive receptivity. Once I resented you for this withholding and controlling. I saw it as your lack of generosity, your selfishness. Perhaps it is. Yet it was you who taught me the thrill of that moment, that pleasure just beyond the peak of frustration. Just beyond the moment of despair.

I have found that pleasure since, without you. I have found it while making my best, and hardest, paintings. I'd forgotten where I felt it first.

You have always relied on surprise—it is a key component of control, is it not? Even as I straddled you on all fours, running my tongue ever so slowly down the center of your chest, stopping to rest my cheek against that hollow in the middle, you sat up abruptly, taking me by the shoulders and setting me down, facing you, with my legs splayed.

We were like two children about to play patty-cakes. I was irritated, for a moment. Then it was you on all fours and me leaning back on my hands, a neat reversal. You running your tongue down the center of my body.

You stopped at my lowest rib. Traced its contour with your fingers until they were under me and you were supporting me with your arm.

Ever so gently you laid me on the down comforter.

You said, "I want to see what you taste like. I want to see if I remember."

I closed my eyes.

Your response was immediate, a muffled "mmh," not intended, particularly, for my ears.

I did not doubt for a moment that you did.

It is morning.

You have gone.

The sun glares on the white surface of the lake. The snow glistens. Rays of light glance in all directions. Tiny rainbows sparkle from countless minute prisms.

Barney's dog Peary runs an irregular spiral near the spot of last night's picnic. His nose grazes the snow-covered ice. His energies are focussed. He is concentrating, following a scent, searching.

I am looking at my most recent canvas.

How stupid I have been.

To think memory can be discarded, like worn clothing.

To think the present can exist without the past.

Outside, Peary has completed his spiral. He has narrowed his search down to a point. Dug away the soft layer of snow. His determination does not waver. He presses his nose to the ice, scratches at it with his paw, trying to expose what lies frozen beneath the surface.

I see now: painting is no more a language of immediacy than life itself.

Two weeks ago Barney posed for this canvas. I assumed it was Barney I was painting.

Now I see it is not Barney's neck I have painted. It is yours. Your adam's apple, protruding like a knee.

I am tempted to abandon the canvas. Begin a new series. Find a new landscape from which to work. But perhaps I can resist that temptation.

Perhaps I will paint in the eyes. I wonder which version I will use. Narrow, cushioned by the generous flesh of innocence, or widened by sights too numerous to recall, yet not forgotten.

Weather

Cecilia Woloch

Wise souls move through the dark only one step at a time.
—Jim Harrison, *Letters to Yesenin*

There is this thread which is really nothing
but seems to be holding us all together
let's call it the weather of God:
how, mysteriously, you draw someone you hoped
you had lost back into your life,
or maybe he's asked for you, for unknown
reasons of his own.
Anyway, there you are, in your sunglasses, saying
you don't remember, saying
that wasn't you who threw bricks at his back
door, years ago.
It was someone else, and her hands were tied.
Then you turn away and pretend to go
but the air is suddenly knotted.
You can't move forward,
some death has your heart.

One Day It Happens

I am a woman trying to understand love.
I am trying to understand how the uprooting
exhilaration of the first months of expressed
passion can become, in a short period of time,
the source of pain, of loss of self.
— Jane Lazarre —

The old folks say,
"It's not how little we know that hurts us so,
but that so much of what we know ain't so."
— Toni Cade Bambara —

Mum and the Planet Earth

Carolyn Cooke

Jim would not marry Mum—she asked him to. He rubbed her feet on the sofa bed downstairs while she got up the nerve. She asked him, "You don't think I'm an old fossil, Jim?" and Jim had to say no. Upstairs in Mum's room I read a biography of the planet Earth. The idea behind the book was that Earth is alive in the same way you are alive, and that evolution, like ordinary life, is punctuated by jerks.

Mum met him in Montreal when she went up with the other science librarians from our state. She called me at home to say that an artist had asked her to dinner in the Underground City, which I thought must be one of the wonders of the world—a city underground.

She brought him straight from Montreal to our house. I jumped when I heard her calling *Molly* up the stairs, as if I were committing a crime against nature, instead of sitting up in Mum's bed, reading a biography of the earth.

"Oh, here you are," Mum said. She stood in the doorway of her room with her overnight bag in her hand. She had on a short black dress and pearls. The air around her smelled of French perfume and black coffee. It was seven-thirty in the morning.

"His name is Jim," she said. "He's ten years younger. He's thirty-two."

"Is he married?" I said.

"Of course he isn't *married*," Mum said, as if Ned hadn't been married the whole time.

She stood in the doorway in her black dress with her bag in her hand, as if she were waiting for someone. "He's an artist, Molly. Maybe the next Cézanne—or Whistler! Now rise and shine! Get dressed! Come meet *Jim*! I'll make some coffee."

But I had waited all weekend to hear about the Underground City. I thought the secrets of the earth must be there—lava pools, the mantle of continents, the layer between the crust and the core. Roots branching out and connecting in soft tunnels that smelled of sod: this was how I pictured a city under the surface of Earth.

Mum put her overnight bag down on the floor. She pulled her earrings off her ears and stepped down out of her shoes. "The Underground City?" she said, throwing clothes out of her drawers and brushing her hair. "It's like a shopping mall."

I put on Mum's fisherman sweater from the bottom of her bed and followed her downstairs. Jim was standing in the living room looking at the gold rug with the stains on it, and at the plaid sofa bed Grand gave us when she got her new one, and at the bookshelves spilling out science books, and at the science books and magazines piled up on every table and mug-rings on the tables and coffee mugs everywhere but on the covers of books. I tried to see for myself what this house would look like to someone who didn't know us, but you can't do that. And then I saw hanging down from Jim's wrist the straps of a green backpack and a sixpack harness with five cans of beer.

"Jim-Molly-Molly-Jim. My daughter, Molly, Jim. Pat down your hair, Molly," Mum said.

Jim looked up at us coming down the stairs. He wasn't any taller than Mum or me. He had short yellow hair and brown eyes, and he was wearing old khaki pants with paint on them and a blue sweatshirt and black work boots. Except for the beers hanging down in his hand he looked like Wayne Charpentier from my high school—he looked interesting. Mum looked like an adult in her dress.

"Hey!" Jim said.

"Hi!" I said.

I was a little worried about the beers. Six months ago, after Mum's ex-boyfriend Ned went up to dry out at Kelly Six, Mum and I went to the discount store and bought seventeen coffee mugs, every one a different color, for just the two of us. I said, "What for?" and Mum turned around with all these yellow and pink and blue coffee mugs in her red plastic basket and green and black and white coffee mugs in her arms. "Because I am going to need seventeen coffee mugs, is that all right with you?" Mum said. And it was true—when Mum stopped drinking she did need seventeen of them.

The rain on the roof sounded like someone up there pounding his fists. We spent the day playing Yahtzee, Mum's favorite game, but only when we play for money—a quarter or a dime a game.

To make it real, Mum said.

She kept pouring coffee from her thermos on the floor. She drank coffee the way she used to drink wine.

"Did I tell you, Molly, that Jim's a painter? Probably the next Cézanne," Mum said.

Jim dropped the dice in his cup and marked down a Full House. His face turned red. "I may have been drunk, but I never said that," he said.

"Oh, it's all right, Jim," Mum said.

"It's just, you wouldn't call my work impressionistic. It's darker—"

"We're on your *side*, Jim," Mum said. "How are you going to get anywhere unless you mythologize yourself a little? Cézanne didn't do any really serious work until he was forty."

"Basquiat was dead by the time he was thirty, or in his thirties," Jim said.

"Who?" Mum looked up from the dice.

"Basquiat—the painter."

"Contemporary?" Mum threw all the dice back in her cup but fours.

" He killed himself a few years ago."

"Three of a Kind, darn it." Mum threw all the dice in her cup and handed it to me. "Be serious, Jim. Dead at thirty? What kind of a genius could he be?"

Jim popped another one of his beers and held it out toward me. "Do you drink, Molly?" he said.

"Not really. I'm fourteen," I said.

Jim moved the beer in the direction of Mum. "Lucy? You don't drink at all?" he said.

"—No," Mum said.

"I guess that's good, hey?"

Mum raised her shoulders. "I don't know, is it good?"

Jim swallowed beer—we heard the bubbles breaking. I could see in Mum's face that she was listening too. She picked up her coffee mug and took a sip. "You drink too much coffee, though," Jim said. "It'll get you, hey? One way or another."

She won, as usual. Columns of quarters piled up around her on the floor, then Jim and I signed I.O.U.s on the back of old score sheets that had Mum's or Ned's or my name scribbled on them.

Mum bit her pencil between her teeth, shook the dice in her cup and spilled them out.

"Darn it," she said. She grabbed all five dice and rolled them out again. I was always proud of the way she wasn't afraid to throw everything back in the cup and start from go.

"Yahtzee," she said, and marked it on her pad, her ninth Yahtzee since lunch at noon.

"Unbelievable," Jim said.

"Talk about unbelievable," Mum said. "Your friend Cézanne didn't go to his own mother's funeral."

"Why not?" Jim asked her. He poured beer down the inside of his glass.

"He was *painting*. Your roll, Jim."

Jim took the dice-cup.

"You can bet your bottom dollar he went to his father's funeral, though," Mum said, and poured more black coffee in her mug. "Children honor their fathers. I know I did."

"How do you know all this stuff, Lucy?"

Mum sipped her coffee. "I told you—I'm a science librarian."

Mum rolled twelve Yahtzees, a record. She kept counting her piles of change, and when it wasn't her turn, she went through old score pads and told Jim about the time she rolled six Yahtzees, and all of them were fives. "Remember that, Molly? Wasn't that something?" Mum said.

I remembered three or four.

"Not that day," Mum said. "It was the time Coot Williams brought us those tiny scallops. I rolled six Yahtzees almost in a row and all of them were fives." Then before anyone could say anything else Mum put her hand on Jim's arm and said, "Jim, Molly thought the Underground City was really a city underground."

"I did not!" I said.

"You did too!" said Mum.

"Not!" I said, ashamed in front of him.

By ten p.m. I was upstairs in Mum's room, reading:

> *If the early atmosphere of earth had contained oxygen, life as we know it never would have formed. The oxidizing effect is seen clearly in the red planet Mars, which is covered with rust. The result of Oxygen as a life-force evolved long after life began. How did life begin?*

Mum's voice drifted up: "The tension is in the little toe, Jim."

"Like this?"

"The toe *pad*, and the outside of that foot, *yes*."

Her voice rose through the cardboard walls. Mum bought this house when she could afford one, after Grand died. Her idea was to sell it and make a killing when the property values went up, and marry a man, and move.

"Ooomm, ooh, Jim. My feet. Are yours."

The library Mum works in is on the Old Beach Road. The first thing she does when she walks in the door is peel off her stockings and drop them in the hall. At the lab, her job is to get the card catalogue up to date and on computer in the next ten years. She does a little every day. Mostly what she does at the library is read the books, or look through catalogues for books the library should buy. That's why our house is filled with science books—new books come all the time in the mail.

Mum likes picture books and atlases and magazines like *National Geographic*, *Science*, *Nature*. On the wall of the library she has a twenty-foot long map of the world which locals come to see.

At home, when it's just the two of us, she sits with her feet in a casserole dish of Epsom salts and reads a science book. She wears a pair of magnifying half glasses with red frames to read so she won't get lines around her eyes from reading books all day. "Listen to this," she says, and then she will read out loud a long article about how earth was created from the explosions of a dying star.

"The little *toe*, Jim. All the tension stores up in my feet."

Our house vibrated with Jim's rubbing. Mum's laugh turned like a tape on a reel. Then I heard kissing sounds—loud kisses, not on the lips, I knew for sure, because she still was laughing.

"Like this?" Jim said again.

"My God, that's it—the little one, yes."

I kept reading about the biosphere—the trilobites and sharks.

Mum said, "Jim, do you ever think about marriage?"

I skipped a few pages to *Panspermia*, the theory that life arrived on Earth in seeds from outer space.

"You going to get your shotgun now?" Jim said.

"Haha," said Mum. Her laugh floated up through the walls.

"Look at me, Jim," Mum said. "I wouldn't get fat or old or nag you."

"Are you kidding?" Jim said.

"Just so you know—I could be interested," Mum said.

I tried to read the biography of planet Earth at Mum's desk. Then I climbed into her bed and read.

When I woke up I heard her breathing in the doorway. Her bare feet slapped the floor and she sat down on the bed, started patting my hair.

"Is he staying over?" I asked. I sat up and moved out from under her hand.

"Do you mind, Molly?"

"Why should I care?"

She grabbed my head and kissed it. "See how pretty your hair is when you just comb it?" she said.

Her arm bumped into the biography of the earth, which I had spread open on the bed. Mum snapped off her laugh and got serious. "Oh-oh," she said. "You are breaking the back of this book."

In the 1960s, some people still had faith in the idea that Earth was not necessarily the center of life in the universe, but because of all the carbon dioxide in the atmosphere most people didn't expect to find life on Mars. The optimists felt that there might be life, or at least oases of life, or even that the gases (chaos) around the spaceship might seed life on Mars. During the first

Life Detection experiments, NASA thought about sterilizing the spaceship before they sent it up in case the atmosphere around the ship might seed life on Mars. The optimists said, "Even if the gases that clung to the spaceship *could* seed life on Mars, wouldn't that be something, to seize this chance to share life with another planet?"

Imagine everyone on Mars reading in their science books about *Panspermia*, the theory that life arrived in seeds from outer space.

The churches said it would be playing God. Most scientists felt it would be unscientific. They decided not to sterilize the spaceship. And when they got to Mars there was no life. It was a rusty, dead planet.

They stayed downstairs. For a long time I could tell from Mum's sounds that Jim was rubbing her feet.

"You shouldn't drink so much coffee. You'd sleep better," Jim said.

"Would I?" Her voice rose through the walls.

Jim's voice, too low to hear, sounded reasonable. Then he said, "Lucy, you are some filly!"

Her voice levitated up the stairs and through the walls, thick as a body, levitating in her room before my eyes.

"I could sit for you, Jim. I used to do that at the Art Students' League in college. I'd love to do it."

"Whoa, Whoa, Lucy, hey? " he said.

"But I *want* to. I have to tell you the truth, Jim, don't I?"

That night I dreamed we were crawling in the Underground City. My place was between Jim and Mum. The most beautiful part was the blackness and the brownness—the gray slimy walls of the city, the shadowy crimps in the rocks, the black pools, the brown cool air. Everywhere was a mud smell, an old, pure smell, damp green. The gum soles of Jim's boots looked like green quarter moons.

Mum was afraid of the dark and of the height. It was true there were heights underground. We pointed our flashlights and looked at the stalactites and the bats. Mum pulled my boots. "My eyes don't adjust to the dark, do yours? I thought that shadow was a chasm."

I was surprised Mum wasn't all that interested in the geology, in the rocks, in just being underground between the surface of the Earth and its core. But to me, Earth was more beautiful than the surface of the world. It was just what I expected—it was deeper. We passed pools and I smelled the water, the decay of organisms. Orange-yellow salamanders stood on the walls with their wet eyes looking straight ahead, ignoring us.

"Hey." Jim reached out and touched one so gently it didn't move.

Mum screamed. The sound echoed further down in the city like a second Mum waiting down there and screaming.

Our flashlights caught Mum's face in two circles of yellow light. "What is it?" we both screamed together.

"It was nothing," Mum said.

We came to a fork in the path, to two long tunnels leading down into the bottom of the city. Jim said, "Do you want to go on?"

"No!" Mum screamed from in back.

Jim and I looked at each other, streaked with mud. We both wanted to go on.

"I've had enough," Mum shouted all of a sudden. "I hate this city!"

"Well," said Jim. "I'm going on." And he disappeared into the darkness.

Mum pasted herself against the slimy wall. Her voice echoed high in the cave. "Which way did he go? For pity's sake, follow him!"

We crawled in the direction I thought Jim had taken, a black tunnel leading into a deeper blackness. Already I couldn't be sure whether Jim was really solid—or whether he was a gas.

Mum was in a bad mood in the morning. We ran out of coffee, for one thing. Jim complained that our coffee mugs were full of cracks and hostile bacteria, and drank a beer for breakfast.

When Ned went to dry out at Kelly Six, he promised his wife he wouldn't see Mum anymore. His wife came to our house. Mum made coffee for her—Mum had a glass of wine. I went upstairs and opened a book. "Mostly I don't blame you, I feel sorry for you," Ned's wife said through our cardboard walls. "You weren't Ned's problem. He knew he couldn't come to me in that condition—I wouldn't have him. You won't ever find me that desperate, walking down to the package store at all hours of the night. You want my advice, liquor is a terrible thing on a woman. You don't sweat it out the way a man does."

That afternoon we went out and she bought seventeen coffee mugs so she wouldn't have to think twice between having a cup of coffee or opening up another bottle of that Gewurtztraminer she used to drink with Ned.

Mum's feet were killing her. She stored all her tension in her feet, especially in that little toe. If Jim could just work on the little toe for a while, on the toe *pad*—the toe pad really was the *point* of pain.

We sat around the kitchen table. Mum kept her coffee mug on the table in front of her, and once in a while she would forget she had run out of coffee and try to take a sip. Jim drank another beer. He had on the same blue sweatshirt and khakis as yesterday. His green backpack hung by its straps across the back of his chair. I wondered what Jim carried in his backpack if it wasn't clothes.

Mum had her bare foot up in Jim's lap. Her other foot was on the floor, wrapped up in some space age fiber sock.

"Is anybody hungry? I could open up a can of Welsh Rarebit for lunch. We could play a little Yahtzee," she said.

Jim looked at his watch for the zillionth time. "No—thanks," he said.

Maybe it was just that I was closer to Jim's age, but it was the first time I saw what we looked like to someone who didn't know us—especially Mum. When had Mum changed? She was the same person, but in a different way. I wondered when she had stopped being a science librarian in her heart. Jim stopped rubbing Mum's foot and patted her toes. I understood how he felt. Mum's feet are endless when it comes to rubbing them. She looked up from her feet. "I know you'll be back, Jim. You owe me $3.75 for Yahtzee, don't forget."

After Jim left Mum read downstairs and soaked her feet in the casserole. I climbed in her bed and stacked up science books around me. All morning we skimmed science books and science magazines and picture books, and wrote our notes on index cards. We would not make a permanent mark in a book.

Between catastrophes, life evolves. The blinding changes happen suddenly—a whale standing on the shore looks down, amazed as his feet fall off in sand. An ape swings down from a rock and stands up straight! But who among us would sit and wait? We walk through the jungle, distracted by life, our eyes peeled for progress. We want to watch ourselves evolve.

She slapped a book shut and pounded into the kitchen on her bare feet and slapped the kettle down on the stove. "What a Bozo!" she said into the air. Something smashed against the sink. "What a jerk!" she said. Another smash, and a third. "For Pity's sake!" she said. I held my place in my book with a finger and went to the head of the stairs out of curiosity, or something, waiting, listening, holding my breath, counting. Smash, smash — ten, twelve, fourteen. She had mugs all over the house.

The Puppets

Patricia Meyers

Standing here hacking at this bloody chicken breast, I'm convinced that most of the murders taking place in everyday life must be conceived in the kitchen by some irate housewife pondering some injustice, and wielding a butcher knife. As my knife glides through the buttery flesh of the chicken, I observe a bloody spot near the bone, dark crimson red, and I think of Arthur's head. It is a round, perfectly bald head except for a few fringes around the edges where he always has a red, bloody spot, where he's scratched at it in times of extreme agitation, rubbing at it when he's thinking hard until it's sore and bleeding. It's been like that as long as I've known Arthur. I can almost hear his Mother say, "For God's sake, stop that. It looks bad enough already." You'd think a man like Arthur would have enough sense to stop messing up his head without his Mother having to tell him. But some people are like that. In need of someone else to pull their strings.

I hear a scratching noise outside my door; Green Eggs, the dog, is asking politely with his eyes if he can come in. As he pads in silently, I look at the kitchen clock. It's almost nine-thirty. My thoughts turn from dinner to love, or the lack of it in my life, and I softly stroke the silken, wavy coat before me. Green Eggs licks my cheek, a nice gloppy, wet kiss, and receives a piece of last night's hamburger.

"You're my kind of man," I tell him. "You still eat red meat, you're loyal to the hand that loves and feeds you, and you're not afraid to express your love in return." Green Eggs yawns loudly. He'd rather bay at the moon than talk politics or business and stay home with me than go out with the guys.

The telephone on the kitchen wall rings. The principal of Auburndale High School wants to know about Archie, my son. "This is his third tardy in the last two weeks, Mrs. Elliott," he tells me. "We just want to make sure you are aware that he is not getting to school on time. One more tardy or absence this semester and he will be expelled."

"Oh, my God!" I think. I stand here daydreaming about the dog, and completely forget my son, who is still upstairs sleeping. As my guilt sinks in, I rush to the third floor, my son's headquarters. This huge old house with its huge mortgage and three floors which I am unable to heat, is my legacy from my husband. Cruel and unusual punishment: I can't sell it and I can't afford to keep it. I moved Archie up to the furthermost reaches of the house, up with the birds, because I feel he functions best if separated from other humans at this time of his life. It is my belief that from age thirteen to twenty, as the body grows, the blood supply is cut off from the brain, and the teenager is rendered temporarily insane. I'm not 100% sure about the temporary part; that's only wishful thinking. My friends who have these beings living under their roof, tell me to hold on, the condition tends to reverse itself.

"Hold on to what?" I always want to ask. But I don't. I follow the trail of clothes and other various paraphernalia up the back stairs, trying not to break my neck as I climb over it. Two plaid pairs of preppie underwear and one with hearts; green and peach towels, my hairbrush that's been missing for ages; a reeking blue sock with a hole in the toe, and a tennis racquet. On the landing there are two pairs of duckhead trousers starched stiff enough to stand alone in the corner and an old Christmas card; an unidentifiable piece from the engine of his friend's Cherokee jeep and a jacket I have never seen before. On the hall table I see a pair of gold earrings (not mine), books, letters, bills, and pieces of old corsages.

Finally, I stumble across some old army boots and make my way through the glass doors into what used to be a ballroom. It is totally inappropriate for the deafening rendition of "Go Ask Alice" that my overgrown baby boy has somehow connected to his alarm clock, so that the alarm beeps in time to the music. You would think if he's smart enough to do that, he'd be smart enough to hear it and get up in the morning.

He sleeps serenely, half dressed in a Rugby shirt, boxer shorts and Argyle socks, cowboy boots clutched in his arms, my sleeping beauty waiting for God knows what to bring him back to life. His beer belly peeks obscenely over the tops of his boxers. I tiptoe as close to his head as I can, before I yell, in my loudest Eastside Cheerleading voice, "Fire! Fire! Fire! You must leave the premises at once."

I know, as a good mother always knows these things, that this will work. Besides, it makes me feel better to scream and shout. I hope I scare the living daylights out of him.

"Mom, what in the hell? You woke me up." I put on my wooden mask face and say slowly and calmly, "I sure hope you like to make hamburgers and pump gas because the way you're going, it looks like that's about the only two choices you may have left in this life, if you're lucky. The principal just called and said this is the last tardy for you. One more and you're suspended. Finished, Kaput."

"It's your fault, Mom," he says in a groggy voice. His hair stands on end and his eyes are red and swollen. "You didn't wake me up. You don't care if I get to school or not."

I just smile and say, "I can see it now! When you're twenty-six years old, I'll get up at five, dress and catch the bus to your place, come in, get you up, and then sit there for an hour or so while you go back to sleep. I'll wake you again and again, until it finally takes, then I'll catch the bus back home."

"Are you crazy, Mom? I won't be able to afford a place of my own at twenty-six. I'll be right here with you. I'm not going anywhere, so quit your worrying. I don't know why I can't get up in the morning. I want to. But when I go to bed I start thinking and I can't turn off my mind. I start worrying about you and Dad, and what's going to happen to me, then I can't go to sleep. So I get up and go downstairs and watch TV all night. In the morning I'm too tired to hear the alarm."

I sit down on the edge of his bed and trace the pattern of the old quilt he has always used. It's called "Wedding Ring." Just endless tight little circles linked together closely with thread, little circles that never get any bigger, just smaller and frayed around the edges.

"Nobody ever promised it would be easy," I say gently.

"I'm beginning to think I'm crazy or something. Wired up wrong. What did that doctor tell you?"

"He said it was like someone else was pulling your strings. Two hundred dollars to tell me that." I shake my head in disgust.

I can still hear him saying, "I suspect a sleeping disorder, Mrs. Elliott. It's almost as if someone else is pulling his strings. We'll have to go into that a little deeper on your next visit."

"I told the idiot you certainly did not have a sleeping disorder. You could sleep through the Second Coming. Your problem is getting up, not going to sleep. You get up fine for fishing trips, and out of town football games. It's school and work that keep you sound asleep. But I wouldn't worry about it, if I were you. I'd concentrate on getting to school while you still have one to go to."

He looks lower than a snake's belly, so I give him a hug. "I don't think it's mental," I say. "Just hormonal or a seasonal disorder. Nothing permanent. It might be, though, if I find you've been putting substances you shouldn't in that nice, firm body of yours." I look down at the quilt I've been rubbing hard between my fingers. He protests loudly. Too loudly, I think as I leave the room.

The clock on the wall in Piggly Wiggly says eleven o'clock as I push my grocery cart through the aisles. I think about how rich we would all be if we didn't have to eat. I start to get that old sick, churning feeling that starts in my stomach and soon fills me completely. I look at the chicken and again think of Arthur's head.

"How about some nice flank steak, Mrs. Elliott?" the butcher asks, smiling.

"No, thanks," I say, "I've got enough already," and make my way to the checkout counter where I wait in line behind a lady dressed in a pink cashmere sweater, designer boots, and several gold chains. She's waiting on change from her food stamps. Her friend, Shirley, the cashier, has run out of change because it has been such a busy morning. I wait impatiently while they discuss the new raspberry-flavored Perrier water the lady is buying. I think how fortunate I am to live in a country where the government treats its less fortunate citizens to raspberry Perrier. If things don't change soon, I'll be sipping right along with all the others.

The clock on the wall now says eleven-thirty and I realize I'm going to be late again if I don't get out of here. My heart starts to pound and I feel my blood pressure rising as I think about the endless day stretched out before me.

I'm twenty minutes late when I leave the lawyer's office and head for school. There are no legitimate parking spaces to be found. I've driven madly around the campus for the last twenty minutes considering every opening. There are only two possibilities—handicapped or the fire hydrant. I choose the fire hydrant and pray that nothing burns as I run off to class. Dr. Carpenter gives me a dirty look as I slink quietly to my seat. This is my Death and Dying Class. I'm trying to get a degree so I can become a real estate broker, and it's the only course available in this time slot. As far as I'm concerned, being dead and selling real estate do have something in common. But being a single parent requires that one be able to make a living, and thanks to that transparent little blonde who walked into my husband's office last year, strutting her youth and her promiscuity, I am now a single parent.

Opening my notebook I write my name in the top left-hand corner. It doesn't look right. Dr. Carpenter talks about the light at the end of the tunnel, something that happens to us all when we die. I think of that beautiful, numbing, forgiving light, and long to see it. My thoughts move from the light to Dr. Carpenter. I'd really like to be a teacher, standing up in front of students. I'd make them want to learn. I'd teach them to laugh and feel good about themselves. No, I wouldn't. That's a big lie. It's all hopeless anyway, I would tell them, so close your books and go on home.

My mind wanders back to the lawyer. He had said in his best snake-oil voice, "Mrs. Elliott, we don't want to be greedy, do we. I think under the circumstances, Mr. Elliott is being most generous. After all, he does have another wife and child that he must support now."

"And whose fault is that?" I asked him. "Who created the circumstances that force me to live on air and very little else?" I was so full of rage I had to leave the room before I lost control completely. My thoughts swell with hatred for the snake-oil man. It's not his fault, I tell myself. He's not the one who divorced you. Then I think about the chicken soup and try to remember whether or not I turned off the stove.

One day I'm going to write a book and call it "Under the Circumstances." It's a heavy load, all that dead weight. I carried it better when I was young because I was so light. My brain hadn't yet overloaded and my body sagged. Now I have to balance my thoughts very carefully in order to keep my psyche afloat.

Arthur, my ex, the one with the head problem, never had to worry about staying afloat. I paddled for both of us and held on for dear life, thus enabling him to finish medical school and specialize in neurosurgery. "Noo-ro-surgery," I've heard women whisper, with total respect and admiration, as if speaking before God. "How wonderful." They should have been rowing the boat. I specialized in husband support, I might whisper reverentially. You know, making a living, paying the bills, housecleaning, raising a child, gourmet cooking, yard work, social planner, etc., etc., infinitely more complicated than neurology. Only now I suffer from noo-ri-tis, a continuous pain in a nerve associated with paralysis and sensory disturbance.

The teacher asks us to tell him the five stages of dying and I can only think of four. Denial, anger, acceptance, withdrawal. Why can't I think of the fifth one? What is wrong with my brain? Maybe I'm coming down with Alzheimers.

I look at my blank piece of paper and hear Arthur's voice, patiently explaining the nerve center to Archie. He was always so patient with everybody else. "The nerve center is a group of nerve cells closely connected with one another and acting together in the performance of some function." I think of this group of nerves, banding together for a very special reason, to convey some motion or sensation, and I feel a nervous impulse to stand up and shout, it wasn't my fault. I never stopped performing, transmitting, conveying, carrying or caring. But I know it's too late to do any good. The nerve center is dysfunctional, defunct.

I hate being labelled. It's a lot like being coffined, locked up in a tight, tiny box, with the lid nailed down. I know the fifth word, but I just can't get it to "step forward." I never wanted to be divorced. I only wanted to keep on paddling in the same boat I had climbed into so long ago. I paddled so hard and so fast I didn't notice the boat had sprung a leak and was slowly sinking. When my hindsight kicked in, I did notice how fast and sure Arthur swam away on his own, with strong, unfailing strokes, never once looking back, toward someone else.

My divorce started the night I went to see Batman. Arthur was working late and Archie invited me to go to the movie with him. After the movie, Archie and I walked arm in arm, singing snatches of the theme song. We were having such a good time, I decided to splurge, and on impulse we walked into Antonio's. "This used to be your Dad's and my favorite restaurant," I told Archie. "When we were first married."

We had been seated and were waiting for menus when I saw them, holding hands and leaning across the table, as if they couldn't get close enough.

Arthur was smiling, and his eyes never once left her face. While I watched, she reached over and touched his cheek. I knew I should leave before Archie saw them, but I no longer had the power to move.

"Please give me a chance," I begged him the next day. "I'll change, do anything you want."

"Don't make this harder than it is," he told me. "I have no choice. I love her." He had scratched at the red spot until his whole head was splotched and bloody.

I feel sick, like I'm going to throw up. I do my magic trick, closing my eyes for a minute, folding up all my thoughts into a small black square, and shrinking them down to nothing. I float slowly down through the warm, dark nothingness. Down, down, very slowly, until my heart slows, my stomach calms, and I feel better. When I open my eyes, Dr. Carpenter is looking straight at me. He thinks I've been sleeping. I smile at him to show I'm awake and alert. He looks away.

Across the aisle a young man deliberately rubs his knee back and forth against the rear end of the young girl sitting in front of him. She turns around and makes an obscene gesture with her finger. Things could be worse, I tell myself. I could have strayed into a sex class. It really wouldn't matter, though. I'm still going to end up buried in a white Cadillac, selling houses I've never lived in to people I don't even know.

Dr. Carpenter points to the blackboard with a white piece of chalk, making his point, whatever it is, and when the bell rings, I realize I didn't even hear the assignment. I collect my notebook, purse, and other paraphernalia and start toward the door.

"Ms. Elliott, could I see you for a minute, please," Dr. Carpenter asks. I walk to his desk in a daze, unable to speak.

"Are you having some kind of problem?" he asks gently. I look at his left hand to see if he's wearing a wedding band. Hallelujah! He is not.

"You've been late for class the last three sessions. You also seemed to be having some difficulty staying awake in class today. Am I that boring?" He runs his fingers through his thick brown hair while he studies me. God, I was in the same fix as Archie.

"Heavens, no," I said, turning red. "You're very interesting. I mean your class is."

"I'd be happy to talk to you if you have a problem," he says, sitting on the edge of his desk while he waits for my answer.

"Maybe that would be a good idea," I say, looking at his shoes.

"Why don't you meet me at the College Inn at noon on Thursday. I'll buy you a cup of coffee." When I nod, he takes my hand and gently squeezes. "But only if you smile," he says, flashing all ninety-two of his pearly white teeth.

As I walk across the campus, thinking about the meeting, I wonder what in the world I will tell him. I decide to tell him my father died, and I'm not over it yet. I'm smart enough to know death wins you more sympathy than divorce. "Get over it," friends say when you mention divorce. Not "I'm sorry!" like in death. Either way, it's loss of life.

"What am I doing?" I ask myself. I'm not going to tell him anything. I'm going to cancel my appointment and do my homework on closings instead. My hands feel sweaty and my chest hurts from all the walking. I sit down on a bench to rest for a minute and check my watch. It's 5:00 p.m. and I feel I ought to report my whereabouts to someone. I can't get used to the idea that I'm free and no longer have to report in. I feel like the woman on TV. The one who says, "Help, I've fallen and I can't get up."

I walk another block before I stop and change my mind again. I certainly am going to see him. I'm going to tell him that I hate him and I hate myself and I hate this whole damned world where nothing stays the same, where people just come and go and change their minds and rationalize their shoddy behavior by mouthing lofty words, where nothing means anything, not even marriage, and every day it all changes.

I'm almost to the library when I slow myself down. It's all true, I tell myself, and nothing I can say or do is going to change it. I'm no more than a speck, here only for a minute, likely to be blown away at any instant. And the truth is, I really need the death and dying man.

Believe this, believe that, believe me, trust me, he'll say. I'll bring you the light, the numbing, forgiving light. I feel it all starting again, inside me, and even knowing how it's going to end before it starts doesn't stop me. I quicken my steps.

When I get in sight of the street where I'm parked in front of the fire hydrant, I look up and see my car, my old and faithful friend, perched obscenely on the back of a city wrecker, being towed slowly down the street in the direction of the city lot. I stand motionless, watching it pass slowly out of sight. My faded old white car with its high, rounded top and its rusty red spots, dented and desolate, bound securely to the wrecker by invisible ties, being pulled somewhere it doesn't really want to go.

Abandonment

Patricia Halloff

Are those tears in his eyes over this? Yes! He places his cup so carefully you'd think it held nitroglycerin on the table; he glares at me, he spits out, "SUGAR! You did it again, Carol!" The way he glares, good God, face like doomsday, finger pointing at me over this minor thing. He is crazy. Clattering to his feet, a monolith of melting muscle and chagrin, sinewless, cocoa foam beading his ratty blond mustache, he shakes his head over my crime as I sip to determine the extent of it. "You DUMPED it in AGAIN. You EYEBALLED it! DIDN'T YOU?" So much the worse for me, he's right. Yes, yes, I nod. "All the spoons were dirty." "Yes, of course, Harold's diet is of no importance," he raves. "Carol's given up, so why shouldn't he? IT DOES NOT MERIT HER CONCERN!" "Knock it off," I tell him, but he won't, voice weakened by self-pity, down two tremulous octaves. "You are uncaring," he says. And experience shows he will go on and on in that victim's drone if I don't, tired as I am, sighing, sighing, get up, take his damned cup, dump my sin down the sink, take out the cocoa and go about making amends.

"Mea culpa! Mea culpa!" I even beat my breast. He doesn't laugh. Brooding, he hurls himself into his chair, a piece of junk from his father's store, fixes his eye upon me, twists an earlobe, scratches his matted hair. "It's been a bad day," he says.

It was necessary, he tells me, for him to storm out of the store again—accused once more of undermining because he was overheard telling a starved-looking woman in a threadbare jacket that the recliner she wanted to buy her crippled husband was not solid rock maple as tagged. "MY SON IS MISTAKEN!" His father, rabid Nemesis, had leapt from the murky shadows of the ill-lit store. Frightened, the poor woman had backed up, abandoned her purpose, and made for the door, feeling her way around outdated plush sofas, ersatz oak end tables, monster lamps, hulking recliners. With Pop in hot pursuit. "HERE WE DON'T DEAL WITH FRAUDULENT MERCHANDISE!" he perjured himself at the top of his lungs. Then after her escape, all efforts to retrieve her having failed, sputtering venom: "AND YOU, YOU JERK! YOU DO NOT SET STORE POLICY!" "And you! Where is your heart?" Harold had asked him, his voice trembling even in the telling. " 'Is money your only God?' I asked him," Harold tells me, moon face flushed and harrowed. "MY STOMACH IS MY GOD, YOU TOTAL LOSS! GET OUT OF HERE BEFORE I LOSE MY TEMPER!"

It goes without saying, I don't have to ask, he went to Unity and Peace where he spent the rest of his day in meditation and grandiose scheming. I don't know whether I want to kiss or kill him, this convert to a cult with only eighty-five disciples, this furniture salesman who can't lie, this latter day celibate who clings to his side of the bed like a barnacle so he won't fall from grace into the middle where he might touch me. I put the cocoa I made before him. "Drink it," I snap. "I'm going to bed."

But not to sleep. I listen to trucks roaring by twenty-five feet from the window; I listen to tires squeal, horns honk, planes rumble. Sometime later, after prolonged contemplation before the shrine he has set up on our dresser, Harold topples into bed. The mattress heaves and settles. "We've got to get out of here!" he groans, hulling, puffing, pulling the pillow over his ears. He is like an elephant on its back, trumpeting indignation. "I CAN'T STAND THIS NOISE!" "Go to sleep, damn it," I beseech him. "Put in your earplugs." "Oh my God, who can talk to you?" But in minutes he is snoring away. I am the one who watches headlights chase shadows across the ceiling, who thinks: For this, I lost my mother?

She invades my thoughts every night as I struggle to sleep; she rarely comes near me in the flesh. Once in a while, at what she feels are decent intervals, we meet in smoky airport cocktail lounges, she en route to places of pleasure. During these encounters I can barely make out the bitterness in her mascaraed and shadowed eyes. "You put on even more weight, Carol?" she said on her way to Palm Springs last year. "Maybe if you got rid of that perm and streaked your hair?" she twanged upon her return from Madrid six months ago. "Join a weight group, my treat," she offered. "And Harold?" she wonders occasionally, examining coral nails.

Yes, my mother has abandoned me, an obese embarrassment, to the bed of mahogany veneer where I toss and turn across an uncrossable gulf from a husband she considers a klutz, a wimp, a flake, unable to fend for himself in a world which is her oyster. For my mother moves fast in flinty circles, her wardrobe always au courant, her toenails frosted coral too; she sports five gemstone rings on her bony white fingers and stays thin as her smile. "You were such a charmer until you were twelve," she remembers over a third margarita, drinking to her departure to Cancun. "Oh, you still have the pretty face, Carol, but you sure as hell don't look like a ballerina anymore."

Mainly she lives in the present, as far from me as imagination and a good income take her, because she long ago washed her hands of eating disorders, seedy furniture stores, wacko sons-in-law who cry and have tantrums. A low-flying plane shakes the window. I watch blinking red lights slide across black sky, skim past moon and clouds, and I think of my mother. Away on one jet and back on another, she flies the planet like a bird of passage, leaving me behind with the oversized egg I laid.

For breakfast, when dieting, Harold eats grapefruit and dry toast and drinks catnip tea. He meticulously dissects the grapefruit into thin wedges, each of which he chews thirty times, but when he gets to his toast he wolfs it down, barely chewing at all, his brown eyes watching me gobble cornflakes with honey and guilt, muffin with jam and self-hatred, coffee with sugar and remorse. "Self-indulgence," is his gentle pronouncement. "Pollution of the body and soul." I pay no attention. Jerk, I think, jealous jerk. But I say nothing. "You know why you overeat?" He always asks prior to telling me. "Because you root yourself in mundane matters. Because you disenfranchise your higher self." He savors his tea in small sips, his smile beams supportiveness. "A wise man said: We all need a sense of purpose." I am unable to keep still another minute. "Enlighten, revered guru," I say. "My undivided attention attends you, learned master." For a minute he says nothing, his lip hangs open, and I am sorry I said it. But soon enough he rallies and, calmed by the peace that passeth all understanding, he smiles a seraphic smile, finishes his tea, and makes some sort of mystic sign in the air. Already his thoughts have elevated him to peaks on which I can find no trails. He picks up his folder of inspirational literature and makes for the door, murmuring gently, "Have a nice day."

Maybe guilt over my gluttony and sarcasm is to blame for the way I feel driving to work. Tension scrunches beside me, prodding my stomach. "DIE!" I scream at a cretin who cuts me off. All one hundred and eighty pounds of me lean on the horn. Abandoning resolution, I light another cigarette, waiting for trouble. On the car radio angels herald glory, peace, and mercy mild. When I pull off the highway into Arcadia Garden Center, it is ten minutes later than it should be and Billy's pickup, damn it, is already there.

"So you made it." From the middle of the slouched barn that is now Arcadia, his words echo toward me though cavernous gloom where cartons and crates of seasonal items await unpacking. I clump across the bare wood floor grooved with brackish dirt, some of it, I have no doubt, from the ancient days this thing was slapped together, and sit at the cash register. This is where I have sat for two years, taking money and bagging purchases for people who garden during growing season and decorate for holidays (including Halloween) when frost closes them down. It is arctic in the winter here—tropical plants in our squalid greenhouse wing, with its plastic dome torn here and there, don't stand a chance. Today, the indoor thermostat reads sixty and I don't even think about taking off my jacket. Bill's cheap radio crackles with carols; tattered flaps of plastic on the greenhouse roof slap angrily in a rising wind. All over the floor are opened cartons: yuletide greenery, balls, angels, fake trees and merry statues of polystyrene. A lone customer rooting around the clearance items has discovered a statuette I know (thanks to Harold) to be Gonesh, an Indian god. "I'll be darned," he says to me, rubbing its trunk. "Where in hell did this damned creation come from?"

And WHOOOSH! It is as if his irreverence has called down wrath from the world above! WHIIISH! All hell breaks loose. A crazy flapping, a frantic swishing, a terrible turbulence in the air. Instinctively I shield my head with my arm and look around to see, good Lord, a bird in here! A berserk wanderer beating wild wings, she bumps into the ceiling, swoops down in a terrified loop, soars up, and spirals out into the greenhouse. I am not far behind. "BILLY!" I scream as she lights on a metal strut where she clings. "HURRY! HURRY! FOR GODSSAKES!" By the time he trudges through the door like a carthorse dragged out of pasture, she has completed several panic-stricken circuits and crash-landed on a crossbeam at the far end of the greenhouse dome. "Oh yeh," Billy says. "A titmouse. A titmouse did that another time." Then he cranks himself up to leave. "Wait!" I cry, "you're going? *You're not going to get it out of there*?" The bird is breathing hard. "And just how you think I'm gonna do that, Carol?" he asks. "How you plan I get myself up there?" "But she'll die!" "Nothing I can do about it," he croaks. "I want this damn thing," the customer calls over, waving Gonesh. "For my wife."

When Billy goes to lunch I try to rescue her. Like a circus elephant on a stand, up on one foot then the other, I balance on the planked plant table under her. I wave a rake in hopes she will fly through a torn flap. But all I do is frighten her into spins and dives so I give up, afraid she will kill herself on the struts she keeps flying into. Jittery and shaken, I climb down. She retreats to her far perch. The picture of despair, she roosts, winded, head drooping, wings ragged. I can't stand this. How many birds, I wonder, do this? Fly into places they can't get out of? I light another cigarette. I take dishes away from plants and fill them with bird seed; if he doesn't like it, tough. I put out dishes of water.

Billy returns, happier from a few cans of beer, and spends all afternoon screwing up our Christmas display. He places fake pines, spruces, firs all over the gouged floor. I squint through shadows into the icy greenhouse; I can barely see the little form we are leaving to the cold, cold wind. "What about her?" "Could be he finds his own way out," Billy says. "Can you believe it? I got three dozen balls on my list they didn't send, the SOBs."

All the way home I think about the bird and how to get her out of there. Maybe Harold will know. But Harold isn't home yet. When I turn the light on in the apartment, a note on our dresser hits me between the eyes. I grab it and read: Harold will not be coming home tonight, or ever again. A cold sweat prickles my skin.

Dear Carol. The time has come for me to follow my bliss and fulfill the purpose for which I have been put on our planet: i.e., to help bring unity and peace to a world morally unsafe, a world in which I can no longer in good conscience live without trying to change it. Carol, the events of last evening and this morning, your unconcern for me along with the venal materialism that poisons my life, have convinced me an existence outside U&P is no longer tolerable. My toxic father, our plastic friends, even YOU, Carol, are caricatures of true human potential. In U&P I have found my family. We nurture one another. We care. By the time you read this, I will be on my way to Arizona, to a community of love. A residence of God wherein lies Nirvana and, hopefully, surcease from yet another depressing cycle on earth.

There is no censure in my heart. Indeed, I pray for you and the elevation of your earthbound soul. Moreso, he writes (moreso?), *if my prayers uplift you to a point of renunciation of your misguided view of, your aversion toward, U&P (which rests, however you may deny it, on a base of sin, ignorance, and envy), and you wish to join our family, we will open our hearts and doors to you, lead you, through meditation and good works, to the peace that passeth all understanding.*

He ends: *I bless you. I pray for you. But I do not bless my father! I BEG YOU, CAROL: DO NOT GIVE HIM THE ADDRESS BELOW!! DO NOT TELL HIM ANYTHING, THE SOB!! Don't try to phone, there is no phone. (No sugar either, ha! ha!) Don't write if it is only to change my mind. Yours in Unity & Peace, Harold.*

In the clutch of panic, shivering like a terrified dog, I dash about the apartment, yanking open the closet door to find his backpack gone, wrestling open warped dresser drawers to find them empty, jerking open the medicine cabinet to find all diet pills taken away. "Oh my God, this is awful; oh my God, this can't be." I'm breathing so heavily I almost don't hear the answering machine click on. I turn up the volume. "HAROLD! HAROLD!" squawks his father, "FOR THE FIFTH TIME I'M CALLING YOU, HAROLD! WHERE ARE YOU, HAROLD? WHERE WERE YOU TODAY? YOU THINK BECAUSE YOU'RE MY SON YOU CAN COME AND GO?" I turn down the volume. I light a cigarette. Like a maniac I lunge from here to there, looking for this and that, finding it gone, until the gorilla below hammers his broom on the ceiling and brings me to a dead stop.

The sword has fallen. I fall into a chair. *This* is my punishment for wishing this in my heart. For calling him dingdong with my inner voice while he snored beside me in abstemiousness. For mentally condemning him to death when he bowed and scraped before his Moloch of a father, his large doughy face crumpled like a fallen popover. *This* is what I get for calling him crackpot and advising him to drink Lysol if he wanted to be pollution-free when he started in about refined foods, vegetarianism, bodily contamination. But Harold, Harold, I didn't mean any of it! I love you! Come back!

Back and forth I pace accompanied by the broom, smoking, sniffling, remembering the first day of high school when my best friend Muriel and our group, noses in the air, walked right past my house where I waited for them to call for me. Shock. Mortification. "It's you're too fat, Carol," Muriel explained when, crushed and humiliated, I cornered her later. "You don't hack it." She looked down upon my saddle shoes; up at my peter pan collar, my uncurled rat-brown hair. "We want to be popular. Boys don't like you." And they had stuck to it. "Me too! Yes!" Harold had cried when we'd confided over coffee and cream pie after Psych 101, two overweight rejects. "My God!" he'd rejoiced that day fifteen years ago. "An almost identical experience! People," he had pronounced, enthusiastically stirring three cubes of sugar into his coffee, "are sad parodies of what they may be."

My heart is drumming, a bomb about to explode and blow me to pieces, as I head for the kitchenette and a waterglass of red wine. All I want is to sit in my chair and drink my wine and not think about this. So I drink until the head-splitting trucks and the window-rattling planes no longer bother me. I stare at a sky which somewhere along the way has turned black. Another glassful of wine, eight bran muffins, and a pack of cigarettes later, I crawl into bed like something wounded crawls into a cave to die, and pass out.

Dear Harold, I write in my muzzy thumping head, the morning after, at my station in Arcadia. *I don't know what to say to you. Is it possible you think I am not concerned about you, my big bear? I, who have always (or nearly always) . . .*

NO! Am I crazy? Am I a doormat? A punching bag? Am I supposed to have a limitless capacity for compassion and self-abnegation? Am I supposed to be a martyr for his cause? The gelding. Don't I have feelings too? Awful. I feel terrible. My stomach lurches and thumps along with the poor titmouse who is still with us: circling, diving, flailing in the greenhouse in her failing attempts at escape. Earlier, Billy had shuffled in with a six-foot ladder, trudged up its steps and waved a pitchfork back and forth, yelling "HO! YO! DUMB BIRD! YO! HO! Get bird! Shoo! SCRAM!" But fear-frozen, she wouldn't move. So he clambered down again, dragged the ladder away, I took an Alka Seltzer, we resumed decorating for Christmas.

Harold. So I am expendable? What the hell concern did you expect from a wife you abandoned months before this final cowardly desertion? A note because you couldn't face me? Maybe you are crazy, Harold, if you really expected loving care, support for your craziness with that lunatic fringe, beatified bliss over my Life as a Nun?

As the morning wears on the letter grows in my sick head like invasive nettle, its accusations sending out stinging hairs of righteous indignation and betrayed hope, its mea culpas putting forth tender shoots of love and repentance. Dank, tomb-like air wafts in from the greenhouse. For some time I have heard no beating of wild wings, only silence. I am sick, a mess, in awful condition, as we hang garlands and angels and I compose diatribes and entreaties in my aching head. When Billy goes out to lunch I climb up on a table, I wave a hoe, I plead with her to find her way out. But she won't even fly anymore. Beak buried, eyes half-closed, she doesn't budge. She has not touched the seed and water.

Dear Harold, I write, climbing down. *We were soul mates. How could you do this?*

The phone rings. I run back to the barn. "NEVER MIND CAN I HELP YOU!" my father-in-law bellows. "HE CALLED YET? YOU GIVE ME THAT ADDRESS, CAROL! I'LL GET THAT LUNATIC BACK SO FAST HE WON'T KNOW WHAT HIT HIM!" I don't bother to answer, I hold the phone away from my ear. "UNITY AND PEACE! CRIMINALS WHO STEAL CHILDREN!" he hollers.

You were all I ever had. You were the one person in the world I could trust.

We unpack soldiers, lanterns, santas, all animated and musical, and place them here and there.

Granted, I was nasty when you set up the shrine on our dresser. Absolutely, I should have always measured and weighed your food. OK, I used some obscenities lately. BECAUSE I WAS AT MY WITS END! MISERABLE!

It's almost six. Billy turns off the overheads and Arcadia is transformed into a land of enchantment. I hate it. The blinking lights and lurching gestures of the animated figures make me even dizzier. When I look into the greenhouse I see her, still out of reach, puffed with misery in the semidarkness and cold. Cold as your heart, you bastard, Harold.

I don't care about you? I am sinful, ignorant, envious? And what about what you did to me, you paragon? What describes you, you fouled-up shit? What words describe this abandonment? Perfidious? Crazy? Heartless? You tell me, Harold. And while you're at it, tell me what am I supposed to do now?

I stand in the middle of wonderland with throbbing head and pasty mouth wishing for bed and oblivion. In the greenhouse she perches, resigned, quivering above a banquet of seeds and water. I am sure she won't fly down to eat, or fly at all again. I know she will die here, a flutter away from everything necessary to sustain her life.

Unlocking the Door

Deborah Shouse

"When I was a girl, my mother . . ."

The words float into my mind like a tantalizing red scarf, waving in the distance.

Evelyn nudges me.

"Susan," George says, "I was asking your opinion on the marketing brochure. Do you think it adequately represents our software capabilities?"

The scarf beckons. I look at George and say, "Well, it seems a little too technical. I'm wondering if you could soften it up with some user testimonials."

George nods thoughtfully. "Good idea. Evelyn, do you have some people who would testify for us?"

I move closer to the scarf. Its color is a humming crimson, vibrant, energetic. I reach for it and hold nothing.

"Something is happening to me," I tell Evelyn after the meeting. "My mind keeps wandering."

I fold my hands together and sit back in my chair. I look around my office and focus on the needlepoint picture my mother created: a cat curled safely on a hearth.

"What do you mean?" Evelyn asks.

"I keep thinking about my mother, but I don't know what I'm thinking."

"Maybe you should call her," Evelyn says.

I have avoided calling my mother. Her interest in me is unsettling. I imagine her, sitting on the battered plaid sofa, sipping ice tea amid the pink flutter of empty sweetener packets, consulting a book called, HOW TO SHOW INTEREST IN YOUR DAUGHTER'S LIFE.

"Oh, hello, dear," my mother says, answering on the first ring. Her voice is taffy sweet, like I might stick to it and never get loose. "Uncle Don's in the hospital."

I bite my lip. Instead of saying, "Good," I say, "What's wrong with him?"

"Heart attack. It's pretty serious."

I try to say something comforting but all I can think of are Don's eyes, a narrow dark tunnel.

"How's Fred?" my mother asks.

"Fine," I answer. I have a lurching sense, like I have eaten and ridden a roller coaster. Fred broke off with me more than two weeks ago, but the way I miss him feels like yesterday. Probably he is fine. Probably he's relieved to be free of me. Men have told me I am difficult and I now believe they're right. Something happens when I get close to a man. Some mangy cat crawls into my heart and I pull away and build myself a secret nest, sharpen my claws.

"Well, I hope you're watching out for yourself," my mother says. "You can't be too careful, living in a big city and all."

I know she is staring at the television while she says this, I hear the clink of her tall spoon against her glass, stirring the settled mound of sweetener into a flurry.

After I hang up, I dial Fred's number. He answers on the second ring, his voice smooth and low, like a minister's.

"Hello?" he says again, when I can't get the words to move off my tongue.

"Hi," I say. "I miss you."

I hear his inhale, the letting out of his breath. "I miss you too," he says.

"Do you want to have a cup of coffee sometime?" I feel like a child reaching out to something blobby and big in the darkness.

"I want a full relationship with you, Susan. I don't want to tiptoe around, acting like we're just friends. We're more than that and you know it."

Part of me wants Fred to hold me and promise me I am good, beautiful and smart. Part of me wants to slam down the phone.

"I have to go," I say. I press the receiver against my chest and Fred says, "Susan, are you still there. Susan?"

I think of our last time together. We came here after dinner and movies. I lay on my bed, dressed in my suit and Fred rubbed my back, whispering his love. No one had ever said love so many times to me. I melted with the safety of it.

"Give me a kiss," Fred said and turned me over. Dutifully I raised my face. Yet something in me hardened. My hands marched into fists. I felt like scooting backward and folding my arms across my chest.

"What's wrong?" Fred asked.

"I don't know," I said. I was standing on a warped edge of a knife, ready to step down into nothing rather than let him touch me.

"I don't understand you, Susan," Fred said. "I thought we had a good relationship."

"We do," I said. "Don't leave me." I clutched the bottom of his sweater and gripped his hand. I knew how it felt to have them storm out, that hollow lost feeling, alone in a dark field, with no light and no landmark.

Fred stood up and I followed him.

"I can't take your ambivalence anymore," Fred said. "When you decide what you want, let me know." As I watched him put on his coat, I felt like a soldier giving up everything to keep the enemy at a distance.

"Susan, are you there?" Fred's voice at the other end of the receiver is strong, demanding. Gently, I hang up the telephone.

"When I was a girl my mother took me . . ."

At work, images of my mother haunt me. She is holding my hand, dragging me someplace. By the way I'm struggling, it must be the dentist. I hate my mouth wide open and not being able to swallow or talk.

"Something is wrong. I think I'm going crazy," I tell Evelyn. I call her because I am scared. My brain won't let go of me. My brain won't even let me walk down the hallway to her office. Pictures of my mother flood me, during meetings, at lunch, while I work at my computer.

"Tell me what's happening." Evelyn's soothing voice reminds me of Fred. He liked it when I was vulnerable and scared.

"Images of my mother just push into my mind. I don't know what to do."

"You're probably trying to remember something," Evelyn says.

"I can't imagine what," I say.

"When I was a girl my mother took me . . ."

Even at home, the words flirt with me, then fade. I want to pull on them, like they're the string that opens a mystery envelope. I want to pull them into consciousness.

"When you were a girl you were so sweet, so obedient," Mother says. She calls to tell me Don is out of intensive care. "Our friends thought you were the model child."

"I don't remember anything that happened before I was twelve," I tell her.

"Not even your birthday parties? Not even the time you and I went shopping at Sears, and I let you buy everything you wanted?"

"No," I say, wondering if she is making this up.

"So I spent all that money for nothing," Mother says. "That's the thing about children—they never appreciate you."

Fred used to complain that I didn't appreciate him.

"You don't open up to me," he said. "You don't talk about your feelings. Why don't you trust me?"

"I talked about how mad I got the other day at work," I said, feeling like a child with a C+ report card.

"But you don't talk about what's deep inside, what you feel in your heart," Fred said.

I searched desperately for some deep lost feeling, some swirling complex emotion I could unearth and present to Fred as a token of my love. But my heart is elusive, hiding bravely in foreign countries. My heart is a coy, sly and hollow ruler.

My mother plays bridge twice a week and volunteers with the church circle. She bakes cookies and visits older ladies in nursing homes. Many people describe her as sweet.

On holidays and birthdays, I send her presents. I talk to her weekly, yet I cannot feel her sweetness. She is a fence that lives between me and something important.

"When I was a girl my mother took me to visit Uncle Don."

The pictures come first, while I am deep in morning traffic: Mother squeezing my hand too tightly, dragging me out to the car, shoving me in the back seat, pulling me into Uncle Don's house, leaving me there, while she went out. I ran after her and she ran faster, locking her car doors against me.

"Take me with you!" I shouted.

My mother shook her head and roared open the engine. I stood in the street, the exhaust clouding me, until I heard Uncle Don saying, "Get in here."

He stood on the porch, fists on his hips, his stomach swelling his flannel shirt. I knew he was counting to ten. If I wasn't on the porch by eight and a half, he'd hit me with his ex-wife's dirty hairbrush.

"I hate Uncle Don," I tell Evelyn. I call her every afternoon. By three o'clock, I can barely concentrate on my work. Walking down the corridor, through the vending area, past the copy room and into Evelyn's office is impossible. I hold the receiver with both hands. My ears explode with every laughing, talking voice that moves past. Only the gentle words of Evelyn calm me.

"Why do you hate Uncle Don?" Evelyn asks.

"I don't know."

But riding down in the crowded elevator, I see an image of my childhood self, my face pressed against Uncle Don's storm door. If I stood here while my mother was gone, I would be safe. I hung onto the door latch and hoped somebody driving by would rescue me.

"You're letting the air conditioning out," Uncle Don said. He put his hand on my shoulder and led me into the living room.

"Give me a little kiss," he said.

I stared at the planks on the wooden floor. He raised my head and battled his tongue into my mouth. I felt like spit-up hot dogs on the side of the road. His tongue suffocated my screams.

"Be a good girl so your mother won't get upset," he said, gripping my shoulders. I stomped on his foot and he slapped my face. My cheek sizzled. I hoped my mother would see the welt and ask me, "What happened?"

But my mother never saw.

If I don't call my mother, I feel guilty. When I do call her, I feel irritated.

"I hope you lock your car doors," my mother says. "I'd hate to see anything happen to you."

"That's not true," I say. Really, the words just blurt out.

"What?" I imagine my mother's face hardening.

"You left me with Uncle Don all those days," I say. "You don't care what happens to me." Another woman has spoken these words, not me. Another women is spilling tears on an important marketing document.

"I don't know what you're talking about," my mother says. "I hope you're not coming down with something."

"You act like something's chasing you," Fred says. "Slow down, so we can talk." He has asked me to go for an afternoon walk in the park. The trees are gallantly shedding and moist leaves cushion the walkway.

I look at Fred, the openness of his face, his gentle slenderness. I long for his arm around me. But I step briskly ahead.

Fred catches up with me and grabs my shoulders. He pulls me to the side so a mother with her stroller of two sleeping babies can pass.

"Leave me alone," I shout, my voice a sharp stick from out of nowhere. I pry his hands from me.

Fred's face turns pale and his jaw grows rigid.

"Shhh," Fred says, the words hissing from clenched teeth. "Someone will hear you."

"I don't care!"

Fred steps toward me, pushing me further away from the sidewalk. A man and woman in matching blue jogging outfits slow, then race on.

"Please don't shout. This is nobody's business but ours," Fred says. I remember Uncle Don's cold whisper as he laid me on the tweed sofa, "Shut up and keep quiet. This is between you and me." I remember the sweaty dog taste of his hand clamped over my mouth, the endless hard hurt of him, and the sullen slackness of his face afterwards.

"I can't keep quiet," I shout at Fred. I raise my arms and push him. I see his hurt, his puzzlement. I want to shove my voice back down my throat. I want to apologize but old glue sticks my lips together. Fred walks away. Too late, I reach out for him.

"When I was a girl my mother took me to Uncle Don's and left me there."

"I think my uncle abused me," I tell Evelyn. "My mother knew and didn't do anything."

"Your mother seems so sweet," Evelyn says. "Are you sure she knew?"

I bite my lip, wondering if anyone will believe me. My mother's goodness is so well documented.

I remember standing at the bathroom sink and scrubbing at the marks Don made from sucking on my neck and chest. I was frightened by their angry redness, so I walked naked into the living room, where my mother sat on the plaid sofa, drinking ice tea, watching television. I stood in front of her, so she could see me. My mother set her glass on the coffee table and tore into a white packet of sugar she'd taken from a restaurant. Then she stirred.

"I can't see with you standing there," she said to me.

"Yes," I tell Evelyn. "She knew."

"You poor thing," Evelyn says and I exhale, relieved that she believes me. Relieved that I have finally said it.

I wait outside of Fred's building after work. The sidewalk vibrates with people striding intently, hurrying toward their next moment. Fred walks with two women, his head down, as though he is listening. I call his name twice before he sees me.

"Yes?" he says, as though I am a bill collector.

"Do you want to have dinner together?" I ask. While I wait for his answer, I create a map of the words I will use telling him about Don.

"Why?"

"I figured out what was going on with me," I say. I am brave with the sword of my knowledge. "It was my uncle. He . . ." I think of the dish of plump colossal black olives I left in my refrigerator. When I unearthed them, weeks later, they were shrunken, hard and shriveled.

"I'm listening," Fred says, primly. I see my mother's arms folded across her chest and her eyes, staring past me.

"I think my uncle abused me." I have flattened myself against the rough brick of Fred's building, my hands clenched.

"Oh, Susan," Fred says softly. "Let's have dinner and talk."

He holds my inner elbow as we walk to a divey Italian joint, down the block. As he puts his arm around me, I sigh and match my steps to his.

In the restaurant, I twirl spaghetti around a fork and tell Fred about Uncle Don. I feel like I am reciting someone else's memories.

"I'm glad you shared this," Fred says. I see the warm way he looks at me, yet I feel like an abandoned house, the openings boarded over with rotting wood and rusting nails.

He hands the waitress a fifty dollar bill and she steps aside to inventory the contents of her apron pocket.

I stand, straighten my suit coat and Fred reaches out to hug me. As his arms stretch toward me, my feet step backward. I see how deeply I have hurt him. I want to say, "I'm sorry. I love you." But my lips are glued. Fred walks away, through the revolving door, past the plate glass window scribbled with promises of "Home-Made Italian Cooking." Meanwhile, the waitress counts his change, announcing each dollar like she is teaching first grade arithmetic. I scoop up the pile of fives and ones and run out to catch Fred.

"You forgot something," I shout, waving his money, running toward his car. But Fred drives past me.

"When I was a girl my mother left me at Uncle Don's and he sexually abused me."

I have been to hours of therapy. I have screamed at my mother, but only in the therapist's office.

"I'm baking brownies this week," my mother says when she calls. "Want me to send you some?"

"I'm going to therapy," I say. "I'm working on what happened with Uncle Don."

"I have a new recipe from the Eastern Star cookbook," she says. Her voice is a cardboard fan moving fast in the heat.

"Why did you make me go over there?" I ask. "Why did you let him hurt me?"

I hear the jumble of her television, her swallow as she drinks her tea.

"You don't understand what it was like," she says.

My hands sweat around the receiver. I wait for her to explain. I hear her tear open a packet of sweetener and stir. I hear her open the tube of lipstick she keeps on top of her TV GUIDE. I imagine she is painting on a new mouth. Her silence is a pillow over my face.

"Besides, that was years ago. There's nothing I can do about it. Now, Susan," she says, "I need to know about those brownies. I hate it when you ignore my question."

My question lies like dusty gravel in my mouth, in my heart. "Send me some," I say.

She comes to visit and brings me a peach-colored sweater, a box of Whitman's chocolates, a pink flannel nightgown, the kinds of things I liked when I was a teenager.

"Thank you," I say. I look at her and try to love her. But a dead grey cloth replaces my heart.

She sleeps in my room and I sleep on the sofa. In the night, she walks to the kitchen and stumbles into a chair, bangs into the counter.

"Ow," she says. "Oh, my knee."

I don't turn on the light and ask if she is OK. I lie there, pretending I am asleep, closing my ears against her cry.

The End of a Marriage

Joanne Seltzer

Three years after the death
of her sainted husband
she learned from her daughters
that he had abused them,

sexually, all the girls
and probably the boys
as infants and children.

She who was once a rock
is now a dervish—now
howling dark secrets—now
collapsed into silence.

How to divorce a man
who has been dead three years?

Cherchez La Femme

Deborah Fruin

The morning of Duncan Jones' funeral had a real New Year's Eve feel to it. I walked right up to his front door without dread, although I'd always thought of it as the house where unhappiness lived, and never understood how Addie could call it home. I knew that the next day she could put the place up for sale, consign it along with all memories of her marriage to the slag heap of disasters and start from the beginning all over again. Pass the champagne.

"Jesus god, it's you, Helen," she said with weary contempt, as though I were a late arriving maid. So maybe it would be New Year's Eve without the funny hats and noisemakers. I didn't pay much attention to Addie's attitude. Addie was imperious. She insisted, ordered, belittled, even sneered, and a lot of people took offense, but not I. For one thing, I knew she hadn't always been that way. It was a survival skill she'd learned after years of exposure to Duncan's blast-furnace personality.

"Who were you expecting?" I asked, wondering if I had arrived five minutes later would I have missed her. For years I'd been having the same dream: Addie speeding ahead in a convertible roadster, the kind of streamlined, shark-finned vehicle the Looney Tunes wolf always drove. I try to follow, but she is driving very fast, weaving in and out of traffic, making it difficult and dangerous to keep up. We are going somewhere great; I have the feeling of exhilaration that comes when you just can't wait to be there. She slips through the next yellow light, makes a split-second, four-lane change and her retro-rocket tail lights shrink in the distance to matchheads, then disappear. I lose her.

"The police," she said.

"Is that all," I said relieved. "I'll make drinks." I veered off toward the bar, a high-art hunk of raw concrete that brought to mind a slab in a morgue. "The cops aren't going to bother you today."

Addie was curled up on the couch like a coiled spring. I handed her a cocktail and asked how she was holding up, but she was in no mood for pleasantries. She brushed aside my question with a motion that made her drink slop out of her glass.

"I expect they want to arrest me." She sipped her drink waiting for my reply, her dozens of gold bracelets and necklaces jangling impatiently. It was a sound I found oddly unnerving. Duncan had given her a fortune in gold jewelry, 24-karat bribes for his countless transgressions.

"No they don't," I said, forgetting how much she loved provocation. Leave it to Addie to cast herself as the star of a crime she'd never have the nerve to commit.

"They do. They think I did it," she said. "Isn't that the last laugh?" She took a long draw from her cigarette and flakes of grey ash drifted down the front of her black silk gabardine. I'd worn the wrong thing. Linen on a transcontinental flight. Big mistake. I knew I could never be as soignée as Addie, but I looked pathetically disheveled and that would never do.

"What difference does it make what they think?" I said, I was blasé about the police. Since I had been with her the night of the murder, they had called me two or three times in New York with questions, all of which had led me to conclude they suspected one of Duncan's business associates. "Do I have time to change before the limo arrives?" I asked.

"I suppose you think I killed him, too," she said, sounding exasperated before I had a chance to answer. I knew all too well that she lacked the spine even to leave him, much less murder him. So many times I offered to pay her way to New York. She could have stayed with me rent-free until Duncan was out of her system. She'd always turned me down. Once when she'd hinted at wanting out, I'd used my contacts to find her a piranha of a divorce lawyer, but she never followed through. I'd hung on to the hope that the next time would be different.

Until last week, that is, when I saw how dissipated she'd become. I begged her to leave with me before life with Duncan did her in. She said sure, next time I came to see her, she'd leave with me. Then I knew he'd almost won. I'd been fighting the battle from 2000 miles away when Duncan had her under the influence every day. If he hadn't died when he did, I know she would have forgotten her promise to me as soon as I was out the door, and there's no question in my mind that the next time I saw Addie it would have been at her funeral.

"Of course you didn't kill him, but almost anyone else who knew him could have," I said. Duncan had been a magnet for every freeloader, con artist, small-time politician and big-time gangster that passed through town. He was an elaborate drunk with intellectual pretensions and mob connections who didn't have any choice but to pick friends who'd just as soon kill him as look at him. It had scared me to think that if Duncan wasn't the death of Addie, one of his gun-slinging sidekicks would have been, but now that he was out of the way, I didn't have to worry about those other guys, either.

"Look, Addie, I need to give this suit a press. Where's your iron?"

"Christ! Crawl out of the goddamn thing," she snapped. "I'll take care of it." Duncan had cured her of nearly every kindliness, but she did care about me, it just galled her to let it show.

"Thanks," I said stripping down to my half slip and bra, "but you know, I think you're worrying for nothing. Just questioning the guys who made death threats against Duncan will take the police at least a year," I said. He had been a philosophy major at Berkeley in the sixties with a lucrative sideline in drug dealing. He had, in fact, been so successful as a pusher that when he graduated from college the organization he worked for rewarded him with a sinecure of sorts as a liquor distributor in Oakland. Not the nicest business; not the safest territory, but tantamount to a license for minting money. Easy money, but with a high price tag attached. In Duncan's case that meant he always carried a loaded pistol; when he dined out he always sat with his back to a wall, his eye on the door. Addie met him in the seventies when we were students at Berkeley and she was working as a barmaid near campus. I thought he was nothing but a hood who'd read Heidegger, but unfortunately Addie found his mix of brains, danger and ready cash irresistible.

"You're wrong. Duncan had more friends than enemies," Addie said, draping my clothes over the shower curtain rod and turning on the shower full bore. "A lot of men envied him. He was an outlaw. A lot of women wished they were me."

I'd heard this line before, and I thought I understood where it came from. Addie is the only person I know who actually got what she ordered from life. She set out to marry a rich man, and she did. Even back in high school I can remember her saying, "I want a man who's got nothin' but money." And that's what she got. She never said so, but I think she believed that because she married Duncan for his money, she was obligated to put up with whatever he dished out. No matter how corrupt, obnoxious, misogynistic he became, she'd say he was "brilliant, satiric, a sardonic wit," just like a bought and paid for Hollywood hack servicing her client. I'd never said a word against him because I was afraid he'd kill our friendship and she needed me more during the years she spent with Duncan than she ever had before.

"Addie, you can't be so naive!" I said. "He believed everybody was his friend because he was so egomaniacal he couldn't see they were only suffering his company. They'd laugh if he pissed in a beer mug on the bar top because he carried a gun and was fond of waving it around when he got drunk enough."

"It was that gun that killed him," she said as though she hadn't heard the rest. We waited in her bedroom while the steam did its work on my suit. She licked dry lips and started another cigarette, the fourth since I'd arrived, closing her eyes, drawing hard until the tip burned red hot. When I was with her I wished I smoked, too. She made it seem like such a thoroughly satisfying thing to do.

"Can you honestly say you're surprised?" I couldn't believe she hadn't seen something like this coming for years. If I'd been Addie I'd have known the number of the police morgue by heart and called it every time he was an hour late.

"I came home to find Duncan with his head half blown away! You can't begin to imagine my surprise. And the police think I killed him," she said.

"Widow Jones, why don't you forget all about this. I gave the police my statement and they seemed satisfied that you were too drunk to drive anywhere. After the funeral we'll catch a plane to Hong Kong and spend some of the bastard's money," I said. That's all I really wanted, the old Addie back. When we were girls we were always together and there was always a party. The invitations may have been in her name, but she always dragged me along. She's said I kept her in one piece. I suppose that you could say I was the perpetual gal pal played by Eve Arden in black-and-white movies, but there was more to it than that: she was more fun than any boyfriend, and I understood her better than a husband ever could. To this day I don't think I'm ever more than halfhearted when she's not around.

"What do you say to Hong Kong, Addie?" The steam had begun to leak in wisps from beneath the bathroom door. She said nothing. Her five-karat diamond flashed with each drag she took from her cigarette, and I noticed for the first time that her hands looked old. Cigarettes and booze—and whatever or whomever else had helped kill the endless empty years she'd spent as Duncan's wife—had turned her delicacy to a coarse pallor, reduced her willowy figure to stretched tendon, raw nerve. She had once been movie-star beautiful, black hair, pale skin and eyes the color of mica. She had an inimitable glamour, even as a child, and that alone could have taken her as far as she wanted to go. She got as far as Duncan Jones.

"Why did he die?" she asked. "I can't remember much about that night."

"It's just as well," I said. If only I could forget. I had spent a sodden weekend with Duncan and Addie, and the last night we had dinner at one of Duncan's watering holes. By the time Addie and I arrived he was expounding to his coterie of sycophants and hangers-on his sexual fantasies involving Ayn Rand. I felt quite sure none of his audience had ever heard of the woman. Addie had been drinking wine at home, but at the restaurant she switched to scotch.

"Did he piss somebody off?" she wanted to know, as though it were possible to keep track of Duncan's insults.

"No more than usual. We ate. We drank. He was giving Dondie a pretty hard time." He had been ruthless toward the hapless, sloppy man, whose loyalty was pathetically worshipful. "I'll bet you'd like to get in Ayn Rand's pants, wouldn't you?" Duncan had taunted Dondie, pinching his fat friend's cheek. "Or how about hers?" he'd said, gesturing toward me. Dondie had laughed too long and loud, until he was sobbing for breath. I'd pitied him.

"Duncan was rough on Dondie?" Addie said skeptically, checking her makeup in the mirror.

"Yes, but, my god, he must be used to it by now," I said. Dondie had been sulking in the background for as long as I could remember.

"Duncan was always careful with Dondie," Addie said. "He's related to the big shot. He gets the whole damn shooting works now that Duncan's gone." This was better than I'd expected. I'd assumed the liquor business would be the last dead weight anchoring Addie to this unhappy life. But she was free. This time when I said come with me, there'd be nothing to stop her.

"About nine o'clock we left the restaurant for the airport," I said. By that time Duncan was drinking double shots and giving a critique on pieces of ass he'd had up to and including a comparison of his wife's sexual inventiveness to that of the college girl waiting on our table, of whom he claimed intimate knowledge.

"Did I drive?" Addie asked.

"I drove. And I kept the keys," I said.

"That's why I couldn't find my car," she said with completely unexpected ferocity. "That's why I had to take a cab home. You decided I was too drunk to drive?"

"Are you suggesting that things might have turned out differently if you'd had your keys?" I said, my own anger rising to match hers decibel for decibel. "Well, you're right. You'd be dead today, too. You'd have crashed your car or arrived home just in time for a face to face with the murderer."

"Maybe you're right. Maybe not," she said. "I'm just trying to figure out what went on. You didn't think I should drive, yet you left me alone in an airport bar with a total stranger, a potential homicidal fiend? That's not like you, Helen, you might have to turn in your mother hen feathers."

Good old Addie: go away, come here. She's full of bravado as long as she knows rescue is near at hand. I didn't want to tell her how fed up with her I'd been that night. We'd arrived at the airport almost two hours before my flight. I was determined to sober her up enough to convince her to come with me, but she headed straight for the bar and ordered a shooter. I told her she was killing herself and if she'd only break away from Duncan she could start a new life. "And live like you?" she'd said. "On forty grand a year in a tenement walk up? I don't call that living, Addie. I call that being worse than dead." It was the liquor talking, of course, letting loose some of her Duncan-fueled rage. It pleased me to know she felt safe enough with me to aim her anger my way.

She'd downed her drink, ordered another and proceeded to hit on some poor sap on the next bar stool, half in his cups, whose flight to somewhere had been delayed six hours. Pickups, she had told me that weekend, had become something of a hobby for her.

"I had a plane to catch," I reminded her. "Besides, you're a big girl. I figured you could take care of yourself in a clinch with a traveling salesman better than you could in a head-on with a semi."

"It wasn't much of a clinch. We went out to the parking lot. We were just going to climb into the back seat for a little kissy face. But we couldn't find the car," she said.

"How annoying. Whatever did you do?" I said as if it were laughable when instead her offhand confession made me want to weep.

"We found an open car in the long-term parking lot."

"Well, there's your alibi."

"I don't remember his name."

"You mean he didn't even tuck his business card under your bra strap?"

"The police don't believe me, either. They know there was a guy, but they think I left him in the bar, came back here and killed Duncan."

"You certainly had a motive." I said. "Anyone in the restaurant who heard his topic of conversation that evening would say it was justifiable homicide."

"I never listened to that bullshit. What was he spouting about? Sex? Duncan didn't have sex with me or anybody else. He drank himself to impotency every night," she said. "You never did understand his sense of humor, Helen."

She was wrong. I understood all too well what kind of a joker Duncan was. When they were first married, Addie had wanted to go back to UC and finish her degree in American literature, but Duncan ended that dream with a one-liner, "So what's your thesis going to be?" he asked her in front of me and forty other people at her twenty-first birthday. "A comparative analysis of Jack Daniels and Jim Beam?" That night she'd cried in my arms. He'd hurt her pride and diminished her dignity, and back then those things were still worth tears to her. I told her to ignore him; reassured her that she was bright and could graduate with honors. But she'd given Duncan the benefit of his doubts, and quit school.

Later it was a baby she wanted. A desire which, on the occasion of their tenth wedding anniversary, Duncan saw an opportunity to belittle. "I'd be happier," he'd said, "if the seed I plant in you grew a money tree. At least then I'd know the fruit of my loins would be well spent." By then, Addie was long past tears, but it had sickened me to hear her laughing right along with him. The next week she'd had her tubes tied, and I did the crying for both of us.

Then, not so long ago, a lonely and depressed Addie had decided at my urging to meet some new people and make a few friends who didn't have rap sheets and prison records. But Duncan had just laughed at her striving for respectability. In the middle of a fund-raising luncheon Addie was hosting, a drunken Duncan careened into the room and loudly advised her, "You'd have better luck as a social climber if you dumped these dames and slept with their husbands." She didn't flinch. She kissed him, and poured him a drink, but later I found out she'd acted on his advice. The only way she knew to repay Duncan's insults, I guess, was to inflict more degradation upon herself.

"Do you think the police will believe he was impotent?" she asked. "Or will they think I'm lying?"

"Why don't you tell them the truth?" I asked. "Tell them he abused you, but you never fought back. Tell them you never really loved him. You were just too afraid to leave."

"Love!" she hooted. "What would you know about love?"

"I think I know something about it," I said. I was still half naked and shivering, but Addie looked colder than I felt. I reached out to her. "I've always loved you."

She turned from my empty arms, but I couldn't let her go. Not today. I grabbed her hand and kissed her open palm. It was cool and dry as a dollar bill. Then our eyes met, and I saw in hers the same contempt with which she'd withered legions of panting men. She didn't see how much deeper my love could be.

"Get dressed," she said opening the bathroom door. The steam had turned it into a sauna, even the walls were sweating. "The police will be here any minute."

"Stop worrying about the cops, Addie. They're not going to arrest you," I said. I pulled the skirt on. It felt like tugging on a wet bathing suit.

"How do you know?" She took a deep drag on her cigarette and tossed the stub end into the toilet.

"I'll turn myself in first," I said. I was trembling now in my clammy clothes.

"That is big of you," she said. "But even martyrs need motive and opportunity. You were on an airplane."

"No. I wasn't," I said. "I took your car. I came back here."

"And? You're saying you saw the murderer?"

"I'm saying I shot him," I said. She just looked at me incredulous as though she were waiting for me to take the words back, say it was all a joke. I said nothing.

"I thought I heard you say you loved me. Now you say you killed my husband? What kind of love is that? You sick, stupid cow." She slapped me, hard. I grabbed her wrists and she struggled against me without much conviction, finally sinking to the floor where I held her close. She was sobbing. At last I'd broken Duncan's spell.

"Addie, it was him or you. Another year—hell, another week—with him and you would have been dead. I had to save you," I said softly. "And I did." I felt such relief and joy cradling her in my arms, stroking her hair. There would be no more nightmares of Addie close enough to touch, then swallowed up by blackest night. She would soon thank me for what I'd done. And I would have my Addie back.

"You still don't get it, do you?" she said after a long, quiet while. "A man like Duncan is hard to find. Most of them expect love, or at the very least sex, but I can't stomach romance, and what's between the legs matters even less. A nice fat bank balance can make any prick interesting. I could even fall in love with you if you had a million or two." She stood up unsteadily and began to pull earrings from her ears, rings from her fingers. "Get out of that sack cloth you've got on," she instructed. I tugged at a zipper and sleeve to comply.

"You're well off now without a man," I said. "You have this house, the car, everything Duncan had. A rich widow can have a good time in Manhattan."

"I'll bet. Too bad I'm not one. It doesn't belong to me; it all belongs to Duncan's business associates. The house, the Jag, the condo in Maui, every pair of my silk panties is theirs if they want them. As long as Duncan was loyal, he got to keep the perks. It all goes to Dondie now." She began to put on the wretched linen suit. It hung on her piteously. "You wear this," she said throwing the silk gabardine to me.

She stood in front of the mirror, checking the transformation she'd just undergone. Wiping off the last trace of lipstick. "Duncan knew the score and we got along fine. But you thought I'd be better off without him." The doorbell rang. "Well, think again," she said letting slip from her throat the last strand of Duncan's golden noose. "How do I look now?" she asked over her shoulder.

"Like nine kinds of hell," I said sucking in breath to fasten her suit coat around me. Even bursting at the seams, I looked better than Addie did at that moment. She opened the door to find Dondie in a suit that looked like it had shared the shower stall with the one Addie had on. She began weeping copiously, as though on cue, "Oh, Dondie, what am I going to do?" she moaned, head in hands. "I'm so alone." He put his mafia arms around her, and of course I knew what she was going to do even if Dondie never had a clue.

So Duncan Jones was dead, but the New Year's Eve feeling had disappeared from the day as fast as the fizz in champagne, and the morning-after hangover was already here. Even before we reached the cemetery, I was craving sleep, but I knew that as soon as I closed my eyes the dream would be back: Addie racing ahead, outmaneuvering me at every turn, slipping further and further away until there's no chance I'll catch up. When I lose sight of her this time, she'll be gone for good. Nothing but darkness ahead.

Since I Fell for You

Judith Serin

He probably won't call tonight. I can't expect it. But I do. My stomach twists when I say he won't. An emptiness expands in my chest. I know the symptoms. I will call him soon. But he isn't home. He wasn't half an hour ago, or last night, or the night before that. And I tell myself that I can't live without his call, can't live through another night of waiting. Though I have, and I will, and more and more the nights are call-less, the stakes are lower, for once it was a night without him that I could not live through, and before that a night when he did not stay till morning.

But I'm alive. My pain tells me. I know I'm obsessed; I know it's hopeless. How did it happen? How did I give myself away? I could have ignored him, that stranger who stared at me. He was nobody then and I was free to turn away, unentered by him, unfettered. I thought his stare was arrogant. I wanted to insult him, to do what an older friend had taught me at twenty—stare back contemptuously, then turn decisively away. But then he smiled at me with such a joy, such a mask of openness, that I was hooked, caught on the jagged corner of his smile. This was at a restaurant, but I always imagine it happened on a bus. As though his smile stuck me to my seat, and I couldn't get off at my stop but traveled instead to a new neighborhood.

The phone might ring soon. At some bar, with some friend, he might excuse himself, walk into a corner phone booth, reach out for the receiver with his brown, veined hand, and tell me he's coming tonight. Or he's there at the bar, with the friend, but he won't call. He's with someone—the woman in the restaurant, the girl he watches at the beach. Before last night she was my greatest misery. He describes the way her legs move, the way an eighteen-year-old's legs make all other women's look flabby and loose. Why should I feel old? He's older than I. But I do. I look at my legs and wonder what's wrong with them. I look at all of my body these days, asking what's wrong. I'm not so old. Why doesn't he speak of me with admiration? Why doesn't he smile at me? I annoy him now. I know I'm doing it and can't stop myself. I see the muscles tightening around his mouth when I ask for something and know I shouldn't ask, that is what angers him, drives him away. The girl at the beach doesn't ask for anything, doesn't even look at him, and that is so relaxing, like gazing at a stretch of ocean and sky. Then he can turn away. I'm always calling him back, always asking for something. It would be so much better if I didn't. If I were very still, if I turned myself into a mirror, if I never spoke, but only sighed with pleasure, reflecting back his prowess, his power, then would he smile at me?

But I can't. The very absence of his smile prevents it, the knowledge that he's giving it, my smile, the smile I fell in love with, to someone else. To many others.

He'll never forgive me for chasing him down. Before I knew him I would never have forgiven myself. That was in my old neighborhood where life seemed to happen mostly in the day: sun flooding the scene, everything so simple and pure and empty. I walked down a long street; I did the familiar errands, stopped at the familiar locations. I was lighter then, freer, imagining that I had a self, that I had choices, that there were things I wouldn't stoop to.

Now I live in artificial light. The dim glow of restaurants, the small yellow squares from the window which crawl across the sheets at night, the sheen of the reading lamp glazing the phone. And when he is here the light turns golden, the whole place buzzes, the air richer, heavier. It eddies around him, pulling me. Always, no matter what I am doing—peeling a tomato, marinating lamb, touching perfume in the hollows of my elbows, taking out the garbage—my attention is drawn to him.

But now, more and more, the phone takes his place. I live with the phone, the way I hoped to live with him. I center my life around it, waiting for his call. If I call him, he is angry or doesn't answer. I'm afraid to shower this evening. Do I dare run out for toilet paper, or can I make it till morning? I am nervous visiting friends, miserable in restaurants. If he comes, the phone will bring him. But now, as so often, it sits mute. And if it does ring, most times I am cheated. It isn't him. I talk quickly. I'm sure he's now calling, angered at the busy signal, giving up. Or it is him and immediately I am disappointed, for I don't want his voice but his presence, and he isn't coming, or he is coming but only for an hour, or, worst of all, he is angry at me. Tonight he will be angry at me.

I knew from the beginning he would be. Walking into our restaurant, I felt doomed, driven by some overwhelming impulse, yet certain I was making myself unhappy. What did it matter? I was already unhappy. I'm not a fool; I knew that I had already gone too far to recover his love. This act, no matter how dramatic, made no difference. I sat alone near the door and played with the pink napkin folded in a fan shape on the table. He came in with her, his hand on her shoulder. She wasn't the girl at the beach; I could tell right away. She wasn't eighteen; she was my age at least. She had dark hair fluffed around her face. Her features didn't stiffen as mine did; she didn't know about me, didn't notice. He did and glared at me while negotiating with the maitre d'. Then he turned away determinedly; that was all the acknowledgment he was going to give me. I should have left, but I wobbled to their table. She looked up from arranging her napkin on her lap. Her face was blank, the only emotion curiosity. Could it be that she didn't care about him? I felt no bristle, no pang in her. His mouth contorted in the effort to conceal his rage. How I wanted his smile then, the simple pleasure at my presence that had taught me I existed. I drooped, my face crumpling in fear. I squeaked out a greeting; he introduced me as an old friend. His voice was thin with hatred. I knew I would be punished. It's been two days; he hasn't called. Will my punishment be permanent exile? That will come, if not now, later. It is as inevitable and unimaginable as death. I sit here, watching the phone, afraid of its ring, afraid of it not ringing. It rings. A charge runs through me. I jerk up, dropping my magazine, my fork. I stumble over my feet. I pick it up. "I'm sorry," I say, "I know it was stupid. I've been so stupid."

"I've only dated her a couple of times." His voice is calm, almost affectionate; he sounds as if he's telling a story. "I don't really know her. She doesn't seem that interesting. I felt drawn to her because she reminded me of a woman I loved. The only woman I've ever loved." He speaks softly, caressingly even. He tells me the woman he loved was aloof, cool and distant. "I never knew what she was feeling, never knew if she really cared. It kept me interested. I felt insecure with her because I wasn't sure she enjoyed me sexually. It became a challenge. I didn't ask, but I watched her carefully for signs of a response. Then one day, all of a sudden, I got it. We were in a hotel; we'd been out late; I was exhausted. Still, there was something so provocative about her as she bent to take off her high heels that I decided to try. I lifted her to the edge of the bed, knelt beside it, slid up her skirt, and licked her through the black lace, feeling her slowly moisten." His voice is low, seductive. He's never done that with me. I press my hand between my legs as he speaks, feel the pulsing there. "Her cry when she came was a high whimper; her hands gripping my shoulder tightened and released. Then she got up, told me to leave, and refused to see me again."

He hangs up. And I am left with the phone in my hand, the moisture between my legs, the pain in the center of my chest, more in my lungs than my heart, a suffocating emptiness. "The only woman I've ever loved." I was sure that he loved me, once, in the beginning. It was all that kept me going: the memory of that love, the memory of his smile, his hands holding my body.

One Day It Happens

Silvia Curbelo

One day it happens: your lover
lights your last cigarette and becomes
a feather of smoke rising through your fingers,
a handful of nothing, a shaft of air.

It is the story of a man
running after a train
or whistling down some alley
while you stare at the long hallway
of his leaving, wondering
how will I live without?

One day the night rides in through the window
and unpacks its usual stars.
You lie on the thin bed
and feel the room
opening up like breath
when the last door slams behind you
final as a shot.

One day you lie alone
remembering the short barrel of his heart,
its single bullet.

It's Only a Phase

Ellen Orleans

Just for starters, can anyone tell me exactly when one's lover becomes their ex-lover? I'm serious. Can you help me out with this one? Here's the picture:

It's the end of a long day. My girlfriend and I are sitting in the beat-up recliners in our living room, flossing our teeth and talking small talk because real talk's been too hard lately and she says "Ellen?"—I know something heavy's coming when she says "Ellen" and not "Honey"—anyway she says, "Ellen, I've decided I need to be single."

"Oh," I say, not believing the words I've just heard, thinking this can't be how it ends, not while I'm sitting here playing with my dental floss. Isn't there supposed to be high drama—a knock-down, drag-out fight, doors slamming, yelling at the therapist's office, lots of crying, making up? Especially, making up?

But no. For me, the end comes with shredded floss wrapped around my index fingers. At 10:15 p.m. we are lovers. At 10:16, ex-lovers? That fast?

I should have known. Should have known that if the first stage of breaking up (you're aware, of course, that breaking up—like everything else in lesbian life—happens in stages) was so strange, that the days to follow would be no different.

So, okay. We've broken up. Just to make sure that I don't go into denial about this fact, the Goddess, the Universe or whoever's in charge of these things, arranges it so that we split up during the week of the Pride parade and Fourth of July parties. This way, I get to see a hundred friends in just one week's time. Friends who ask, of course, how I am, then inquire, "Where's your sweetie?"

So, I tell them that we've been having a little trouble lately . . . well, actually, we've decided to live apart . . . well, *actually*, we're splitting up. Going through the story again and again moves me out of denial and into the tedium stage; in other words, I quickly grow sick and tired of explaining the situation.

I consider lying, telling people my lover recently moved to Nepal to study with a Buddhist teacher, or that she got a Rhodes scholarship to research Victorian lesbianism, or was brainwashed by a cult of dyke separatists and was now living on womyn's land in the Ozarks. But I'm not feeling that creative.

So instead, to keep myself amused, I start categorizing the responses I get.

Response A: "You've really grown in this relationship. I can tell it's been a true learning experience for you."

While this remark is meant to be supportive, if I hear it one more time, no matter how well-intentioned the person is, I'll throw up on her Reeboks. I've had enough personal growth to last into my mid-40's, thank you very much.

Response B: "I'm really sorry. It must be awful for you right now. Let's get together soon and we can talk."

This is a good response and when I hear it I congratulate myself for choosing my friends well.

Response C: "I never did see what you two had in common" or "I'm amazed that you stayed together as long as you did."

These callous remarks are poor responses and when I hear them I admit that I've occasionally screwed up in choosing my friends.

And finally, Response D: "I know this is a painful time for you, but there are a lot of women out there who'll be glad to learn you're available."

This a terrific response, even if it *is* a bold-faced lie. When I hear it, I can't wait for the woman who said it to break up with *her* lover so I can ask her out on a date.

Having categorized my responses as such, I realize that I've left the tedium stage and entered a cynical phase. In fact, it seems I've fostered a skepticism that influences every aspect of the breakup, especially that omnipresent question: "Was it mutual?"

Now, if anyone tells you that their breakup was mutual, they're lying. It's that simple. There's always the one who leaves. And the one who gets left.

In advising you on how to best handle breakups, numerous self-help books and lesbian philosophers will tell you to say that you were the one to leave, or at the very least, to shrug your shoulders in a mature fashion and quietly declare, "It was a mutual decision." Never, never should you admit that *she* left *you*. Supposedly such a statement makes you look pathetic.

But I subscribe to a different philosophy. Even if it was (sort-of) mutual, let your friends know that it was *she* who left.

Why go for this tactic? For one thing, more lesbians can relate to this predicament, because more lesbians have *been* left by their girlfriends than have left their girlfriends. Mathematically, you wouldn't think this possible, but in the actual world, such is the case.

Secondly, by claiming that *she* left *you*, you can count on the sympathy factor. Doleful statements such as, " I don't know what happened. I loved her so much" or "I thought we had years together ahead of us" are bound to raise compassion and pity in your friends. If you play your cards right, in a few months such compassion can be turned into out-and-out lust. And if that doesn't work, you can at least get a few good meals out of it. (Lesbians can be such fine nurturers.)

Unfortunately, just when I'm feeling comfortable and at home with my cynicism, I move into the depression stage. I wonder why I should bother to get out of bed, or wash my clothes or, for that matter, eat. This isn't a particularly healthy way to live, especially in the long run. So, at this point, I realize that it's critical to look at all the benefits of breaking up. And having built up a substantial list, I thought I'd pass my findings along.

One advantage of suffering through the end of a relationship is being able to blame all your problems on the breakup. Haven't cleaned the cat box in weeks? Tell your friends that that was always *her* job. Just maxed out your VISA buying CD's and cassettes? Rationalize that you are "taking care of yourself," that a little pampering is justified during these difficult times.

Do you keep showing up for work two hours late? Explain to your supervisor that your life's been an emotional nightmare ever since your lover walked out. (No need to mention that you've been staying up to 2 a.m. eating chocolate fudge brownie ice cream and reading Stoner McTavish mysteries.) Yes, if you're good at it, you can milk the trauma of the breakup for months.

Another way I found to cheer myself up is to recall all those quirks of hers that drove me nuts. For instance, she insisted that the two zippers for the tent door always meet up precisely in the middle. That the socks never be washed with the underwear. That the tortillas always be shuffled before freezing them.

"We may not be together anymore," I consoled myself, "but at least I'm free of all those eccentricities."

Funny thing is . . . once she left, I discovered a few things. Like, it really is easier to open and close the tent door if you zip the two zippers right up to the middle. And separating the socks and underwear probably *does* cut down on the spread of bacteria and vaginal infections. And, sure enough, the tortillas do seem to stick together if you just toss the package into the freezer. Oh well, at least she's not around to say "I told you so."

Eventually, I move out of depression and into a healthy sense of self once more. Then what happens? Her ex-girl friend shows up in town.

True, I too am now her ex-girlfriend but that doesn't really count. I mean we could get back together again. This may likely be one of those minor separations we'll laugh about years from now. Right? Hmm, could it be I'm slipping back to the denial phase?

Anyway, having my girlfriend's—I mean my former girlfriend's—ex-lover around makes me realize that in the hierarchy of past lovers, I am currently on the bottom of the heap. In fact, suddenly, my ex-girlfriend's chummy with her ex-girlfriend, the very same woman she grumbled and griped about in the beginning of our relationship. I don't certainly don't want to think about what they must be saying about me.

Finally, when I learn to cope with the fact that she and her ex-lover are becoming true pals and confidants, something even worse happens. My ex-lover finds a new lover. Of course, I stay very adult about it all; I realize that life moves along, we all continue to grow and . . . .

A NEW LOVER?!!! NO!! An ex-lover I could handle. I mean, at least her ex-lover and I had something in common. But a new lover? This is *not* good news. For starters, it's a pretty sure sign that we won't be getting back together. (Okay, I admit it. I never left the denial stage.)

And you know what the worst thing is about her ex-lover? The worst thing is: she's nice. How can I hate someone who is nice? How can I hold a grudge against someone who's cheerful, caring and warm-hearted? Oh, did I mention that's she's also athletic, outgoing, and also quite cute? I bet she even separates her socks and underwear.

So, how do I cope with this new development? Having experimented with a myriad of survival techniques in the past year I consider a) cleaning out the attic, b) eating massive amounts of sugar or c) booking yet one more out-of-state airline flight.

I also consider looking deep into my heart to find that part of myself that is happy for my ex-lover, knowing she has found the loving, supportive companion she deserves. But it's not there. Instead I find a part of myself that says, "Hey. The honeymoon part of this new relationship won't last forever. Soon she'll be grumbling and griping about her new lover. Soon, she'll see what she's missing with you. Really. I promise."

Sure, I know this is yet another bald-faced lie. Still, I like this new voice; in its own twisted way, it boosts my ego and (along with a half-dozen escapist videos) gets me through this latest of traumatic phases. Yes, armed with this bit of cynicism about my ex-lover and her new lover, I know I'll survive.

At least, that is, until the invitation to their Commitment Ceremony arrives in the mail.

Saying Goodbye to Joey

Margaret McMullan

Joey was sitting propped up in bed wearing a white diaphanous dressing gown with ostrich feathers at the cuff.

"Don't I look lyrical?" he said, nearly lifting his arms all the way up. A feather floated from his cuff and on down to the IV tube coming out of his arm. "Angelic outfit number seven."

A year ago Joey had fed me milkshakes after I'd gotten my wisdom teeth removed. He covered for me when I went to Mexico with Michael and he made me chicken soup after the abortion. Now I found it difficult to even look at my best friend, Joey, even though he was laid out in a Lenox Hill hospital bed dying. A lot had happened in one year.

I could see the purple Kaposi's Sarcoma blotches on his skin beneath the gown. They ran all along his shoulders and collar bones. He held out his hand and a bottle of nail polish.

"Do me," he said.

It was Joey's birthday and I gave him a Minnie Mouse night light. I also baked him a cake. He wanted chocolate, but chocolate wasn't on his diet, so I made him a carrot cake with cream cheese icing. I gave it to Alma Jean, the nurse, so that it would be a surprise. We were timing it. Any minute now Alma Jean would come in, turn off all the lights, and sing "Happy Birthday."

"Happy birthday," Joey's roommate, Scott reached across their nightstands and gave Joey a dog-eared copy of Camus' *The Plague*. On Joey's nightstand there was a page torn out from *American Health*, an article about how AIDS patients should take care of their teeth because soon they would forget how.

"That book is wild," Scott said. "They've all got it, right? The plague. And everyone's saying, 'I can't believe this could happen to me in the 20th century.' "

"You're a sick man, Scotty my boy, but I appreciate the thought," Joey said.

Scott went back to reading his paper. "Yeah," he mumbled. "I'm sick."

I held Joey's cool, thin fingers and started painting.

"They've got birthdays all wrong," Joey said. "The presents shouldn't go to the birthday kid. They should go to the mothers. They're the ones that did all the work."

"So call your mother," I said.

"I wouldn't know what to say. We haven't talked in so long." Joey held his hand out and looked at his wet, orange nails. "It's a strange world," he said. "No one lives where they were born. No one even lives where they grew up. Everyone's all over the place. You end up with makeshift little families in makeshit little apartments."

Michael came into the room carrying pink roses and a box of chocolate turtles. I moved to get up, but Joey said no.

"I brought these," Michael said, looking at me.

"The last time the three of us were together, the two of you were together," I said.

"Let's not get dramatic," Joey said. "My nails are wet."

"So how long did you two last?" I asked Michael. "Any longer than us?"

Alma Jean came in, turned out all the lights and brought in the cake. She was smiling as she sang Happy Birthday, her black face glossy in the light. She gave Joey a bottle of Calgon bath beads. "The kind that really bubble," she said.

She set the cake down on Joey's tray table. Joey inhaled to blow out the candles.

"No, don't blow," Michael said. Alma Jean stopped singing and looked at him. "You can't blow on it. No one will want to eat it then," he said.

Nobody said anything. We all looked at the cake. It was lopsided and one third of it was crumbling. The wax from the candles dripped green onto the white frosting.

"It's probably too late anyway," I mumbled.

"Blow on the fucker and then spit on his piece," Scott said. He fell back into his pillow. His chest rose and fell in quick succession.

"No," Joey said. He reached up and turned on the lights. "He's right." One by one, Joey squeezed the tips of each candle. There were twenty-three candles. Alma Jean had forgotten about the one to grow on.

The Tuesday after Joey's birthday I called my mother in Chicago. She usually had good advice on what people should do for people in the hospital. She once told me it was a good idea to bring people dirty books and magazines, that way they would feel more alive. Novenas were important, as well. A week before her hysterectomy, she told me how to make a novena, and every day before work, I stopped in at a church and placed a prayer written on a slip of paper under a cushion, in a prayer book, or up front where the candles were.

Over the phone, I told my mother everything about how Joey was always cold, about how the nurses woke him up every morning at 3:00 for X-rays because they didn't want him to catch pneumonia, about how he couldn't make himself eat because he would throw up.

"This *is* an epidemic, you know," she finally said. "Don't lick any envelopes, Catherine."

I didn't say anything; what could I say?

"Well, what did your friend want to do with his life?"

"I don't know. I guess he wasn't very focussed."

"Well, *now* he is." And then she let the phone drop while she went after the dog, and I stood there and listened to the receiver on the other end banging on the kitchen floor.

I started to put slips of paper under the cushions of the hospital chapel down the hall. I slipped in just before visiting hours, put a card under the nearest cushion, and then I slipped out. I didn't know what prayers went with what illness so I just wrote down *Pray for him*, and *Make him better*.

"Fear is a rabbit staring at a snake," Scott said. He was in bed staring at the ceiling. Even in the daytime, the smile on the Minnie Mouse night light glowed red.

"He's writing poetry now," Joey said, rolling his eyes. He tapped his temple with his index finger. Joey's face was covered with shaving cream. He was propped up in bed with a portable plastic sink. The pop-up mirror was still down. The room smelled of Foamy Gillette and nail polish and it reminded me of the times Joey had done my nails on Sunday mornings.

"He quit reading," Joey said, moving the disposable razor along his chin. "So tell me things."

"Love is 2 A.M.," Scott said.

"They told him he could go home," Joey said. "But he won't. He said he can't get this kind of reception on his TV at home. Can you believe that? The guy would rather be here." Joey put his razor down for a moment. He was out of breath. Joey wanted to go home, but his insurance didn't cover the cost of any medical care he would need there.

"On the way over, a garbage man mistook me for Caroline Kennedy," I said.

"All right, Cat," Joey said. He brought his hand up for a high five and when I slapped it gently, I could feel how cold he was.

"Loneliness is the smell of one potato baking in the oven. Hope is popcorn."

"Oh, I like that one," Joey said, wiping his face with a towel. Without the shaving cream, without his stubble, Joey looked paler and more gaunt than ever. "I just love the smell of popcorn." Very slowly, Joey lifted the plastic mirror on his portable sink.

"That's *hope*," Scott said. I watched as Joey, without a word, folded the mirror back down again. "You love the smell of hope."

The next time I visited, Scott's bed was empty and neither Joey nor I said anything more about him.

"Glen Campbell is having an affair with Michael Jackson," I said. It was hard to talk to Joey anymore about anything other than food or celebrities.

"Don't," Joey said. "It hurts to laugh."

I turned on the TV and tried PBS, but there weren't any nature shows on. That was the only thing Joey wanted to watch anymore.

"Put me in the tub, Cat. I wanna die clean."

"Joey."

"I mean it."

I used the whole bottle of Calgon bath beads Alma Jean had given him for his birthday; who knew when he would have the strength to get up again.

He took off his nightgown next to the tub. He was wearing a pair of cotton Wonder Woman underwear. Once, I had given him an 8 x 10 glossy of Wonder Woman autographed and framed in gold, and, in turn, Joey stole mascara from Beauty and a miniskirt from Fashion for me. That was way at the beginning when we both worked at *Women*. I wondered what Joey stole for Michael.

I helped him settle into the tub. It seemed as though part of his body was caving in, closing into itself while another part—his rib cage and his hips—were reaching out. His body looked like a piece from a jigsaw puzzle and all at once I wanted to hold him, fit myself to him to fill in the parts that were caving in.

"I should probably tell you not to look, but frankly, my dear, I don't give a fuck."

He sank down into the tub so that the bubbles came up to his mouth. In the tub he looked even thinner.

"Oh, that's good," he said. "Water's good."

"Should I go?"

"No," he said. "Stay."

There was a plastic stool in the bathroom and I pulled it up next to the tub and sat down.

"I feel like I should say something," he said.

"Like what?"

"I don't know. Something like *I coulda been a contenda*."

"You don't have to say anything."

"Yeah. What's to say? You're born, you grow up, you go on a few diets, then you die. The worst of it is I was ready to settle down. I had my recipes and everything."

Already there was a ring around the tub of Joey's dead skin.

"So." I held my breath and then I let it out. "Did you ever cook for Michael?"

"Oh, Catherine. Don't."

"No. I wanna know. You always wanted to meet Warhol, and Michael introduced you. So what else did he do for you? Did he buy you stuff? How long were you two together anyway? How was he?"

"Don't do this."

"Compared to the others. Really. I want to know. Was he experienced? Or was it just a fling?"

"Why are you doing this?"

"No one thought about me in all this. Or did you? Did it make it better that he was my boyfriend? Did it turn you two on that I was right there? Down the hall? In his fucking bedroom? Did that make you hotter, Joey? Did it make him hotter too?"

Joey looked at his toes.

"*You* didn't love him, Joey. *I* did. The worst of it is, you ***knew*** that."

"Why are you doing this now, Catherine?"

"Because I'm sick of being mad at you. Because I don't want to still be mad at you when—" I stopped myself.

"When I die."

"No," I said, shaking my head.

"That's what you meant to say. You don't want to be mad at me when I'm dead. And I'm supposed to make everything all right. Bless you my child, right? Well, you know what? Fuck you. OK, Cat? Fuck you. Just fuck all of you."

I walked home alone that night even though it was a bad hour and a not-so-good neighborhood. If I did get mugged I figured I had it in me to fight off anybody. When I was this angry, Joey used to say, "Cat, the mood you're in, you could kill a small village of pygmies."

When I got back to my apartment, my cat Damn It came out from behind a pile of clothes in the closet and rubbed up against my legs. "Citizen Kane" was on and I made popcorn and sprinkled Parmesan cheese over it then curled up in the pull-out bed. This isn't so bad, I thought. Damn It was curled up beside me licking bits of salted cheese from my fingers. I don't need to call either Joey or Michael. I even thought of ordering a pizza for the hell of it, the kind I liked with Canadian bacon and onions, nothing with green peppers the way Joey liked, or mushrooms the way Michael liked. But I stayed in bed, and shouted out "Rosebud" at crucial points in the movie, the way Joey used to do sometimes when he was at work, pasting up the How-To Section for *Women*.

The following weekend I did not go to the hospital to visit Joey. I went to a party instead on the Upper East Side.

I didn't know Michael would be there, and when I went home early I wasn't at all surprised when I saw him standing outside my apartment building, waiting for me. That was how we had met in the first place at a party. My boss's party. He had been my boss's date.

"Cat," he said, just as he had before.

"Mouse," I said on cue, because that's what he looked like to me.

He took me in his arms. He had changed his cologne, and now he smelled like one of the fold-out scratch and sniff ads on the men's page of *Women*.

Our lips were nearly touching. I breathed in his breath. Was the virus in the saliva? I moved to kiss him and I opened his mouth with my tongue.

"Take me upstairs," I whispered.

He backed away. He ran his hand through his hair as he paced up and down a square of pavement.

"I don't do sex anymore, Cat."

"I'm not lunch," I laughed. "We'll be careful."

He put his hands on my face, and for the first time in a long time I saw how tired he looked. I had read in *The Wall Street Journal* that he had replaced his boss, and after a particularly successful leveraged buyout, he was quoted as saying, "It's a simple formula, 'Fear and greed. Fear and greed.' "

"I got tested," he said. "I could have it. I won't know for a year, maybe more."

"I know," I said and as soon as the words came out I realized how ignorant it sounded. Staring down at the cars parked fender to fender on 78th, I wished I could sit in one. Just sit in a parked car for a while, maybe with the radio on. Then I would start the car, take it to a car wash, cry during the rinse.

"I talk to you sometimes," I said, holding on to the top of the iron gate. "In the shower. When I'm getting dressed."

I closed my eyes and thought about the time he gave me a necklace of fake diamonds. They had, after all, looked real enough in moonlight. "I still like to hear your voice," he said.

I opened my eyes and drew him to me. "You know the stuff that makes fireflies light up? When we made love, that's the way I felt afterwards."

He took one step away. And then another.

"Sweet Cat. You're my princess. You'll always be my princess." He brushed my lips with the tips of his fingers, then he turned and walked away, lifting his right hand in a wave, without looking back.

Word had gotten out about Joey at *Women*, and Joey's former boss was spraying down the phones with Lysol and making everyone in the art department throw out all their coffee mugs. At noon one day, I heard him in the conference room next door, talking to his doctor. He spoke in whispers.

The dim whispers of a TV woke me up that night, the last night the three of us had all been together. We were at Michael's apartment, sitting around on black furniture, blowing up Joey's balloons, getting high, putting together an imaginary time capsule of the eighties. Michael had put in a bunch of Miles Davis tapes. Joey put on his favorite red sequined dress, the one he wore when he won the dance contest at The Underground. I settled on a really good bad movie about aliens and a couple of issues of *Women*. I knew then that that wasn't what I wanted to leave behind. I wanted to say, "This is the high point. This year, this day. Right here in this room. My life with Michael and Joey."

But then I fell asleep and I woke up to the whispers and to the smell of rubber balloons and when I got up, I saw them there on the couch, moving together naked in the flickering bluish tint of TV light.

I did not know why I didn't turn around and leave. I did not know why I stood there in the doorway and watched. Later I would wonder why I hadn't stopped them. Maybe it was because I had suspected something like this would happen all along.

It looked like it hurt. Michael held the back of Joey's shoulders, his own head turned away towards the back of the couch. I couldn't see Joey's face. He had his head in his hands, but then he clutched the arm of the sofa, and I saw his profile.

He was clenching his teeth. He looked like an angry little boy. Twelve maybe. His shoulders were pale and his whole body was skinny and hairless. It looked like rape, so much like rape that I took one step forward to stop it, but then a balloon popped and Joey opened his eyes and saw me.

He said, "Oh." Michael didn't see or say anything and he kept on. Joey moved his hands down to his hips. Was he pointing or was he trying to stop Michael? I stood still in the doorway. More than anything, Joey looked as though he were pleading with me. As though he were saying, please, just this once. And then he squeezed his eyes shut and put his head back down into his hands.

I left the apartment and dressed in the elevator going down. I couldn't remember what part of town it was or even what day. For a minute I thought I was late for work, but then I saw how slowly everyone else was walking, how empty the streets were and I remembered it was Sunday. Easter Sunday.

I fell into a crowd of people dressed up in pastel polyesters and I followed them inside a church.

The mass was in Italian and I sat next to a large woman in a black dress.

"Let us pray," I guessed she said as she fingered her rosary. It was like being at a funeral.

It made me nauseous to think Michael and Joey had done this, knowing I was sleeping down the hall, in Michael's bedroom, waiting for Michael. I wondered if he and Joey had lied to me, if they had started long before that night. And I wondered why I hadn't known. What about the soulful way Michael looked at me? And what about Joey? Where did this leave our friendship?

When the altar boy rang the bell the third time that day, I considered seeing a priest. Bless me, father, for I have sinned. It has been, oh what? fifteen years since my last confession. Where should I start? And what would a priest have to say after all was said? Priests never really doled out advice on anything real. It was always so many "Hail Mary's" and a few "Our Fathers." They never told you how you were supposed to live with yourself, or how to get up in the morning, or how to look your best friend in the eye after he has slept with the man you thought you loved.

Sitting in my office at work, listening to Joey's former boss on the phone with his doctor, I wondered if I had AIDS. I wondered if Michael had it. I wondered how I would ever get over the hurt of losing them both at once.

On a 3 x 5 index card without the lines, I wrote *Love* him. I put the card in my purse and took a cab to Lenox Hill.

Walking through the hospital, I passed waiting rooms filled with women: women with their shoes off, women reading pamphlets on tumors and post-operative care, women reading back issues of *Women*, women asleep, women praying, their heads in their hands, women biting the edges of their styrofoam cups while talking to other women. There were hardly any men in these waiting rooms where phone calls' carried the news of survival or death.

I slipped into the hospital chapel with the prayer card and I saw Joey there, in the second pew, his IV in the aisle.

He was wearing a pink dressing gown. There was no one else there.

He smiled as I sat down next to him. We stayed quiet for a while. Joey stared ahead at a wooden cross behind the altar and I was glad there wasn't a bearded Jesus hanging from it.

"Been drinking your energy drinks?"

"Yeah," Joey said. "I call 'em Scotch and Sodas now."

His face was even thinner than before,

There was so much that I had not known about Joey. That time I saw him inside a bar on Christopher Street drinking with two thugs in leather, it was as though he had been another person altogether, a person I couldn't even begin to understand. And then later, when he started up with Michael, he came to work later and later until finally he came into the art department at noon one Monday, bleary-eyed and shaky, and his boss handed over his empty Wonder Woman mug and told him he needn't bother laying out June, July, August, or any other month for that matter.

It had not been unexpected. There was talk in Articles of Joey doing a lot of coke, and he had been seen at Area and at the Palladium nosing up with business types until all hours. One assistant said that he had played the mermaid at Visages and at midnight he had taken off his scales while hanging upside down from the golden ring.

Sitting in the church pew beside Joey, I wondered if you could ever really understand those you love.

Maybe there was a How-to article in this: How to know someone. Follow them around all day, every day until you realize you never knew them. How to keep loving your best friend after you've hated him.

"You know what I'd like to do?" Joey said. "I'd like to strike a deal with God. God, I'd say. I swear I'll never have sex again. If I could just have my life back."

He looked down at his hands. He petted the maroon-colored fur on the cuffs of his dressing gown. Then he looked at me. His eyes were glassy and a little red. "I'm sorry, Cat. I'm really sorry."

I touched his lips with my finger then put my arm around his back. I could feel his rib cage.

"I don't think I really loved him anyway." I took a deep breath. "I loved that he liked me and what I said, or maybe what I wore. Some days it was my hair. When I finally told him that I loved him, it was more like something I wanted. It wasn't really how I felt about him. I might as well have been saying, "Let's get the car washed. Or yeah, let's have some wine with lunch."

A woman came in and sat in a pew across the aisle. She held a pamphlet called *Christ and Cancer*.

"What do you want?" I asked Joey.

"I wouldn't mind being on the I-10 to New Orleans. Ever been to Mardi Gras?"

"Na."

"Well, shit, Cat. You never showed your tits at Mardi Gras?"

The woman with the pamphlet got up and left.

"Was it my breath?" Joey asked.

I smiled and took his hands. They were cool and bony and his skin was as delicate as a moth's wing.

"Sometimes I think it would do me some good to stand in front of an elephant, but it would just be too real," he said.

I pressed my forehead on his shoulder.

"You're such a good friend," he said. "It's a shame we can't grow to be old friends."

I didn't want to lift my head because I didn't want Joey to see me crying. I thought of everything I still had to do for him. I hadn't brought him a box of chocolates yet, the kind he liked from Bloomingdale's. We didn't have many pictures of each other. I should have made him a scrapbook to look through. Nothing seemed enough. I tried to think of people to call, but I wasn't sure whom he wanted to see and whom he didn't.

Joey hummed the beginning of the Mr. Ed song and rocked me back and forth. His skin still smelled of the Calgon bubble bath.

"See the sea gulls?" he said.

I looked up. He had his eyes closed.

"Yeah?" I still had the prayer card in my other hand and I slipped it under the cushion where we sat.

"Let's feed them," he said. "Let's throw them some bread."

We were watching "Breakfast at Tiffany's" one afternoon, when Michael came in with a bag of oatmeal cookies from a health food store and a dozen red roses.

"They say oatmeal's good," he said.

I stood up to go.

"No," Michael said. He looked at Joey and then at the roses. "I mean, stay." I nodded and sat back down while Michael brought another chair around to the other side of Joey's bed.

"Bet they're better than what Cat made," Joey said. He winked at me and opened the bag of cookies. He took one out, looked at it, then set it on his nightstand. "We're trying to learn her how to cook."

Michael smiled.

"You've put on weight," Joey said.

"If you don't eat everybody thinks you've got it," Michael said. Then he looked at the rail guard. "Sorry."

Joey shrugged. A new nurse came in.

"Where's Alma Jean?" Joey wanted to know.

"Lucky enough to have tonight off."

"This is a famous man before you," Michael said. Joey and I looked at one another and then at Michael. "He works for Warhol. He and Andy, they're like this." Michael crossed two fingers.

"No kidding?" the nurse said. She was taking Joey's blood pressure.

"I wanted to do one of those piss paintings but he was already through with those," Joey said, winking at me.

"Can I have your autograph?" the nurse asked.

Joey laughed and only realized she was serious when she gave him her prescription pad on which to write. He took the pad. The nurse took a cap off the pen in her pocket and gave that to him too. He was smiling as he pressed the pen to the pad. He made a motion to start, but then he looked up. He wasn't smiling. He was crying.

"I," he said, swallowing hard. He looked at me then at Michael. "I can't remember how to spell my name."

That day it didn't seem right to just leave, but Michael was gone, and visiting hours were up.

"I could sleep here, you know."

Joey looked across at Scott's old bed.

"You don't want to do that."

I nodded absently.

"OK." I put my hands on my lap as if to rise. Then we looked at each other and I couldn't move.

"Say good night, Catherine."

I wanted to hug him but he bruised too easily now. I stood up to kiss him, but he stopped me.

"Wait," he said.

He took a Kleenex from the box on the nightstand and laid it over his lips. "OK," he said, the Kleenex moving as he spoke.

I shook my head. I took the Kleenex away and then I put my lips to his.

Whatever Happened to Harry?

Susan Ito

My mother called today and told me about the trouble in your family. "Those poor Yoshidas," she sighed. "So sad." She talked in a hushed voice about how your father finally died of stomach cancer, how for the last year of his life he ate nothing more than vanilla pudding and okai, boiled rice soup. Then she told me about your mother's diabetes, how it made her go blind, how it turned her feet into swollen purple eggplants.

She was right; it *was* really sad, and I told her not to tell me anymore. But then she told me about you, how you go to your mother's house every day, bringing groceries and clean laundry. She told me you give her a hot bath, that you lean over the steaming water and scrub her yourself.

"Poor Harry," she sighed. "All alone, no wife, just taking care of the mother. Sad life, *neh*?"

I brightened at this mention of your name. "He's all alone?" I asked. "Never got married?"

"No. *Kawai soh, neh?* I feel sorry for him. Think about it, all day working at that advertising company, then all night and weekend nursing her. Terrible."

I thought about it. The image of you, driving across the Golden Gate Bridge in the evening, carrying paper bags full of cereal and TV dinners, made me smile. It softened the hard core of rage that I usually feel when I hear your name. Perfect penance, I thought. The idea of you serving a life sentence taking care of your parents, good people I had always liked, is more satisfying than the violence I usually wish on you.

Usually, I think about grabbing your collar with both hands and slamming you up against a wall like they do in the movies. Your feet would dangle down helplessly, your flimsy glasses tossed to the side of your face. My fist would grow to the size of a honeydew melon and I would punch your belly until your eyes popped. This is what I would have done to you, back when I was twelve, if I had known what you were going to do to me.

But I didn't know. You were twenty-two years old when I met you, Harry Yoshida, almost too old for the Japanese American Community Youth. I was eager to leave the children's program to join that hip group of teenagers. I had just had the braces taken off my teeth, and I had traded my black horn-rimmed glasses for contact lenses. That summer, I felt myself filling with possibility. I had a low-cut peasant blouse to go over my new breasts. I had hot pants, nothing more than denim panties. I hung on the edges of the Youth, tantalized by the jokes, the laughing, the talk that was a maze of unopened secrets.

I was especially taken with you, with the wooden box of paints you carried everywhere, the wild bright colors that bounced off the walls of the Community Center rec room. They let you paint murals there, over the ping-pong table: fluorescent paintings of Japanese samurai warriors in tie-dyed robes. I stood next to you for entire afternoons while you painted, inhaling the smell of linseed oil and turpentine. I washed your brushes. We didn't talk much, but I knew you were aware of me.

One Saturday, you asked my parents if you could take me to the Museum of Modern Art.

My mother was impressed. "How nice, Harry's taken such an interest in Diane," she said. "Like a big brother."

I knew it was really a date, and I fretted excitedly in my room, trying on every combination of clothing that my wardrobe held. I had never been kissed by a boy, and I wondered if you would hold my hand. You did.

First you bought me a cup of coffee, and we sat in a small café outside the museum. I tossed my hair back and drank the stuff black, sipping it slowly through my teeth. It tasted terrible but I knew that to ask for milk or sugar would make me look like a little girl. You talked about the exhibit we were going to see, names of painters I had never heard of. I just nodded. I was staring at you, your hair brushing the edges of your shoulders, the black bandana around your neck, and I wished my girlfriends from Taylor Middle School could see how cool you were.

"You should know good art," you said, and I nodded solemnly. Then we stood up and went into the gallery and you took my hand, slowly swinging my arm as we walked in front of the large framed paintings. That would have been enough for me. I would have written about you in my diary, Harry, I would have scribbled your name in the margins of my three-ring binder for months to come.

But I never wrote your name down; I never wrote a word about what happened, not until now. You drove me back to my street, out in the Avenues, and parked the car fifty yards from the house. We lived in one of those pale boxy houses the color of Necco wafers, right at the edge of Golden Gate Park. Some song was on the radio, *Mah beautiful woh-man*, and you grinned, looking over at me. "Just like you, Diane." You touched my cheek and said those words, told me I was beautiful.

I nearly fainted. Here it was, the romantic life, right at my doorstep. I tilted my head back slightly, the way I knew women did, and felt your heat moving toward me. A *kiss*, I thought. *I'm going to have my first kiss*. But your mouth, so gentle with flattery, was nearly violent on contact, huge and wet and full of teeth. Your tongue was a crazy snake, slithering over the roof of my mouth. I made myself respond with enthusiasm, even though I wanted to gag, to push you away. I was desperate for you not to figure out what a child I really was, a baby without a clue. You were smooth, professional, the way you unhooked my bra with one hand and slipped off my shirt. I lifted my arms obediently, like an infant, and then sat there, bright white under the light of the street lamp.

You pushed your face into the side of my neck, moaning and saying "God, Diane, you're fantastic." I believed you, giddy and terrified. You clawed at my pants, the zipper opening with a tearing sound. Your fingers, with jagged unclipped nails, kneaded the flesh through my cotton panties.

You gasped into my neck, "Does it feel good? Yes? Do you like this?" Your eyes were closed, and it seemed you could barely breathe.

It didn't feel good, Harry, not in the remotest sense. It was red pain. But it appeared that this grinding thing you were doing, this mashing down on my sex, was supposed to feel good. I whispered, "Yes."

As you crawled over me, licking and biting like an animal, I lay with my head pressed against the car door. I didn't say anything until, like a lucid nightmare, I heard a familiar voice pierce through the thick wet fog of the windshield.

"Wait," I whispered. "Stop."

It was my father, walking our shepherd mutt, Yakamashi, right past the car. They were taking their usual route through the park, where I knew they would take one lap around the polo fields. My father was singing radio jingles. "K-EZY," he crooned. "Easy, soft and lo-ow . . ."

Immediately you disowned me. You flung yourself to the opposite door, muttering "Shit, oh shit, he's going to kill me." I trembled on the vinyl seat, pale and absolutely naked. My twisted pants clung around one ankle. I saw the outline of my father through the fog, walking briskly, pulling the chain around Yakamashi's neck.

I prayed to God to let me die at that moment, but I didn't die. My father didn't peer in the windows. He didn't rescue me or kill you, as I was partially hoping he would. He kept walking, pulling the sniffing dog away from the car door, and then his voice dimmed and disappeared through the sweating glass.

You waited just a second or two after my father dissolved into the darkness. I thought that would be the end of it, but you came back to me, renewed and unashamed. This time you unzipped your own pants and took out this thing, poking out underneath your shirt. I had never seen an adult one, not alive like that, so large and tough and shiny. You told me to touch it, and I patted its hardness like the head of a cat, with the flat surfaces of my fingers held tightly together. I had no idea what I was doing, that was obvious. You became impatient and said, accusingly, "You don't have much experience, do you?" Ashamed, discovered, I shook my head.

You rolled your eyes. You tucked yourself back into your pants, and quietly told me to put on my clothes. While you combed your hair, looking up into the rearview mirror, you said, "There's this really good book. I think you could get a lot out of it, Diane."

I liked to read, and I was relieved to have a conversation to distract me from the humiliation of trying to work the clasp of my bra. "Really? What's it called?" I was expecting a title about modern art, something I could learn about the paintings we'd seen.

You told me to look for *The Sensuous Woman*. "It's out in paperback," you said. "You can probably even find it at that bookstore near the museum, in Opera Plaza."

I nodded obediently, making a note of it in my head, and lifted my white T-shirt from the dashboard. For a moment I thought of waving it out the window, like a surrender flag.

You picked up my hand, kissed it on the palm. "Listen, Diane," you said, "maybe you're a little young for me. Let's try this again, maybe, when you're, let's say, sixteen?"

I wept into my bathwater that night, Harry. I didn't want to wait until I was sixteen. I had crossed a line that night with you, an invisible border to the other side of childhood, and there was no going back. I thought of the way you had kissed me, like a drowning person, and it made me shiver. I felt as if I had failed some critical exam in your car, and I vowed to buy the *Sensuous Woman*, and that I would study all the things you had found so lacking in me.

After my parents went to bed, talking about how much they liked you, I lay on the carpet, tracing my finger around the cut-out heart shapes on the Matisse postcard you had bought me. My boyfriend, I thought. I have a boyfriend named Harry Yoshida. But that was the last time you called me, or took me anywhere.

A month after our date, you showed up at Community Youth with a new girlfriend, someone close to your age: Pamela Shimizu, the college girl who had tutored me in math one summer. I was devastated. I wondered if Pamela did those things with you in the back seat of your car, those things that I couldn't. I almost asked her, but then a month after that, you were alone again and she had a new boyfriend, a Jewish guy named Neil. I guess you know that they got married, a long time ago, and that they have a little boy.

After a while, your insistence on being part of the Youth seemed pathetic. You were so much older than any of us junior high and high school kids. There was that day during the Cherry Blossom festival. You and I were going up the elevator of the community center. We hadn't spoken in years. I remember the way you looked at me, and then you said, "Didn't you just have a birthday, Diane?"

"Yes." I looked up the crawling numbers as the elevator lurched its way to the sanctuary.

"How old are you now?"

I held my breath. "Sixteen."

"You've sure grown up, Di." You reached out, pulled my arm so fast it hurt, and then that sensation of your mouth on my face made me feel like throwing up. The door opened then, and the light from the auditorium flooded in as I jumped away. Your mother was there, browsing the crafts table.

She waved a Japanese paper kite at me as I stepped out, and called my name. "Diane-chan! Did you get a new haircut? You look so pretty today."

That was the last time I saw you, Harry. You know that I finished high school and went on to the University in Hawaii. I don't come home that often. There are lots of men here with dark, spiky hair like yours, and sometimes I think it's you on the street, or standing in line in front of me at the market. I get a tight, burning feeling high in my stomach until they turn to face me, and I realize it's someone else.

My mother sees you every now and then when she goes to the Community Center. She tells me that you paint all the banners for the festivals, flying like brilliant, airborne fish over Post Street. No matter how old you are, you're still her favorite Japanese boy, and she calls to tell me what you're doing, little things about your family.

I'm sorry about your parents, Harry, I really am. But I can't help feeling satisfied when I think of you, sitting on the edge of the tub next to your mom, and she's running her hands quietly over the surface of the water. The way you gently, gently lift off her kimono, and sponge the soft pale skin underneath, and then scoop the rinse water over her back with a plastic teacup. How you go to her, every evening, to help her bathe, while the neighborhood girls walk by under the window, and you hear their high sweet whistles, calling their dogs home.

Rough Slices

Reneé Ashley

What I want, what I really, really want, is to break the cat's neck with my bare hands and toss its body into the woods somewhere behind the house. But I can't. Of course I can't. And the reason I can't is not that I am afraid that the cat will claw me to shreds in the process, and it certainly isn't from any fear of Deb's wrath once she finds that the cat is missing, but simply because, if I did it, that rotten cat would haunt me. The scene would grow to gothic proportions in my mind—widescreen, dolby sound, 3-D, the works. I'd live it over and over again, bigger and louder each time, and then that lousy secret would weigh on me like armor until I either went mad from it or died, one or the other. So I can't do it, or won't is more like it. I mean, it's not worth killing myself over wanting to kill a cat. But it is the thing that I would really, really like to do.

The stupid animal is pregnant again.

Here are the things that are happening: 1) in just less than four weeks, Jake's daughter Deb will be moving out never to return according to her, and we, as she puts it, can bet our lives on that, just as we could also bet that she isn't taking her cat with her. And 2) on the same day, Deb's younger brother, Bernard, is going to live, permanently, with some aunt somewhere in the West who is still in touch with his mother, which means that there will be just the two of us left here, namely Jake and me.

And then there are these things: because of his divorce, the house will have to be sold; Jake and I will have to find another place to live, and then we will have the grim process of moving itself to contend with. And, on top of all that, there's even more: I'm not really certain that, without the stress inherent in what began as, and has remained, a very difficult situation, well, I'm not sure that Jake and I will have much to say to each other after the kids are gone and the distraction of the move is done with.

Worrying about all this stuff is wearing me down. I can actually feel my faculties failing me, my normal acuities rounding off like pumice stone. The constant grating of nerves and wills around here abrades my strength, takes little just-bearable layers at a time until, finally, I realize that all those small but rough slices have added up and I'm in real pain. It's like when you crawl around on your hands and knees on the rug, like when I was playing with that first litter of kittens for instance, and then after so much of it you find you just can't do it anymore because all those little layers of skin that have been scraped off, a single, nearly unnoticeable layer at a time, have finally left you hurting like hell. Like rugburn. Anyway, I am no longer up to my former levels of patience. I sleep more now to get away from it all. And when I am awake, well, I blow easily, much more easily now that it is nearly over.

And, of course, we, Jake and I, haven't talked about it, but the tension is taking its toll on him too. It's obvious. He's just not quite as sharp as he used to be. He doesn't seem to think quite as quickly or to move as fast either. He has completely lost his preoccupation with making love. And there are small things, little things like not shaving, and not throwing his shirts in the laundry, and he never, ever washes the car anymore, never. Now his shirts lie scattered around on the floor, building up in the corners of the room like the paper cups and hot dog wrappers that blow into the angles of the cyclone fence at Paulie Park. Sometimes, even, days later, he'll pick one up and wear it again. It's not like him. And the Chevy, well, the Chevy looks like it's actually held together by the dirt. You can't see through the windows at all. But it'll change back. It'll be better for him once all this is over. It really is a crime, but, after all, they are his kids.

I've been Jake's mistress for over a year now, though they don't really call it that anymore. I have lived in this house with him, this house his children have grown up in, this house still *half-owned* by his estranged wife, and God knows it has not been easy skating, though certainly I am the first one to acknowledge that I have no one to blame for my hanging around but myself. No one forced me.

Nearly every day I am reminded of that.

At the height of each domestic squabble, every time I want to knock out the walls of this house with my bare fists, every time every single repetition of each irritation forces me to see that it is more, more than simply going against the grain, I tell myself, "It is a temporary situation." I remind myself that the nasty barb of Deb's and Bernard's *resentment* will disappear, bloodlessly, altogether, when they themselves finally do. I tell myself that those plans are already laid, and that the ubiquitous essence of his wife, that nimble Ghost of Christmas Past who never shows her face but who forever holds the key to the front door high above my head, will be exorcised when the divorce comes through. I keep telling myself that all the ugliness and disappointment will evaporate and that Jake and I will live idyllically beneath the oaks and maples forever and ever, and that our greatest burdens to bear, our worst afflictions, will be mosquito bites in the summer and shoveling snow in the winter.

Of course, this is nonsense. But, for the most part, it gives me pleasure to toy with it.

Now, though, there is no way to get around recognizing that that particular chapter of my life here has come to a close. The period of real striving is almost over; peace is near at hand.

It is a dangerous time.

The sure things change now. The blacks and the whites, the all-too-soon-deciphered biases and moods, the bloated jealousies, the tantrums, both feigned and real, all that turns foggy at the edges and blurs, merges, then drifts off, vaporous and steamy, moves away to nebulously point the way to a world of possibilities. All the myriad transmutations of Yes and No. It's staggering.

Then one day I open my eyes and I see another approach, a whole different side to it. Insight hands me the perspective of balance, the Janus-faced, the twofold vision of what is within the realm of possibility: the kids will move off to their chosen worlds, worlds they enthusiastically deem better and brighter than Jake's and my own, or they will not. They will be happy, finally, or they will not. The house will sell and Jake will either salvage enough from the split to put a down payment on another, a smaller house I would imagine, or he will not. And, of course, it has been left unsaid, but we will make it together, Jake and I, or we will not.

It is these sorts of times, these topsy-turvy slippery times, when absolutely nothing can be counted on but the not being able to count on anything at all. It's these times that really add the years to a woman's face. There should be some sort of steps you could take to prevent it, but, really, when you think about it, there is no prevention. So, to Jake's silent displeasure and my own vain chagrin, I check the mirror nightly for new lines around my eyes, creases at the corners of my mouth, new, subtle disfigurements in the name of Life itself. All too frequently I find them. And so each night in a great show of tedious regime, I cleanse my face, cleanse, cream and cream again, rubbing only upward at the neck, manipulating the skin, teasing it, persuading it to defy gravity, begging it not to betray me before I am ready. I stroke only upwards, upwards and out at the eyes, upwards and out to keep them from hanging down like the eyes of bloodhounds.

And so, anyway, now the wretched cat is pregnant.

Her name is Fedora. Jake and the kids had her when I got here, but she's still a relatively young cat, sleek when she's not pregnant, and other worldly looking. I can see now, after having learned all that I have in this last year or so, that Fedora was another of Jake's attempts, however misguided, to make up to his children for the fact that their mother went off and left them. And there were even more of them back then. Three kids. The eldest boy was in a head-on collision somewhere near the western border of the state some time after she left. I don't think he was driving, but he was killed. His head was severed from his body. I heard it from a neighbor who assumed I knew. But nobody talks about it here. Anyway, the wife went off before that ever happened, went off and left them all, left and established another whole sort of life, a life, all those years ago, without them. I guess Jake got the cat to fill some of that empty space.

The family really needed *something*.

Anyway, not too terribly long after I got here, Fedora had that first litter of kittens. She had a hard time, too; lost two of them. Three survived. But she would have lost those three as well if I hadn't been here, if I hadn't caught on quickly and helped her. Stupid cat. She didn't even know what was happening to her. She ran around the room trying to escape the pain like the devil himself was after her and she was dropping kittens on the floor, fresh from the oven so to speak, as she ran. Even at the time I thought it was a mighty dumb cat that didn't even know what kittens were about.

And then, well, as far as that particular batch of kittens went, I have to admit my own complicity. I was just as guilty as the rest of them. It's pretty obvious, I guess, that I'm a sucker for small, furry, helpless-looking things. And they kind of grew on you, those kittens. I literally spent whole days with those little ones, chasing them around on the carpet, unsticking their little soft claws when they got stuck in the nap of the rug, playing tickley-cat-feet games and rubbing their bulbous little tummies while they lay on their backs and tried to swipe at my fingers. But then there was the dog to be dealt with and I had to choose. And, of course, one tends to choose one's own. It's only natural.

Before we came to live with Jake, we moved around quite a bit. Web is part something—enormous, Irish Wolfhound maybe, who knows. But whatever he is, he is big. He is big and he chases Fedora. For sport only, but that doesn't seem to count much in his favor from the kids' point of view. Or the cat's. But it's not his fault; it's in his genes. Anyway, since we have come to live here, the cat has taken to living in high places. Mostly it lives on top of Bernard's punching bag platform in the basement where Webster can see it but can't reach it, which is fine with me but it drives Web mad.

Fedora, though, does all right for herself. She obviously gets down now and again because she was pregnant back then and is obviously pregnant again now. And that's some trick if she doesn't get down. And there are the mice. Periodically I find the generous offering of a dead mouse, a gift I'm sure, usually in my closet, mutilated on the wooden floor beneath my good dresses, sometimes in the kitchen on the linoleum where I stand by the sink to fix dinner and wash dishes each night. And I have been singled out for the honor, it seems, because no one else in this house gets dead mice in his closet or beneath his feet. Anyway, it just shows that she does get down more than they tend to think, so they shouldn't feel too sorry for her, because, quite obviously, the mice didn't commit suicide and Fedora didn't get pregnant twice by sitting on top of the punching bag platform. If nothing else in this life, I have learned how *that* part works.

The point is that when the cat had that first bunch of kittens, mother and spindly mewling brood were sequestered in Deb's room in order to save them from Webster. 'He never would have hurt the kittens, and despite all the dramatics he wouldn't have hurt Fedora either, not on purpose. But they stayed behind Deb's closed door anyway. Which was fine. It was Deb's protective streak, her idea, and wise, I suppose, but I still felt, somehow, though I never said, that Webster had been unjustly accused and that he should have been, oh I don't know, recompensed somehow since he only wanted to play with them.

It didn't matter because in a very short while the arguments began on another note anyway.

There was no way we could keep the kittens.

So, Deb was going to see that the kittens were given away. It was, after all, her cat, and she knew that. To hear her talk was a kick in the teeth: Yes, of course, they were her kittens and therefore it was, oh my, uniquely her responsibility to dispose of them, and she was going to, oh of course she was going to, but she never really quite got around to it, you see, for the life of a popular young woman is busy, oh so busy, and quite ridiculously difficult, trying really hard to the point of not having time, not having any time at all for anything that even vaguely resembled giving the kittens away.

It was really beginning to wear.

And in the meantime the kittens were growing, rising rapidly above their kittenness, leaving behind their little plaintive squeaky mews for resonant, life-sized meows. In short, they were soon to be cats and no family in its right mind would take them off our hands once they were cats and we were going to be stuck with them forever if something wasn't done quickly. Deb, obviously, had washed her hands of the problem by ignoring it. So Jake and I had to do something.

We boxed them up and we drove them down to the A & P. We found ribbons, pink for the girl, who looked just like her mom, and then blue ones for the boys, and we tied them loosely around their little kitten-almost-cat necks and settled the three of them, nestled snugly in their Heineken box with a bit of blanket, into one of the store's big shopping carts. And then we stood outside the automatic doors of the store hawking our wares. Jake and I would take turns. We'd hold up one at a time, up near our faces where people could see it, and we'd cuddle it, nuzzle it, make the usual huggy-lovey-kitten-fuss over it.

People, of course, went haywire over them with their little ribbons. All of those who showed an interest, however, didn't necessarily want to take one home with them, but they loved to pick them up and to pet them and coo little kitten endearments at them and then hand them back to us and go on their way, kittenless.

By dark, though, the box was empty except for the piece of blanket.

Each kitten had been kissed goodbye as we'd handed it over, one hand at its shoulders, the other cupping its little behind to support its weight. We'd given them to people who, while wandering into or out of the market with their supper on their minds or in their hands, promised soulfully, people who, at my insistence, swore that the kittens would get their shots and their flea collars and regular 100% nutritious meals and that the folks themselves would be very careful not to step on them or to let toddlers pull their heads or legs off. I made each of them promise to be very, very careful not to run over them with his car. I did all of this, of course, so that I could tell Deb that each went to a good home. I went through it all in good faith. But, inevitability such as it is, the attempt was predestined to failure.

Deb could have gotten a degree in histrionics that night.

And now, well, it's so easy to see what we did wrong. We were fools not to have taken Fedora down in the box with those first kittens. Now, because of that mistake, we've got to go through the whole crazy thing again.

And then all this other stuff is going on and, while it is, I'm still thinking about all this cat stuff and time is passing, passing like crazy and developing a funny way about it. And as all the impending changes get nearer and nearer, well, time and everything else sort of gets away from me.

I am braced for change, but, still, the magnitude of it scares me half to death: all of a sudden everyone needs something done, everybody wants it done today and, of course, their entire future wellbeing depends solely on the alacrity with which I attend to their needs. No one else can do it. No matter what it is. And, of course, nobody is satisfied. Ever.

And time whips me around like I'm caught at the edge of some terrible eddy.

Then it speeds up even more and gets crazy, crazy, a bottomless pit, insatiable. Things around here get ugly, uglier than normal more often than not. Everyone is on edge; everyone is angry. We all act as though some fiat has been handed down, some imperative that states that vicious arguments must accompany each decision, a sort of rampant justification of whatever choice has been made. No single maneuver is exempt, and we all get cheap and mean from the heat of it. It becomes evident that we are *all* being changed here, moving or staying. It is out of any single person's control. So we all eat and run. Nobody gets his phone messages, bread or milk, gin or dish soap. No one will face another. We seem to always be out of. For a week now, we have needed cat litter. No one has clean clothes. Everyone is furious. And by the bottom half of the third weekend, no one is speaking. There is some relief in that.

And so time, like the rest of it, just speeds right on past without me. It slips by like it's greased.

On packing day the air conditioners are not working. It is a poor beginning. Early in the day, the disposition of the single working fan provokes so much spleen that Jake eliminates the problem by throwing the fan through the window and onto the rocks that lead to the driveway. Fedora is full to bursting with babies and is yowling in the heat. Web is prostrate on the cool cement of the laundry room floor. The kids are heavy with confusion. They do not know whether to burst out in song or to hang their heads. They do know well enough what it is they want; they just do not know how to play this particular game at this particular time. Perhaps years from now they will have figured it out. But now it is hot and terribly humid and we are all on the verge of exploding, from the heat, from the near-steam rising from our own sluggish bodies. The tension marks the air, ragged, between us, and voices rise and snap like needle lightning, like thin, splintery thunder, emotional and sharp. And the only silence comes during the moments when they look into their father's eyes.

Deb's room is undergoing massive deconstruction. She is rolling all her clothes into compact balls and shoving them into athletic bags and a backpack. Sweat makes her hair stick to the skin at the side of her face, at the back of her neck. At seventeen, she looks like an old, frantic washerwoman. Books dragged from her closet, from beneath her bed, from shelves, dogeared, cracked-spined, old Judy Blumes, dog stories, mysteries, all are warped and darkened from moisture, from age; all are dropped mindlessly into boxes and set aside. She does not care at all for these. Jake will dispose of them after she is gone, I am sure. Against her rear wall, beneath the high window, stuffed animals are in a heap. A pepto-bismol pink cat with feet like a bear's is peeking over the top through a single rhinestone eye; an enormous green monkey with wire in its arms lies face down against a small brown bear and a plastic Winnie-the-Pooh on a stick whose arms and legs are free to jiggle when the stick is hoisted or dropped. Deb is past all this now. These are baby toys, gifts from boys who no longer interest her, fair prizes, souvenir adolescents' baubles. They are kicked to the side. She cannot bear to throw them away, nor can she admit she wants to take them with her. It is hard on her. I can see that. I do understand. I watch her as she tears posters from her walls, rock stars and softly blurred photographic prints with sentimental, bad verse; they are literally ripped down, then crumpled like so much old newspaper and stuffed into the open mouth of the yard-sized green garbage bag she has begun to fill with the discards from this life. The bag sits on the floor, listing to one side, swollen, amorphous, a green molten monster. She is clearing out and she is glad, she tells me.

Bernard's approach is worlds away. He is impassive and deliberate, quick. Five minutes after he has begun, he is ready to walk out the door. The clothes he recognizes as useful have been carefully folded and packed inside two open brown paper sacks that sit on the floor at the foot of his dresser. He has bent the tops of the bags over, twice, carefully creasing the double fold with his fingers. All this care and yet, when he passes me in the hall, he is carrying the bags as though even they are meaningless, meaningless or empty. As he brushes past me, he tells me over his shoulder, "Throw the rest away." He is done here.

He has another life. So, he walks out the door and he sits on the steps while he waits for Deb to finish and for his father to drive them down to the bus. And then, except for the order he has left behind, it is as if he has never been here. His room is silent and he is waiting to leave. It has always been like that with him.

I fantasize the way it will be once they have gotten on their busses: I will ransack the house for dried-up orange peels, for dirty dishes, single socks, and old homework. I will strip this house clean. Then I will vacuum, dust, wash the place down, disinfect it, a purge, erasing all traces, eliminating all evidence that they have ever been here at all. When the house goes up for sale, it will be immaculate, empty except for what little Jake and I will choose to live with, a lesson in minimalism. I will have painted, by then, where their dirty children's hands have left black trails like tire tracks on the walls.

After Jake and Deb go out, I walk to the door and look out. I press my face against the flimsy plastic mesh that passes for screen nowadays and I let what there is of the afternoon breeze be sieved through onto my forehead. I see Bernard stand and move towards the car while his sister and father come down the stairs. No one speaks as the three of them walk away. No one touches. The breeze is more than I had counted on and I can feel the skin across my brow contract. I pull my face away from the screen and brush blindly at the imaginary dirt that I am certain has stuck to my skin. As the Chevy pulls out of the driveway, I reach up to lift the hair from off the back of my neck where it is clinging to the sweat, clinging, in this heat, as though for its life, and then I sink down onto the cool slate of the foyer and I cry.

I am still like that when Jake pulls the car back into its space in the front of the house.

When I hear him, I try to pull myself together. I can hear his keys jiggling, inadvertently, in his hand as he walks up the cement path to the door. He walks like a tired man. And, still, by the time he reaches the steps I have not yet risen.

He opens the door and moves across my outstretched legs without even grazing me, without a word, without a glance, and then, when he gets to the edge of the living room, he turns and asks me, calmly, with just a hint of curiosity, of weariness, where I'll be going.

It makes me stop.

Then, I think I have misunderstood him. I cock my head, bend it to the left, in his direction, a pose like "His Master's Voice," but I cannot get my breath.

I stand quickly.

"What do you mean?," I ask him, slapping at the seat of my pants with my hands. Any trace of tears that was left has dried in that moment. I watch him intently. I wait.

His face is set and he is gaunt, angular. He is watching me watch him. When did he become so thin? When did his bones take on such a sharpness?

Why haven't I noticed this before? Is he ill? There are grey shadows beneath his eyes, shadows like carbon paper smudges or ash; they have spread across all his features and down his thin, bristly, corded neck. He is a pewter sculpture, or stone. He makes no response. And when he finally speaks, his answer reaches my ears but it does not take hold. His tone, however, is unmistakable. There is no way to misconstrue the voice itself.

I look in his direction, but, really, I am no longer looking at the man who stands there. I am already somewhere else and I am thinking that I don't know what to say. My lips part without any direction from me.

"Jake? What do you mean?" My voice is soft now, hushed like water rolling over sand. My hands are still at my sides. By now the question is rhetorical.

Jake lifts his eyes, holds them steady, wide; they are egg-shaped now, elliptic, set deep into his face. He is slow to move but he does not falter. He looks weary, sick; unruffled, but leaden. He takes a single step in my direction and then he stops. Right then, I almost believe that he doesn't see that I am cut, cut deep, to the bone, and horrified.

There is going to be no way around this man.

In an instant, I think of all I must do in order to leave. I must dig out my suitcases, pack, sort my things from his; I must collect my clothes from the cleaners, do the laundry before I go; I must be certain to remember the winter clothes from the basement closet, the skis from the shed, the boots. I must gather Webster's leash, his blanket. I wonder where his brush is. A water bowl. And Fedora. What about Fedora? The kittens aren't even here yet. The thought leaves me short of breath, makes me angry. The last time she had trouble. She needed me. It could easily happen again. She might need me again. I really shouldn't go before the litter comes. It is only days, it can only be days before they are due. Last time she didn't even know what was happening to her . . .

I turn to Jake. Any pride goes. I plead silently, with my eyes, with my posture, for him to tell me I can stay, that I am misunderstanding him or that he has changed his mind. My eyes smart, they burn as though I've gotten something in them, something poisonous; they bite and water, flush themselves clean, diluting, removing whatever it is that is causing the pain. I peer at Jake, turn my sorry eyes on him, refuse to turn away, to cry, not now.

He looks as though his eyes will close, as though he would sleep right this moment if he could, but he returns my gaze steadily. "Where will you go?" he asks simply.

"What will you do?"

The House with the Aqua-Colored Bars

Carol Potter

Walking up the steep-cobbled hill today,
I was suddenly tired of my solitude, one boney
thought after another pulling itself

through my head. I was thinking all I really
wanted was your arms around me, to feel your
body moving with mine, to hear you tell me

you love me, that you want me. I was thinking
I was done with this self-lone trip
when I came hard-breathing to a house with aqua-colored

bars guarding each window, and I could hear a woman sobbing,
"I can't take it anymore! I've had enough.
I can't take it. It's all over," her grief

breaking into the air—her grief was everywhere
electric in the street. She didn't care
if anyone could hear. It was all over. I couldn't tell

if she was on the phone or if this was
happening in person. I was breathing hard
from my climb, my heart yammering in my chest,

my breath fast and quick the way it goes
when making love, when coming to the top
of that climb in a lover's hands, her mouth

pressed against mine. I miss you and think of you
often, but when I heard that woman sobbing
at 3 o'clock in the afternoon, I said to myself:

Let me walk by that house and keep on walking.
I don't want it. I don't think I could take it
one more time. I stood beneath her window

looking down at the city. She has a spectacular view.
Pink bougainvillea in full
blossom; she can see all the way across the city

to the mountains and the lake gleaming between.
Tonight, in my house, I think of that woman
on the hill. Exhausted, I imagine, all that

weeping. The wind has picked up, is blowing
the flowers on the trees, is tapping
fat-pink blossoms against my windows.

Fever

Lynn Kanter

Perhaps it was an acoustical trick of the new house, but Ellen's hearing seemed to be particularly acute that evening. The round, hollow tones of a mourning dove outside her window; the quiet hiss of vegetables steaming on the stove; the drone of a television from the house next door—each sound came to her crisp and discrete as letters dropped through the mail slot.

She could even hear her own headache. It sounded like rock music booming from a car parked so far away that only the bass was audible.

When the phone rang, with its exaggerated cricket's chirp, she snatched it up instantly, before it had a chance to make that ridiculous sound again.

"Hi, El. It's me." "Valerie! How's it going out there?" Ellen slouched in a corner of the nubby off-white couch and closed her eyes, picturing Valerie's bright round face surrounded by curly dark hair.

"The usual. Trying to cram two weeks' work into a few days. Then just when I'm ready to put my feet up and relax, there's some dinner meeting or something that I have to go to. These D.C. women are really intense."

"Tell the truth. You love it." Ellen unclipped her barrettes and fluffed out her shoulder-length blonde hair. Maybe that would ease her headache. "You get to indulge your workaholic tendencies, without me there to try to make you do something frivolous, like take a walk or go to bed."

She laughed. "Yeah, you're right. And it's nice to know my labor's going to a good cause, for a change." Valerie was a financial consultant for businesses in the Minneapolis area. Two years ago she had started doing some work for feminist organizations in Washington. Now she spent about eight days a month in D.C., and it seemed to Ellen that their life together was defined by absences.

"The best of both worlds," Ellen agreed cheerfully. "You get to bring home the bacon *and* be politically correct."

"Ellen, you bring home the bacon too. Just not as much of it."

"No, I bring home—I don't know, the marmalade or something. Teaching English to high school kids may be a noble profession, but I'll never be in your tax bracket, that's for sure."

"Yeah, well. Taxes aren't everything."

There was a pause. Ellen could hear the glassy percussion of ice cubes, the soft "pop" of a cigarette as it left Valerie's lips. She smiled as Val's vices came home across the telephone line. "You sound tired. Is Celeste taking good care of you?"

"What do you mean?"

"She seems to be tied in to all the groups you work. I just wondered if she was still looking out for you."

"I know my way around now. I don't need much looking after." Val took another sip of her drink. "How's the house coming along?"

Ellen heard a metallic clunk on the other end of the phone. It was a familiar sound, but one she couldn't quite place. "I just finished unpacking the last few boxes—we're finally all moved in. We have to hang the pictures, but I thought I'd save that until you get back. Honey, where are you calling from?"

"The hotel."

"Oh, good. Do you have the number? You forgot to give it to me when you left." Ellen almost hoped she didn't. She didn't want to get up and hunt for a pencil; it was so pleasant there. slumped on the sofa with her eyes shut.

"You know, I don't have it handy. I'm in the bar."

"It's quiet there."

"Well, I'm in a little alcove. Listen, El, I have to get going. There's a meeting later tonight, and I haven't had a chance to go over my notes."

The metallic thunk rang out again, and this time Ellen recognized it. Her eyes flew open. The clean lines of their living room leapt into view. She bolted upright and her vision blurred around the edges in time with her throbbing headache.

"You're not at a bar. I just heard someone set a pan down on a stove. You're in someone's damned kitchen. What's going on, Valerie?"

Ellen heard a sharp intake of breath. "I'm at Celeste's," Val replied quietly.

"Why did you lie? Do you think I care where you have dinner?"

"It's more than dinner," she began in a low, choked voice. "I didn't know how to tell you—"

The earth slid sideways. Ellen slammed the phone down with both hands. Black dots vibrated before her eyes, and she pictured, crazily, the poppy seed bagels that Valerie always brought home from Washington. She put her head between her knees and took deep, quivering breaths.

Valerie was having an affair.

With Celeste: spunky, savvy, red-haired Celeste. Sophisticated Celeste, with her dry humor, her silky phone voice, her Capitol Hill townhouse that

Val described in such admiring detail. Vivacious Celeste, whom Ellen had never met but nonetheless felt she knew, because Valerie talked about her so much.

And no wonder.

Head hanging between her knees, Ellen smiled grimly. No wonder Val spoke about her all the time. She understood the impulse perfectly. When Valerie was out of town, Ellen mentioned her as often as possible because it made her feel closer to Val simply to say her name.

Ellen sat up slowly and dug her fingers into her scalp. If she didn't hold on to it, her head would explode. The pain was acrobatic; it ran down her spine to all her joints, then leaped back up to her skull and started over again.

She tried to remember when Val had first started chattering about Celeste. Was there a moment when Val had changed, when she had stepped off the plane with a new, secret smile in her eyes? When Ellen loved her, in their high white bed, did Valerie's thoughts fly to Celeste? Had Ellen not felt the absence in her arms?

The phone chirruped again. Ellen yanked out the cord and hurled it against the empty white wall, where it made an ineffectual slapping sound and slithered to the floor.

Hands clasped behind her back, Ellen paced the gleaming wooden floor of their living room. She crossed and recrossed the spare rectangular space, accompanied by the squeak of her tennis shoes. Their new home sounded like a basketball court, and she had never noticed before.

What else had she missed? What else had passed through her life unseen while she graded papers and read novels? Ellen felt like a cartoon character of the fifties, immune to gravity as long as she didn't realize she had stepped off the cliff. The instant she looked down, she was doomed.

Valerie was having an affair.

It had all been a lie, then: the intimacy of daily life, the murmured dreams of their future, the faraway world of Washington, in which Val worked late, and ate lonely room service dinners, and slept in cold empty beds, longing for Ellen.

No doubt Valerie did work late in Washington. But she came home to another woman, a woman who could arrange meetings and make introductions, a woman who cooked dinner, banging pots on the stove. A wave of nausea surged through Ellen when she thought of what happened after dinner.

She couldn't believe it: she was actually sick with misery. First her lover had betrayed her, and now her body. Suddenly it occurred to her that perhaps she really was sick. She pressed a hand to her forehead. Blazing!

Ellen found this strangely comforting. She was not falling apart; she was merely coming down with something, some kind of flu or virus.

Long ago she had discovered a fitting companion for despair. Now, as if she had been only waiting for an excuse, she hurried to the kitchen to seek it again. Ellen grabbed one of Val's packs from above the refrigerator, ripped off the cellophane, and lit a cigarette. It had been five years since her last one.

The slug of minty white heat hit her in the back of the throat. Gagging, she tossed the cigarette into the stainless steel sink, where it died with a hiss. How could she have enjoyed cigarettes all those years, sought them out, even paid for them?

And how could she have lived with Val for so long, reveled in her company, cherished her habits, while all the time Val was a stranger? Because surely, if Valerie could share with another woman her early morning caresses, her hoarse, tender cries, then Ellen had never really known her. At all.

She sifted through her memories like photographs in a box. The nights she and Val sat up late in bed, chortling over old movies and eating ice cream out of the carton. The sweet notes Val left her in such improbable places: pinned on a bath towel, hidden in a cereal box, tucked into a textbook. The car trips they took together, speeding the hours by making up silly songs about their travels—False, all of it false.

Ellen turned off the flame under her strong-smelling overcooked vegetables. She poured a glass of orange juice and slopped some on the spotless formica counter. Her spill and the bright copper-bottomed pots hanging from a rack on the wall provided practically the only color in the pristine white room.

Perhaps she should go on a shopping spree and fill the house with hideous dried flower arrangements, huge glass jugs of stale potpourri, framed drugstore prints of cowboys and hunting dogs. Valerie would hate that. It would serve her right.

She took her glass and wandered into the bathroom, where she tossed back three aspirin and studied herself dispassionately in the mirror. Strange: her entire world had changed, yet she looked just the same.

Her blue eyes were dry and glittery with fever. Her thin straight hair was as blonde as ever; she had to look closely to find the streaks of silver. Her broad forehead was scored by three worry lines, straight and even as if they had been drawn with a ruler. Newer, finer lines fanned out from her eyes and lips. The skin beneath her chin was beginning to sag. So what? Naturally she had aged over the years they had lived together. So had Val. But that couldn't be the problem, because Celeste was older than either of them.

Ellen frowned at her reflection. Why had they installed these stupid marquee lights over the mirror, anyway? The place looked like an operating room. That was fine for women who put on makeup each morning, but she and Val certainly didn't need it.

One corner of her mouth turned up in a sneer. Celeste probably wore makeup. She was probably the kind of lesbian who painted her nails, and wore high heels when she didn't need to, and slept with men on the side.

Ellen turned on the tap and splashed cold water on her face, surprised that the drops didn't sizzle when they hit her burning skin. This was misdirected anger, her therapist would say. It was not Celeste's job to keep Valerie faithful. But how unsisterly of her, the feminist queen of D.C., to get involved with a woman who was already in a committed relationship.

If she knew.

After all, Valerie had lied to Ellen—lied every time they made love, every time they made breakfast, for god knows how long. Who could guess what she had told Celeste? We have an open relationship. My wife doesn't understand me.

Ellen snapped off the lights and strode into the bedroom, where she searched the built-in white bookshelves as a passenger scans the airport crowd for a familiar face. They were all there, her old friends—Fay Weldon, Alice Adams, Mary McCarthy, Margaret Atwood—the authors whose work comprised the honors course that Ellen taught and secretly called Straight White Women of the Western Hemishpere.

Infidelity played a part in so many of their plots. Was it possible that faithlessness was so common? Could pain like this abound in the world, ricochetting off the walls like invisible x-rays? And yet how archly these women wrote about love and loss. How casually their characters entered into relationships, changed partners, dabbled with the heart.

Ellen had never loved casually in her life, she knew that for a fact. She didn't think Valerie had, either. Which left her with one conclusion, a conclusion that made her sink slowly onto the bed and press her palms against her pulsing eyelids.

This was not some "Dear Abby" crisis that she and Val could overcome with the help of counseling or conversation or kind friends. They would not survive this. It was as plain as text: Valerie was not merely having an affair with Celeste. She was in love.

But why, then, had Val been so eager to buy this house, which even she could not afford alone? Why had they—just six weeks ago—given up the lease on their old apartment? Granted, it was too small for Valerie's home office with its computers and fax machine, its multiplying file cabinets. But it was the perfect size for one woman, suddenly single after ten years.

Ellen stood, swayed, staggered into the living room. She dropped to her hands and knees and felt under the couch for the phone cord. It was not good for her to be cut off from the world like this. She was sick: sick at heart, sick to her stomach, sick to death of the new chapter in her life which was only now beginning.

Ellen plugged the phone in and curled up on the smooth unyielding floor. High above her, polished wooden beams met in perfect angled symmetry. Tasteful white track lights shone like the winter sun, distant and bright, but creating no warmth.

She turned her head towards the large picture window. Out there was the backyard, and beyond it a wooded ravine, as yet unexplored. But all she could see now in the black, black glass was the reflection of a small dark-clothed figure crumpled against a shining expanse of light wood. If she looked closely, she could just make out the pale lost oval of a face, her face.

Ellen wondered where she had left her orange juice.

She wondered when the aspirin would kick in. She wondered where she would belong, now that she was exiled from the embrace of life with Val.

She pictured herself in her therapist's office, splayed out in the fat black leather chair, head thrown back in the strange lassitude that always overtook her during their sessions. Across the tidy teak desk she could see Charlotte with her long black hair and her sharp, inquisitive face, her fingertips meeting in a triangle above the yellow legal pad on which she never wrote anything.

All I'm hearing from you is questions about Valerie, Charlotte would say in her clipped Canadian accent.

That's what I'm thinking, Ellen would reply.

That's what you're thinking, she would repeat flatly. What are you feeling?

I don't know what to feel, because I don't know what's going on. I need information.

Do you need to understand what's going on in Valerie's head before you can determine what you yourself feel?

It's not that, exactly. I'm trying to react appropriately to the situation, but I don't really know what the situation is. It's as if she's handed me a sealed envelope, and I'm supposed to RSVP before I get to look at the invitation.

What do you suppose would happen if you reacted inappropriately?

Look, I'm obviously going to be making some kind of major life decision here. I think it would be nice if I had all the facts first.

But you don't have to make that kind of a decision right this second, Charlotte would argue. (Actually, Charlotte rarely offered her own opinion. Ellen wished she would.) All you need to do right now is allow yourself to feel whatever it is you're feeling. What are you feeling, Ellen?

Sick. Angry. Hurt. Betrayed. Rejected. Stupid.

Why stupid?

Because I should have known. She left a thousand clues: the nights I couldn't reach her; the new hair style she came home with one time; the long after-hours phone calls she made in her office with the door closed. But I never put those things together. It never crossed my mind.

Why not?

Because I love Val. I trusted her.

Is it possible you were merely denying what you already suspected but couldn't bring yourself to face?

Ellen would struggle to sit upright against the warm, skinlike leather. Charlotte, are you saying there's no such thing as trust, only denial?

I'm asking you.

"That's the trouble," Ellen said aloud. "You're always asking me, and I never know."

Clutching her aching head, she sat up, leaned against the couch, drew her knees to her chest. Certainly she would grieve deeply if Valerie had said, "I don't love you anymore," or "I've found someone new." But it would not be this bitter, corrosive misery. The lies had polluted everything.

Trust had been only a visitor in their home, and now it was gone, leaving empty rooms behind. Everything looked different, as if a new color had been introduced into the world. Even small common words, once faithful as stones, now had a sinister subtext. Lover. Sister. Bedroom House.

The telephone trilled, making Ellen jump. She let it ring once, twice. On the third ring she silently put the receiver to her ear.

"Ellen?" It was Valerie: familiar, beloved, unknown. "Ellen, are you there?"

"Yes."

"Ellen, I'm so sorry." Her voice cracked. "I've wanted to tell you for a long time, but I didn't know how."

"So you called me from her kitchen to make sure I'd figure it out for myself. Very clever," she replied in a flat, caustic tone that she understood was to be her new voice when speaking to Val.

"Try to understand, this is something that happened to me. I wasn't looking for it. We never wanted to hurt you."

"We?" Tears crossed her face as slowly as age.

"I—*I* never wanted to hurt you."

This banality was the worst blow, Ellen thought. Their lives—their conscious, correct, lesbian lives—had been reduced to a TV movie. "Where is she now?"

"Who ?"

Ellen closed her eyes.

"She's upstairs," Val answered finally.

Ellen wondered if that was true. For all she knew, Celeste was listening in on their conversation, her cheek pressed to Valerie's as they shared the phone.

Ellen spoke slowly. It was such an effort to form the words. "Are you coming back?"

"I don't know. Do you want me to?"

"I don't know."

"Well, I think we should at least talk. I mean, there's a lot to discuss."

"It's a little late now."

"You're not making this any easier for me."

"Should I?"

"Ellen, you must know how much I hate this."

"I don't know that. I don't know the first thing about you." Despite a decade of intimacy, Val remained a stranger. She would always be a wrapped package, both gift and mystery.

"Look, I'm going to take the red-eye. I'll be there early in the morning. Will you—never mind, I'll take a cab from the airport."

Ellen rested her forehead on her knee. "Okay."

"I'm sorry, El."

"I know." She hung up.

Hand still on the phone, Ellen slid away from the couch until she lay flat on the floor, arms and legs outstretched like someone who had fallen from a great height.

She had a dozen friends she could call, women who would come over and make her tea and hold her hand and tell her that Val didn't deserve her, or that one door closes so another can open, or that all good things must end. But she didn't call. No one could inhabit this moment with her.

This sorrow was hers alone. She must accept it, embrace it, befriend it. It must be, now, her only companion.

Ellen heard her headache recede. Slowly, sounds lost their awful clarity and shrank to their natural proportions. She felt her fever fade to a pinkish glow, like the last pangs of sunset.

Radio and Juliet

Shelley Washburn

Every morning, in the dark before dawn, workers scraped and then dropped big loads that clattered on the ground, shoveled metal parts across the bed of a truck, pushing the pieces until they squealed, and it was too early for such work and it woke her. Juliet lay on her back, then, looking at the sloped ceiling of the bedroom. She was tall, her feet hung over the end of the mattress, and pale. Fifty-five years old, her hair was still blue-black, thick and long. Men said she was beautiful, but she laughed at that. A fine face was nothing, in the end only a face. Her passion was words.

Juliet listened to the stories whispered at work back by the file cabinets, gossip about this clerk or that, someone who shoplifted or snooped in desks, someone who lived alone, wore the same dress every day, wet her pants when she laughed. Juliet listened to it all and at night told her husband everything, adding her own explanations, questions, and answers.

I wonder if May is a virgin? Yes, she probably is, she's so religious. But it seems to me she secretly craves sex. Why else would she go to the prison every Friday night to save the convicts? She's lusting, I'm sure.

The clerks in Payroll said May was a slob, her armpits smelled, no wonder she didn't have a man. Juliet said no, that was not it, May was . . . was turbid, yes, but she loved God with a passion that confused her, she was confused. Juliet worked hard to find the right words to name and explain. This was how she made sense of things.

Her husband didn't understand her yearning for words, the danger of it. Even Juliet didn't understand until the day she climbed the radio tower.

Seven steel spires loomed over William and Juliet Leavy's home on Heathman Heights and then another radio transmitter, taller than the Seattle Space Needle, rose in their midst.

One after another, the neighbors complained to city officials about mysterious happenings: lights turning on by themselves, television programs fading into static, garage doors opening at random.

Mr. Thompson, who lived across the street from the Leavys, told the officials his toaster sang rock songs. "I hate rock," he said.

The scrambled signals and weird electrical occurences were a nuisance, but the biggest concern was their health.

"You're zapping us with microwave radiation when no one knows for sure what these waves do to the brain," said Dr. Tucker from next door. "I beg you, gentlemen, halt construction until further information is gathered."

The city council said, "We sympathize," and gave the go-ahead anyway.

Around the same time that construction began on the new tower, William began to pace the halls of their home, leaving at strange hours to take photographs, to have meetings, there were plenty of reasons. And when Juliet asked him if he had something to tell her, he turned up the collar on his black coat, clamped his lips flat together and looked away, a narrow stare so defiant that Juliet's breath slowed.

I saw May at the market, she said.

Oh, he says, picking up a book.

She's getting married.

He reads his book.

I said she's getting married—to an ex-convict. William?

William glances up from the book.

What's the matter?

Nothing. I'm fine.

When she climbed the tower, the memory of his shirking enraged her. Fine? He said he was fine! She pushed out her jaw and screamed, He's fine!

At first, Juliet wondered if radiation, brain damage, had caused the empty place between them, this collapsing hole that held its shape like a riddled hillock while the insides slipped away. What reason for silence where once there had been words with beginnings and ends, words to sleep and eat and make love by? Juliet had to ferret out the story herself.

Desperate for some clue, she snatched William's mail from the box like a thief. She held his letters up to the light, searching for words, and copied down the return addresses on a piece of paper she hid under a cider press in the basement.

Two days of searching his mail brought the name and address she was looking for, printed in fat girl letters. She looked up the telephone number and walked around for two more days with it memorized, saying the number under her breath. Then, in the middle of cooking dinner, she ran to the phone and dialed, with sausage sticking to her hands. A young woman answered and Juliet hung up. Back at the stove, she turned the burner on high and scorched the meat.

"I made a call," she said to William, intending to tell him what she had done. But their phone machine suddenly snapped on with a jumble of music and what sounded like religious exhortations. "The tower," she said instead. And William shrugged.

On the following Saturday night after dinner, William dialed a number on the phone in the den. Juliet heard him speaking in a low, soft voice, almost a whisper. She heard the voice, no words, but she knew what he said.

She scrubbed at the cast-iron dinner pans. Around and around she pushed the orange plastic scraper under the water, pushed and pushed.

Her husband watched her splashing water everywhere. "So the tower grows, eh?" he said for lack of anything else to say.

She was watching him now, gathering the smallest insults and oversights, the faintest clues and examining them for signs of the coming loss. And when he told her he needed to go out that evening, she was silent and grim.

Juliet followed her husband in her car, though she already knew the address, though she had been by there five times before. She watched him pick up a girl who couldn't have been more than twenty, the age of their own daughter. They drove to a park. Juliet locked her car and snuck into the bushes behind a log where the lovers sat.

The girl leaned on William's shoulder. Juliet squatted down, trying to listen through the blood pounding in her ears. The words, the words, she thought, I can't hear.

From the third platform of the radio tower, Juliet marveled over her wanting to hear. Was she searching for some quirky reason behind William's behavior—the girl was dying, he was consoling her—some sign that William would come back to her with talk again? But what a ridiculous idea. From the first days of his romance, she knew her husband had lost his will for that.

Juliet crawled forward and then felt her knee slide on something soft and wet. She looked down and found a handful of rotten plums smeared across her leg. The purple skin of one was sticking to her shin. She brushed it off and sat up.

She poked at one of the plums with her toe. It looked like a small slaughtered animal, its red guts bursting from it skin. Juliet ran back to her car and sprawled across the seats. The girl had wrapped her arms around him, put her cheek on his chest against the shirt that Juliet had ironed just that morning.

Juliet started the car and drove home slowly, her legs still streaked with red juice.

Once in the house, she went into the bathroom and sat on the edge of the tub. She breathed through her nose in rapid bursts like a sniffing dog or a woman giving birth. She opened her mouth—nothing but little breaths. Off and on, as she climbed the tower, she made those same little panting breaths.

William found her in the bathroom a few hours later, still in her coat, with dirty knees and dry, red streaks on her legs.

"Oh, William . . ." she began, then stopped herself. "I fell," she told him.

So it was a girl, as it turned out a dark-haired girl, and not a word.

Juliet thought somehow the girl could explain the silence, help her name this thing that had been torn from her.

The house was nothing, not sexy or mysterious. It was too brown and too square for that. Tan circles of dry grass spotted the tiny lawn and two overgrown rhododendrons drooped by the door. Juliet parked across the street and sat for a moment pushing her hair around in the rear view mirror. Then she got out and stood before the single-story house where William's girlfriend lived.

She took slow, little steps up the cracked walkway to the front door. She pictured William saying, How could you? How could you? She closed her eyes and pressed the cream-colored plastic doorbell.

"Yes?" said a young woman peeking out the door.

"I want to talk."

"About what?" asked the girl.

"About William. I'm his wife," said Juliet.

A small dog barked somewhere in the back of the house. The girl opened the door wider. "Come in."

Juliet followed her down a dark hallway carpeted in beige wall to wall and into a bare living room. The girl pointed to a futon couch under a long window. "Please, sit," she said.

Juliet sank down feeling trapped in the room with its short ceiling. Her brother had locked her in a trunk, long ago, at their aunt's house and she had screamed into her folded legs and no one heard, not even her brother. And she had pushed and pushed on the lid until something in her exploded. He opened it and pulled her out limp and gasping. She was never the same. That was not his sister he brought up from the box.

The girl fiddled with a pillow in her lap.

Juliet stared. This was herself, thirty years ago. The girl's jaw was sharper, her mouth thinner, but the rest was the same, the same wide face, dark eyes, and stiff, black hair.

William had loved Juliet once, or else why would he want her again so young?

The girl put the pillow aside. "What do you want, Mrs. Leavy? What can we say to one another? I love your husband and he loves me. I'm sorry if you're hurt."

Juliet shifted in her seat. That the girl could be so forthright and only a girl, while she, a woman, found herself speechless, was hard.

"He's my husband," said Juliet.

"Yes. I said I'm sorry. But people change, outgrow each other. You've got to let him go. It will be difficult, but you'll get over this."

The girl seemed calm, reassuring like a nurse who had never had surgery. Such a smooth, clear face. Let him go?

Oh, sure. Just take William Leavy out of my life like you take off an old coat. Try pulling off the first layer of your skin, you little bitch, try being flayed alive. Let him go, indeed.

"What is your name?" said Juliet.

"Elise."

I'll tell you something, Elise. I have years with William, long years. This man you like dug a fish pond for me behind our house, a house we've had for twenty years. And the girls were born there, well, practically. With the first one, William came off the roof to find me squatting on the front porch, crowning. Do you know what that is, crowning? The top of the baby's head was pushing out of my vagina. I have one, you know, a vagina, like you have. The day was hot and he drove fast to the hospital, skidded over a sidewalk for our baby, and held me in his lap and bawled louder than our newborn daughter, a daughter who would never do what you have done.

"Mrs. Leavy, what else can I say . . ."

You don't know anything about him or me. He likes the spot under his left shoulder blade scratched hard, there's a scar there. He listens to radio talk shows all day long, shouting and swearing at the idiots who call in. And he's never wrong, did you know? The neighbors won't speak to him because he let the air out of their tires last Christmas when they parked in front of our house . . .

"You're not the first lover he's had. Probably not the last."

Elise glared. "Excuse me, but I don't have to listen to this. William and I have a special relationship, whether you accept it or not. And if I were you, I'd learn to accept it."

And one more thing. This will happen to you someday. You have thin lips and a hard heart. One night your man will fall into bed beside you smelling of come and somebody else's soap and you'll remember these know-it-all words.

"I think that is all I have to say," said Juliet and she left before the girl could show her out.

She laughed to think of it on the tower. Say? What had she said?

Juliet pushed a button on the radio in her car, a classical station. She got rap instead, thanks to the towers. She whirled the knob on the radio; it was all she could get, rap, beating, shoving the words down, like a force-feeding. She hit the power switch; she was full of words, sick with words, swallowing wads of them in her throat, holding them, the foul taste of them, back.

The air that night was mean hot. The plaster walls felt parched, dusty and warm. The jar of lard on the stove glistened with melted fat even though the stove was cold. Juliet thought that tonight she would tell William everything, about how alone she felt, about his being done with her, his want of her, about the girl, Elise, but mostly, about Juliet's desire for him, still.

She dressed for him, putting on a long blue skirt and a sleeveless white blouse. She pinned her hair in a French braid and snapped on silver earrings. She didn't look so bad, so bad for a woman in her fifties. Why couldn't he see her?

William came home late and found her in the kitchen.

"Where have you been?" she asked.

"Don't start this," William said.

"Start what? I just asked you where you've been. Start what?"

William sighed. "You know where I've been."

Juliet winced. "Let's talk," she said, sitting at the table. The white fan on the kitchen counter hummed and waved the hem of her skirt.

William frowned and sat down at the table.

She touched him with her fingers and he turned away. Juliet pulled back her hand, held it like a wounded thing. This rebuff hurt her, but there was a kind of excitement too. William seemed strange and raw and she was reckless with grief. It was the end—or beginning—of something and she was ready to play it out.

"Tell me the truth," Juliet said.

"What?"

"Do you love her?"

"I don't know."

"You don't know?" Juliet said in a low voice. She made two fists and struck them on the table top. "You don't know? You, I mean us, these years, you don't know?" That wasn't it, what she wanted to say.

"What do you want from me, Juliet?"

"The truth . . . after all this mystery, your silence . . . just the truth." Or maybe some comfort, some kind words for old times.

"I suppose I do love Elise. She's young and beautiful, but it's more than that. She opens my heart. She admires me," said William.

"I admire you."

"Ah, but you are different. You glare and grumble . . ."

Juliet began to protest.

William said, "No, see. Hear me out. You want to know, I will tell you. There is no brilliance with you, only anger."

"Your affairs have made me hard," said Juliet.

He laughed. "Has it been so bad, Juliet? Have you suffered so much?"

"Yes."

He rubbed his eyes. "What can I say to you? You have a tragic perspective. Everything is shit. But things could be much worse for us. I'm content with my life."

"I envy you," she said.

William stood up. Day and night the trucks roared up the street loaded with metal parts to add to the tower, the squawking back-up sirens bleeping. "Do they all drive backwards?" William shouted.

Juliet pushed back her chair and ran to him. She pulled up his shirt and slid down until her nose pressed into the soft hair around his navel. She plunged her whole face into his stomach.

William stared at her and wrenched his mouth like a man choking or ready to spit out hot food.

Juliet sucked in the scent of him, sweet apple wood, and she cried in a tiny croaking voice.

William gently uncurled her fingers from his belt and pulled her upright before him. "No. No. It's too late," he said shaking his head. "Too late for me to love you like that."

Juliet stumbled away from him and hit the refrigerator.

"Why are you doing this?" she screamed. "Why?"

She grabbed a large potted African violet from the window sill and threw it at him, grabbed another one and another, twelve years of blooming birthday violets, and busted them on the kitchen floor.

"Are you crazy? he yelled. "Have the radio waves warped your brain? What are you doing? Stop it. Stop it!"

Juliet smashed another violet. "Bastard! You sneaking bastard!"

He left the room, slamming doors throughout the house. As he walked down the hallway, the wall lamps lit up dimly. "What the hell?" he roared. When he stepped away, the lights faded.

Juliet sank into a chair in the kitchen. This was not it, what she had wanted to say. No. No. It was something about surrender, about giving in. Not these sharp words.

Everything came out wrong, came out badly. She wanted the truth, and when he told her, she said, not that truth, that wasn't the truth I wanted.

She could see him on top of the girl, her black hair stabbing the flowered sheets, legs wide open and William heaving up and down.

The microwave oven on the kitchen counter buzzed. A madhouse. She was mad; it hurt, it hurt. Mad. She smacked the oven. Small voices sang from its sides. She pulled the cord out of the wall. The music played on.

Juliet couldn't say exactly why she climbed the tower. She wanted to send William a message. She wanted revenge, drama, an act he couldn't ignore. But she also wanted answers and the tower seemed to promise them with its signals and lights, its colossal height. A woman might find solace, sense, at such a height.

After their argument, Juliet ran upstairs to the spare room where she lay on the couch whispering the words she could have said. William snuck out the kitchen door around midnight and Juliet slipped into a fitful sleep, waking before dawn to workers rolling up the street in their heavy trucks.

She dressed, pinned a small note to the front door, and drove off slowly.

The sun had almost poked through the horizon, lighting the belly of a thick cloud stretched above the distant hills. Juliet parked in front of the radio tower, found an open gate in the cyclone fence around its base and walked in. The tower stood on three great legs joined by eight platforms, forming a narrow tripod that pulled up to a tight point. Three workers, bent over a set of plans laid out on the ground, missed Juliet's quick leap onto the first steps of a long ladder that led to the top.

It seemed easy to climb, one foot after another, the easiest thing she had ever done in her life.

The men below clustered around a bundle of thick wires.

Juliet waved.

She stopped to catch her breath at the third platform. From the tower she could see the entire city and the silver river coiled around it, see it all without fear. What fall could be worse than this silence between them? Anyway the stairwell was safe, wrapped in a tube of metal bars, and the platform had high railings. The view was spectacular.

One worker looked up. The other two looked up. One pulled out a pair of binoculars. The workers pointed toward Juliet. She waved and began to climb to the next platform.

The workers made big scooping motions with their arms ending, always, with their hands pointing to the ground. Juliet laughed and climbed on.

She sat down at the fifth platform, leaned against the handrail, and panted. The workers were shouting something, but she couldn't hear their words, and one had begun to climb up after her.

In a few minutes, she stood up feeling rested and fit. She wiped her hands and grabbed the bars on either side of the stairs, climbing faster now. The air was clearing and the day looked to be a hot one.

About midway to the next platform, Juliet stopped, put her chin on the step in front of her, and closed her eyes. Her mouth tasted metallic, her fingers stung. Suddenly, the white platform above was too far away to reach.

Oh, God, oh, God. Can't move. Not up or down. Can't anything.

The tower seemed to be leaning or swaying, even, she thought, whispering. She clung on, listening and waiting.

She had tried to find the words to save her marriage, to be spared the pain of change, of all the little deaths that life requires. Now she was willing to suffer, just to get it over with.

Juliet opened her eyes and concentrated on the diamond pattern of the step before her. If she could unravel her yellow knuckles from the ladder, shift her feet from the step where they had lodged, if she could keep from glancing down, she might climb.

Inching, sliding, and then scrambling upward, Juliet collapsed onto the sixth platform.

The sky was vast. She had never seen the city like this before. A huge expanse of small things. Boats and cars moved like slow fish, and the round, white mountains east of the city looked no bigger than a fist.

The platforms of the tower were closer together now and she could see the top, its antennae flagged with shreds of clouds. Except for airplanes, she had never been this high. Not with her own two feet, this high. William was one of those dots down there. She sucked in some air and started to hum.

Juliet began climbing again. Dizziness made it hard to find the steps. Sometimes her foot missed the rungs. The metal handrail warmed in the morning sun and her sweaty hands slid up and down. She tripped up the last set of stairs.

At the top, she hoisted herself onto the tiny platform and kneeled there in the sun and the fierce, silent wind. Her black hair stuck out behind her like the oily feathers of a raven. Juliet scooted to the edge of the platform and gazed at the far-away city.

She was no star-crossed lover, destined to die from mangled messages and bad luck. Her problem was not words, not the girl.

Did May pray for her convict? Pray for his redemption, for her own?

Words carried no redemption—they were stray signals, interference—without experience, without a shifting of the heart.

Juliet stood and sliced her hand through a patch of passing fog.

And then a thing May would call grace.

Juliet heard voices, the barking of a talk show host and his guest, arguing over a sales tax. William's favorite program in her head, her teeth, her fillings, somewhere, a reception clearer than their own home radio. She shifted her arms and the voices stopped. Instead, classical music, a polka, the blues.

Laughing, she twisted back and forth, changing the channels, finally settling on Bach. With her arms up, palms flat to the sky, she caught the sweet solitary piano notes climbing above low, groaning strings. The notes rose and fell, circled and called, utterances for the silent place inside her that spoke nonetheless.

The workman who had come after her thrust himself onto the platform behind her.

"I will let go!" she sobbed and the man, hearing her cry, grabbed for her. But he misunderstood. These were the girl's words, spoken through a woman's heart. It was done, the fearful thing, the unbinding.

"I'll go down by myself," she said to the man, pulling away from his grip.

Now her bold recklessness left her and Juliet, taking care not to fall, sank to her knees. Like a washerwoman, she jerked her hands along the platform floor as she crawled toward the ladder.

The Butterfly Effect

Kelly Simon

Richard's heart is beating against the hollow of Janet's cheek. She can feel the flutter on her skin as she rests her head there. She counts the beats as they lie on top of the comforter, the silvery light from the TV, still on from the night before, flickering over their bare skin. She is watching and not watching the screen. Her eyes are closed and her head is on his chest, his arm around her shoulder. She feels herself heavy and content, intertwined with his body, as if her muscles are braided into his sinews like the drawings in anatomy books.

"The end," he says, echoing the words on the screen. She thinks she feels his heart speed up, or maybe it's hers. He slides his arm out from under her head and lies on his back looking up at the ceiling. Then he swings his legs to the floor and sits at the edge of the bed staring at the carpet.

She pulls the covers up around her neck. "The end of what?"

"Nothing," he says. "Just . . . endings"

She hears the toilet flush, the sink water running, then the peculiar shrill scream of the shower. She lies there waiting for him to come back to bed and curl up beside her as he usually does in the morning. When she hears the beep of the microwave downstairs, she realizes he's not coming back.

She gets out of bed and pulls on her jumpsuit. She goes into the bathroom, brushes her teeth, thinks about washing her face but doesn't because she doesn't want to wake up all the way yet and think about why Richard seems so distant lately. She knows she blows things out of proportion. Richard calls her the worst catastrophizer since Chicken Little.

"Give you lemonade and you make lemons out of it," he says.

She stuffs her toothbrush, blowdryer and makeup in the overnight bag that she shuttles back and forth between their houses. They spend almost every night together but he doesn't want her to move in officially because it would hurt Nancy's feelings. Nancy is his wife.

He's sitting at the kitchen table drinking coffee with his back to her when she comes downstairs. She sets her bag in front of the door, then walks over to the sink, spoons some instant coffee into a mug with red hearts on it, punches some buttons on the microwave. Her arms are folded across her stomach as she looks over at him. He doesn't turn. Ella Fitzgerald is singing Rodgers and Hart. *"You have what I lack myself, and now I even have to scratch my back my-self."*

"Aren't you going to sleep in?" he asks when she sits down. She shakes her head, watching his face, but he's intent on scrutinizing yesterday's junk mail. She'll wait for him to speak first. Maybe he'll say, "You looked so cozy in bed I thought I'd let you sleep," or, "I've got a lot to do today and I wanted to get to work early."

On the counter is a yellow notepad with a book title scrawled across the page. *Midlife Crisis: How to Survive the End of a Relationship,* it reads.

"The end of you and Nancy or the end of us?" she asks, holding her finger-tips steady on the notepad.

He walks over to the record player, lifts the needle from the disk, and turns the machine off. "I'm tired of this record," he says. Janet feels her eyelids quiver. He turns to her. "What are you going to do today?"

"Go home and put my house back together." It slips out. She'd meant to say something neutral, like "I'm going to the library," or "I have some blue-prints I have to get out today." Nothing definite, so that whatever it was would have to come from him. She holds the coffee cup up to her face, blow-ing into the dark liquid, feeling the steam on her upper lip.

"What are you going to do?" she hears herself saying. He looks over at her small heap of belongings in front of the door, then looks back at her with a strange look on his face. She imagines fear in his eyes, feels a lightning bolt of power.

He takes a cigarette from the pack, puts it to his lips, then, as an after-thought, offers her one, crumpling the empty pack. Her hand shakes when she raises the cigarette to her mouth. She flattens the tips of her fingers against the edge of the table until the base of her nails are white, the cigarette squeezed between her index and middle finger.

He sits with his back straight like a child in class. "It's not you, you know." For a long time he says nothing and she thinks maybe he just isn't going to. He concentrates on the backs of his hands, not looking into her eyes.

She's trying to make up her mind whether to say Who is it then? when he says, "You know how I hate to hurt anyone."

"Are you having a mid-life crisis?" she says, keeping her voice under con-trol.

His mouth is smiling but his eyes are not. He looks down at his hands lying palms up in his lap. "Maybe you were it," he says.

He kisses her goodbye as if nothing out of the ordinary is happening. As she eases her car out of the carport behind his house, she thinks: he's picking up the phone right now, dialing Nancy's number. She imagines him gripping the receiver in both hands, waiting for her to answer.

Nancy will be coming out of the shower when the phone rings. Janet sees her walking toward the kitchen, the Mediterranean kitchen that she, Janet, designed for the two of them, a kitchen impeccably tidy, unlike Janet's own. The space that Richard had entered the afternoon they met, ducking his head as he walked through the doorway. The spot where Nancy had uttered the four words that changed all their lives. "Richard, this is Janet."

Janet sees Nancy running a comb through her cropped hair, slicking it back like a boy's as she reaches for the phone.

"How are things going?" Richard will say, keeping his voice casual, without that information-seeking edge to it.

Janet imagines Nancy leaning against the kitchen wall, head down, bunched fingers massaging her forehead. "Why are you calling?" she'll say. A thin trickle of water from her wet hair will sluice across her cheek, bead on her upper lip.

"I just needed to hear you breathe," he'll say.

Janet talks to herself, trying to quiet her demons. *Take deep breaths, stay calm. Maybe The End means the end of him and Nancy.* But she knows that if he's not standing at the back window as he usually does waving goodbye to her, it will mean that it's all over. She wills herself not to look up but at the last second does and as she pulls past, something about the way the sun hits the blank windows making it look as if no one is inside convinces her that she is not imagining all this, that it is her, Janet, that he wants to end it with.

"She's winning!" Janet says aloud in the empty car. All of a sudden she can feel it. She can feel it in the slight hesitation when she asks him what he wants to do over the weekend. Or when he sets the paper in his lap and stares across the room at the TV. Last week, when they were lying together, his hand seemed to stop in mid-caress when he was stroking her back as if remembering another body. What's worse, the more distant he becomes, the more she needs to attach herself to him like a tongue to ice.

"The first rule of life-saving is don't try to rescue someone if you can't swim," she'd said to Richard a few months ago when he talked about how devastated Nancy would be if he filed for divorce. Now her words are coming back to haunt her.

When they first got together, Richard used to complain about Nancy's controlling ways. She was a neat freak. She was cold and angry all the time. Janet could afford to be magnanimous, the voice of reason, then. Lately, he hasn't talked about how awful his marriage was. Janet thought it was because he had simply run out of steam. Now she wonders how she could have been so dense.

The other day he told Janet that he felt guilty about going away on vacation with her because it would hurt his daughter's feelings.

Janet had said, "Are you thinking about going back?"

"It would solve some problems," he said, picking up the paper.

Driving back to San Francisco in the early morning stop-and-go traffic, Janet waits for it to sink in. "It's over," she says aloud. And when that doesn't make her queasy she says, "You're on your own." But even that doesn't work. She explores for damage, probing herself like a tongue to a tooth, surprised to find that she is intact.

Janet makes herself think of all the things she can do to make the most of this new chunk of time. Looking at it one way, she feels almost as if she's just been released from a cramped position and can stretch for the first time in a long time. There's a kind of luxury about it.

From the notepad on her dashboard, she tears a yellow Post-it and presses it to her steering wheel. One eye on the road, the other on the paper, she writes, Start Diet. The writing is wobbly and unstable. It will be easy now with just herself to worry about. Just five pounds and she'll be down to her normal weight.

She pulls a cigarette from the pack in her purse, then shoves it back in the pack tearing the paper. She rolls down the window and drops the broken cylinder onto the roadbed. It's only been in the last few months that she's smoked so much. She examines her face in the rearview mirror. Small vertical lines have etched themselves onto her upper lip. When she met him she looked thirty-five, now she looks at least forty. She reaches for the pen.

Quit Smoking, she writes. She follows it with two large exclamation points. The pressure of the pen cuts two gashes in the paper. Like frown lines, she thinks. Filled with small tentative resolves, she's surprised at how calm she feels, how in charge.

She snaps the radio on. ". . . *the underlying cause of chaos is the multiplication of tiny glitches and irregularities,*" the reporter is saying. "*The notion that a butterfly stirring the air over Tibet today can affect a storm system over California next month is known to scientists as The Butterfly Effect . . .*" Janet switches the station to news. "*. . . no rain in the three-day forecast,*" the weatherman says.

"*. . . an accident on 580 at the Strobridge off-ramp involving a big rig and a compact . . .*" she hears. Richard is on his way to work now. He must be listening to the report. He'll think she was so upset by what he said (or didn't say) that she wasn't paying attention to the road. There'll be a call waiting for her when she gets home. If there is none, she'll know for sure.

She knew what she was getting into. At least, everyone *else* knew it.

"The first affair is a throwaway. It's just to prove to themselves that they're desirable. Then they go back to their wives, watch TV, get fat, and die with a smile on their face," her friend had said. "Face it. You're disposable."

"This is different," Janet had said. "I'm not nuts about him. I'm not vulnerable. It's just a good time."

When had she grown so attached?

Traffic is at a standstill now. She opens the car door. Four cars ahead of her two drivers are standing on the shoulder arguing, their bumpers touching, blocking two of the lanes. The sun seems to be coming from the wrong direction. She feels disoriented. She gets back in the car, leans on the horn. The passengers in the car next to her stare at her like she's from another planet. She looks at herself in the rearview mirror. Her jaws are locked. She hardly recognizes her face.

A half block from her house she finds a parking spot. She positions her Honda to back into the space and the car behind her pulls up close to her bumper. She rolls down her window, waves the driver around. He pulls up even closer, preventing her from backing up. She gestures to the space, signaling for him to pass, but he turns off the engine and dangles the keys at her.

The man in the passenger seat smiles a slow insolent smile, puts his cowboy boots up on the dashboard. The driver rolls a joint, takes a deep drag, passes it to his buddy. Then he leans back against the seat and closes his eyes. Cars are backed up behind them, horns honking wildly. A cop passes by on a motorcycle. Janet rolls down the window and waves him over.

"Officer," she calls. "Those men behind me won't let me park."

"You're holding up traffic," he says. "Go on around the block."

"I've been trying to park here for the last ten minutes," she says. "They won't let me into that space."

"Get going, lady," the cop says.

"But I *live* here," she pleads, hating the whine in her voice.

"Get *going!*" he says, gunning the engine at her, "or I'll give you a ticket!"

She slams the gear into first. Then she pulls around the corner and stops the car, blocking someone's driveway. She turns off the ignition, her heart heaving and crashing inside her chest. Then she puts her forehead down on the steering wheel and cries like she has not cried since she was a girl.

When she walks in the door she avoids looking over at the telephone to see if there are any messages. She'll let herself do that after she showers. She sets down the overnight bag, catching a glimpse of herself in the mirror. The hollows underneath her eyes are violet.

She takes the bedroom phone off the hook before she goes into the shower so that if he calls he'll get a busy signal and try again. She undresses, steps into the stall, then gets out. She walks to the phone and sets the receiver back in the cradle so that there will be some evidence if he calls. The water soothes her. She soaps herself slowly, rinses off, repeats the procedure twice more. Three times means there will be a message. Coming out of the shower, her hair wrapped in a towel, she goes to the telephone. The red light is on, not blinking. No message.

Suddenly she sees her apartment through his eyes, as if it has descended into desperate disorder since she last slept there. Shoes litter the floor, books and magazines are piled on every surface. No wonder he doesn't want to sleep there.

She walks around the apartment seeking out the debris of their affair: the matchbooks with the logo of his credit union that are strewn all over the coffee table and the kitchen counter. The back copies of the *Wall Street Journal*. The bits of paper covered with his tidy printing notes taken during business meetings. She goes from room to room collecting half-finished crossword puzzles, menus from the places where they've eaten, clippings from the travel section (A week in Spain $999), putting them in the trash, furiously reclaiming the space from entropy. All the time she is bypassing the feeling in her stomach. She's learned that when she stubs her toe, she can stop the pain from reaching her brain. She practices that now, almost managing at times not to feel the nausea.

She blow-dries her hair. Then she files her nails. Then she gets the bottle of polish remover, takes off the old polish and repolishes her nails. She tries not to remember his hands as they stroked her back, his palm hovering on a cushion of air barely brushing the fine hairs there; his voice light and tentative as a boy's when he reads to her in bed. She sits for a while at the dining room table, looking out the window at the east hills, trying to summon reasons to despise him. Wind-driven rain hurls itself like handfuls of rice against the window. The panes buckle and sag with each gust as if they're about to implode. So much for the weather report.

She squeezes her eyes shut and thinks about his mouth. How he takes the corner of his lower lip in his teeth when he's thinking. He is not a demonstrative man. She calls his tape and listens to his thin emotionless voice, which suddenly sounds boyish and vulnerable. When the beep comes on, she hangs up.

He's with his wife now! Suddenly, Janet knows it! He's taken the day off from work, driven past her house, seen her car in the driveway. He makes a couple of passes up and down the street before he decides what to do. Then he pulls into the driveway. He parks his Toyota next to hers. The two white cars side by side fill him with comfort.

He walks up the brick path between the terra-cotta planters filled with neatly trimmed purple and magenta flowers, up to the door. He knocks. Nancy opens the door. Her eyes widen. Neither of them says anything. She puts both hands on the edge of the door, leans against it for support. She's wearing a cotton skirt and a T-shirt, sea-foam green with a mauve silk scarf across her shoulders. She has no makeup on. She's not wearing her glasses, so her eyes have that vulnerable searching look that nearsighted people have. He shifts back and forth from foot to foot.

"What do you want?" she says finally. He clears his throat. "I want to come home," he says, reaching for her hand.

Janet shakes her head violently to dislodge the thought. Love is all in your head, she thinks. We're born with this big chunk missing from us, like a giant shark bite, and we go around looking for someone who makes us feel whole. Does anyone really love anyone else, or are we just loving our missing selves? She remembers how awestruck she and Richard were when they discovered they had twin thumbs, the same shape, the same curve, the same folds over the first joint, the moons identical pale crescents.

She makes a cup of decaf, lights a cigarette and sits at the dining room table staring at a basket of wilted freesias. She pours herself a glass of wine. Then another. She is surprised each time she finds the glass empty. When he hasn't called by 5:45 she knows he isn't going to. She turns the volume on the answering machine to low so she won't hear him not leave a message.

In the bedroom, she turns on the TV, sits on the bed with her arms wrapped around herself staring at the screen, forcing herself not to blink. "The underlying cause of chaos is the multiplication of tiny glitches and irregularities," the announcer is saying. Maybe a butterfly stirred its wings over Tibet a month ago and this is the result. She traces the hairline crack at the bottom corner of the opposite wall along its jagged path up across the ceiling, imagines it widening, rending the roof, then the house, cleaving wider and wider until the earth groans—a terrible howling noise—then splits apart.

Her eyes feel heavy and she lies back against the pillow. And there on the screen of her closed eyelids, is Nancy in her Janet-designed kitchen, walking around the center island toward the front door. Janet hears Nancy's feet on the tile, sandaled and soft. Nancy checks herself in the hall mirror, runs her fingers through her hair. Janet hears the click of the latch. Richard ducks his head and enters the foyer. They sit on the couch at opposite ends. Nancy feels a tugging in her throat. Her hand lies on the sofa cushion. Richard covers it with his. Her shoulders are straight. Richard observes how poised she seems. Her coolness never fail to surprise him. He leans toward her, licks his upper lip, delivers his plea. She grabs onto the thin thread of Richard's voice as he tries to give her reasons to take him back, tries to believe in the possibility of it.

Her eyelids tremble as she registers the flatness of his voice, the studied earnestness, the words creating no heat. He wants to do the right thing, but there is an absence of heart sound, the sound of guilt not of love. She says a few words, shakes her head. Richard leans forward, relieved, kisses her awkwardly on the cheek.

Janet hears her own phone ringing. If she were not bound by cords of sleep, she might lift the receiver and hear Nancy's voice coolly compassionate as if she were talking with another grownup with whom she shared an imperfect universe.

And, as if that universe were still intact, one of them might say, "You win."

Italian Supper

Daniela Kuper

The last time I went to Europe I fought with my husband every day. We fought every day in regular life, but in Europe I thought it would be different.

I remember Venice, the moment I knew it was over. Our room overlooking the Grand Canal with its soft morning colors, temples, statues rising from the water, and me throwing open the double windows and leaning out to smell the sewage, or maybe to fall.

I turn from the boats, the perfectly dressed Italians, the everything-you-ever-wanted-in-a-vacation window scene, to regard the man I married.

Chuck doesn't look up.

A woman prays her husband will never stop looking when she undresses. We've come so much further than that. Chuck doesn't notice me at all.

He sits on the bed and fiddles with his things: cameras, lenses, film containers, Woolite, pocketknife, maps, Carmex, compass, coins, guidebooks, and he's got his socks soaking in the bidet. I'm afraid to say anything at all to this man. The words fry up in my throat and turn dumb.

I keep the scene inside, it eats me up all day. We go around these magic streets and it's looking like Cleveland. My husband renders everything around him normal.

The sun starts to go down, lovers prepare to get juicy. You can smell it from the canal, from under their arms and between their legs as they walk by. The sugar spots they haven't tamed yet.

Women's shoulders go soft. Men's lips thicken. Italy makes ready for love. Restaurants change shifts. The lighting softens. Menus have buttery sauces, warm lobster. They touch in Italy. Like Paris, only mustier. Men grab a breast, the rump of the woman they want, give it a wenchy squeeze. The women laugh it off. The children whisper to each other in the tunnels.

I turn to the man I married and touch his arm. He doesn't turn to me. He's looking for something in shop windows, hundreds of shop windows. He looks at fountain pens, pipes, ties, and shoes. I look to see what he's seeing but I don't care about these things. We haven't talked. We haven't played and I know we never will. In my calves and my breasts I know it.

Chuck, I say. *Chuck, we need to connect.* My words are wrong. They are always wrong. *Connect.* Sounds like a plug, a conduit.

Butter to bread, breast to mouth, this is what I want. I want to suck in his tongue for a minute, then talk about strangers. I picture us laughing, and how that would feel, then he buys me something unexpected. Then we make love. This is what I want.

I have lots of time to consider all this because he never answers me. Minutes go by. Time goes by. I touch his arm again but now I have become a nag. He's mad, I've bothered him again.

In Florence, he sits in the luggage car protecting the baggage from *the Italians* because I hadn't bothered to learn train seats are by reservation only.

I get a table from the maitre d' in the dining car with peach roses and white linen because I speak a little Italian and talk with my hands. *Mi dispiace, I* tell him, *I forgot to reserve a seat, do you have room for my husband and me?*

He stops polishing the wine glass and regards me up and down. *Signora,* he says, *could you be able to eat very, very slowly?*

Yes.

Would you remember every bite?

Yes.

Then I have room.

Chuck, the man I married, sits white-lipped in the luggage car, his army jacket so fully functional it lacks only refrigeration to become a model city.

I go to the dining car alone and eye a Swiss man who is just the right age, a little too old. We are the only ones here with the maitre d'. The Swiss man flirts delicately and offers me some of his *Times.* He looks thin, financial, and I like the way his legs cross at the knees and swing slightly.

After a time Chuck comes to the table, laden with fresh arugula in olive oil, Chianti in a hand-labeled bottle, warm focaccio.

The maitre d' stares at him. Chuck is sweating. His jacket weighs fifty pounds. He is sweating from the jacket and the strain and responsibility of keeping everything together for the world.

Half an hour after he sits down, he sees the meal. He sees the veal parmigiana, the buttery risotto, the chocolate wafers, the Alps, the lakes, and the perfect Swiss businessman who now no longer looks my way.

This is romantic, he says. *I've always wanted to be in a dining car,* he says. *Like in the movies. Like Claudette Colbert. Like Cary Grant.* He says all this but it isn't enough. I am a husband's worst nightmare. I want to fuck the Swiss man. I want to fuck the maitre d'. I want to fuck the veal parmigiana because I imagine its rich red sauce staying in places I have hidden since my marriage.

The Night We Say Goodbye

Lin Florinda Colavin

---

you crouch
behind a bulwark
of fear
while i
hurl myself repeatedly
against the barrier
that thickens
with each assault

sharp words
fill the air
their shards embedded
in the massive wall
between us

and yet
in this same place and moment
my heart yearns for us
to fill the night
with whispers
like small raindrops
awakening the love coiled in our bodies

tongue
seeking tongue
snakes
swimming into dark water

where
we could know
what only the body can teach us
how to celebrate
what we no longer hold.

The Last Mr. Wrong

When he is late for dinner and I know he must be either having an affair or lying dead in the street, I always hope he's dead.
— Judith Viorst —

Love was a terrible thing.
You poisoned it and stabbed at it
and knocked it down into the mud —
and it got up and staggered on,
bleeding and muddy and awful.
— Jean Rhys —

Macroscopic Phenomena

Marilyn Krysl

. . . the basic unit of the universe is an event . . . .
Zukav

Brian. He is not attractive at twenty-two, he wasn't attractive as a kid either. Even as a baby he acted limp, puked excessively, and lay around in smelly lethargy as though he hadn't the heart for living. Worried his mother into specialists and Valium (though she had other reasons, too, for the Valium). His life has not been anywhere near bliss. Father a famous research physicist and prestigious university professor, upstanding in the international scientific community. Mother now fat and frumpy, excessively even-tempered, she makes the average citizen of Palo Alto want to scream. She will go through life as she is now, a doily in the computer age. The father sublimates.

This father, this mother: Brian becomes a brain. Thrust into Advanced Calculus at an early age by the name they conspired together to give him: Brian. He is fat and soft. He is ill-shaped. All grace, beauty, stylishness, and verve have slunk inside, impacted in the cortex. Thick-lensed bifocals, honor roll, Merit scholar, he is destined late in life to receive a Nobel Prize. Indeed there will be no escaping such a prize. You think Destiny doesn't exist, we are self-made women and men? This kid is so destined your heart aches. In Rilke's terms he will fail utterly. He will not be able to change his life.

Beth talks intelligently incessantly. It's her method of not thinking too deeply about things she can't do anything about anyway. Majoring in economics. She is smart and a workhorse. Okay looking, a brunette, and completely willing to marry Brian. She has already been looking around, and he is what she can aspire to. Beth promises no *surprises,* none. It does not even occur to her to feel desperate about her prospects. That mild inner hysteria seems denied her, or she herself denies herself such little flurries of scariness. Will Beth turn fat and even-tempered in his arms? Or does she have inner resources not immediately apparent? Or the years, going by, may force her to develop resources. The intriguing thing is that if she decided to have style, she'd become a compelling figure. At present, though, she appears to be eager to nail Brian, this man so unattractive no coed will be persuaded into his sack no matter how prestigious the linen. She is at Stanford, he is at Stanford, last semester of the B.A., then graduate school and the tedious plodding ahead. He has no women: he has friends. Correction: he has, if he wants her, Beth. Anyway, he can marry her and presto, he'll be set, will get to have sex at last. Do not sniff at this, you who have health, joyousness, shapely torsos, and undistinguished parents.

The friends. A crowd of other brains, high school class presidents, some foreign students, mostly men. I like André, mother a French princess, father a Hungarian businessman. He treats Beth with respect, with Laura he's affectionately playful. Every now and then he winks at her and says, "I am lookeeng out for your velfare, darling."

Raoul, Sekiko, Franz. And Manuelo, who fled Spain to avoid Franco's draft. Managed to marry an American high school girl, though the marriage was never consummated. She has conveniently disappeared (who knows where? One believes only some of what Manuelo says), leaving him with American citizenship as long as she doesn't sue for divorce.

A few women like Laura and Beth. Beth tolerated more or less for Brian's sake, though he cannot get up the energy to want her. André and Manuelo try to rig various setups for him, they even contract with a young coed to pretend to fall in love with him. She's convincing, but at the vital moment he's too terrified to get it up. She shrugs and dresses, leaves rather abruptly, he thinks. When she tells André what happened, he has no choice. Matter-of-factly he sighs and pays her. Now these friends have given up. Brian will have to remain a virgin until he marries, there is nothing more they feel they can do.

Laura. Attractive. At first glance your American girl-next-door, athletic, shapely—but with flair! She has style the girl-next-door doesn't. "You are not," André says, "zee average greengo, darling." Great legs, she walks like an antelope. Slings one thigh across the other knee, calf swinging, swinging, as she takes notes. In Aesthetics 495 André whispers, "Watch out, darling, theese eediot beehind you is sneeking looks at your legs." Undistinguished, working-class parents, no help to her, possibly a hindrance. (Act as though you have sprung from the head of Zeus.) There is no history of success, the absence of success is, in fact, a spectacular absence. The problem of sociology taking over personality: son of prof learns to become prof, daughter of housewife learns to stack a dishwasher. There is no escaping history, the trick is to make it work for you. In other circumstances, a moneyed family, say, she might have become a Claire Booth Luce. But she has no capital, none, she's on a scholarship. What she has is style and quickness. She's going places, emphasis on the going. Blazing into the future here at Stanford, citadel of knowledge. Inside a university there is supposed to be immunity, as in a cathedral. To the extent this immunity exists she takes advantage of it. She may become an intellectual, perhaps another Simone de Beauvoir. Possibly there will be a grand passion, the love story of the century, possibly she will move from one painter, writer, sculptor to another. Or cast men aside and become a crack journalist, or make it at the U.N.; her French is fast becoming impeccable. She is talented at languages, digs philosophy, and she has been around, knows the nether workings of the body. A lawyer, a Nepalese student, a high school principal, the editor of the *Palo Alto Star,* briefly. Professor J, who fell in love with her and proposed (she refused). Laura believes in love, she has to believe in love. Laura has inherited nothing but bootstraps, and she isn't buying that line for a minute. As every public school pupil knows, Lincoln is a myth created by the U.S. Textbook Commission. God does not help those who help themselves, she will have to make it on her looks and brains. But this is a weighty prescription: everything is on the line all the time. Laura sometimes envies Beth the ease with which she assumes the world was created for her. On the outside Laura looks lush, but inside *she's* prepared a torso of steel. And steel adds weight; there has to be something with wings, something feathery on which to soar. A belief in love is the ticket. Like helium, it will lift her off. The fifties are finished and the sixties haven't quite got going, one of those moments in history when everything seems possible. She spent the fifties growing up, now here she is: like Cyd Charisse she's ready to dance.

Scene I

Laura and Manuelo were drinking espresso. André, in his room, read Wittgenstein.

"This thing you call love, it's an illusion," Manuelo said, smoking one of André's Gauloises. (André had taken him in hand. "You vant to look like a man, you must shave," André instructed. "Every day shave. Vonce a veek, eetes not eenough for you.") "Sex is real," Manuelo continued. "All the rest, that's in your head." She laughed. Manuelo, lucky to get one girl in six months, maybe he'd never actually had one. Laura could afford to be gracious, let him have, for a while, her exquisite attention. Now that she'd laughed, though, he was annoyed. "You're too young to understand these things," he said. He was younger than she was but pretended otherwise.

"Look, Manuelo," she said, turning serious, "you can pretend it doesn't exist. But you're pretending."

"Illusion," he repeated firmly. "You're going to cry tears over this, sweetheart, believe me."

"I probably will, and precisely because it isn't an illusion."

"Listen, sweetheart," he said, leaning across the table, garlic on his breath, "let Manuelo show you once. Some real sex and you won't want these dreams."

She fell back against the pillows, really laughing this time.

"Let's go to my room," he persisted. "We'll have some wine."

"André," she called giggling. "Help! André!" André appeared in the doorway, took off his glasses.

"Vat's going on? Manuelo, I told you, she doesn't *vant* you. Quiet, please, I beg you."

It's been raining lightly for several days, a wet spring, the azaleas are out fabulously. Kennedy in office for three and a half months, he looks like a winner, he just may be the one. Laura, just coming from a tryst with the lawyer, she's hungry. Of course she isn't in love with him, but while she waits he passes the time. A bit acrobatic, but it will do, interim. Laura doesn't think of a man as a catch; "a good match" doesn't interest her. Her scanner isn't tuned for the neutron star, her scanner is tuned for colliding galaxies. Now she is hungry and her skin glows. Beneath a yellow umbrella she walks quickly toward the Student Union, imagining the grilled cheese sandwich she will order, the glass of milk, the cherry pie. She would like a platter of tomatoes niçoise, but the grill doesn't serve such things, she'll have the tomatoes at home, later. Though Laura and Brian share some of the same friends, they have never actually had a conversation. They've been at the same table with André and the others, conversations everyone around the table plays into, as though conversation is a striped beach ball—if it comes in your direction, give it a push. When they've met, it's been in these circumstances. For Brian's part, you don't take seriously what you can't have. She glances at him casually, he does not hold her eye. Now because of her umbrella she doesn't see Brian. But he sees her. He looks at her, and his guard is down—sweet circumstance that sometimes comes to us. Suddenly he's enjoying himself immensely: watching her when she is unaware of him, outside her window in the dark, looking in. The secrecy of this! People unaware of being watched are naked. She is striking in dishevelment, wisps of hair astray, and in her urgency, the decision in her stride. He can even see the tryst she still smells of, and how very hungry she is. He steps out to rush after her, take her to lunch—and stops: what in God's name has got into him, the impossibility of such rash action! He thinks to retract the energy of his longing—longing that soars from him in an arc—but in spite of the years of rigorous training, he isn't hardened enough to manhandle his response. Besides, his intelligence is uppermost, he knows a good thing when he sees one. He tries, in that split second, to keep his feeling a twinge only, but he's leaned in just a little too close.

The Strong Force binding the nucleus together zaps him in.

The ache of love comes on like instant acne. Unlike a pimple, though, his feeling has a graceful shape, like an oval sphere of light moving through his bloodstream. If he could continue this moment indefinitely, the sight of her back as she walks briskly away—but while time at the subatomic level is sometimes reversible, time at our level marches on. She goes into the grill, lusting after that sandwich.

Scene II

"I'm in love with Laura." Saying it as one might say I wish I were rich. Manuelo looked amused.

"She does not vant you, my friend," André said as tenderly as possible. "She does not vant anee of us."

"She deserves a prince," Manuelo burst out. "She's not interested in a virgin," he added as though there were some score he knew.

"Leesen, my friend, theese eese folly."

"Uh-huh," Brian agreed, wishing for once folly might sweep him up out of logic and calculus into the improbable. He looked at André, a helpless look: save me (But we tried!) In the crunch he was too intelligent not to fall in love with her.

Though he needs to prepare for the Harvard and MIT interviews.

Though she is unattainable.

André told her. When he told her, she thought well of Brian. He has, she thought, the imagination to desire the impossible.

What could be worse than denying oneself a romantic life?

Prison.

Torture.

Early cancer.

The hard labor of the poor in third world countries.

But this is Stanford, not São Paulo. She must struggle to rise—there's nowhere to go but up. He must concentrate simply to stay level; the thrust of Science has already shot him into the upper atmosphere and shows no sign of deceleration.

Scene III

He calls her. What the hell.

"This is Brian," he says. "Look, I'd like to talk to you. Could you go out for dinner tonight? It really would mean a lot to talk to you." Coming from the king of the frat house this speech would be just another line. You pause, though, when such a speeeh is delivered by a real, suffering man in the world.

"Well," she says, laughing, "you are direct."

"How else can I be with you under the circumstances. Listen, I just want to talk to you. We've never actually talked, you know."

"I want to be straight with you," she replied. "I can have dinner, that would be fun. But I don't know if André told you I'm in love with someone. I don't know if he told you that." Both of them know this is a lie told to save face for both of them.

"He didn't, but I'll accept that. I'll pick you up at six, then, if six is all right."

They meet frequently.

How does this happen? Brian keeps proposing they meet, Laura keeps accepting his proposals. They stick to the rule that Laura's in love with someone else, therefore their meetings are platonic. Brian talks, Laura listens patiently. She is so forbearing, deals with him so delicately, that he begins to feel encouraged. Her patience resonates with such benign intent that he is very nearly moved to shouts. He decides to take advantage of this, he'll take advantage of whatever there is. Brian talks, Laura listens, and a kind of steady state comes into being. Things get neither better nor worse. They meet but nothing comes of these meetings. The event of note is that they continue to meet. No meeting of theirs is the last meeting, each time the thrill that it isn't over yet. He gets to be a little whacko, she hasn't told him to buzz off. A little dizzy with the brashness of figuring what can he lose. So he begins to talk his love to her, he talks his life, tells her a novel, trying to build up sympathy for the main character. He takes pains not to bore her, he works for eloquence, lacing his tale with as much panache as he can. For weeks he talks her up, developing fluency, embellishing the basic theme with mad little forays into the ridiculous. He says some fairly bizarre things. "My system hasn't been prepared for you, my system's been prepared for a paper towel." "If I could fuck you just once." "Marry me."

She answers patiently. "I can't marry you. You know I'm not in love with you, I can't pretend otherwise."

He's wildly happy; when she speaks, he devours her reasonable replies. Everything she says is completely reasonable, he doesn't disagree with her for a minute. He appreciates her honesty, he appreciates her agreeing to listen to him. He appreciates her sitting still and letting him look at her day after day. My God, the privilege! None of the others get this privilege; she meets only him in this oddly intimate way. Yes, he thinks, they are intimate! Their friends observe them and make no comment, move a little away, as though to give them privacy. No one, not even Manuelo, teases them. Brian thanks them from the bottom of his heart for shutting up. But it also scares him—if they harassed him he'd remember there is no hope, he'd remember to take this lightly. But they are most pointedly not harassing him. It's as though each friend is privately holding his breath, pretending to be going about business as usual, but actually staring wide-eyed. Like physicists examining an S matrix, their adrenaline shoots up, just watching. They wish Brian well, they go on not breathing for his sake. He gets tearful at the thought of their friends' hopefulness. He and Laura work at encouraging the tendency for hope to exist, to actually exist. He pours his heart and soul into their mutual endeavor. Their effort will not fail on *his* account! To accomplish this he builds onto the edifice of their conversation, and at the same time his brain continuously monitors the keeping of his cool. Get sleep, don't drink too much, think tall, eat slow, read Marx, don't turn around fast.

As for Laura, she is obliged to sip a lot of things slowly. Coffee, orange juice, bourbon, whiskey sours, Manhattans, lemonade, glasses of water. She seems always to have a glass before her. Life takes place at a series of tables and on each table a glass of liquid she is obliged to drink. She has agreed to listen, she has agreed to take him seriously. When and how did she agree to this? Well, she doesn't want to hurt his feelings, there's that. Though she has turned and walked away from bleeding men without a backward glance. She wonders about this, is forced to conclude that she actually has begun to like listening to him. She finds she gets interested: what amazing remark will next fall from his lips? Though he began awkwardly, he is developing a new genre, and this form is for her, exclusive: such talk no one else will hear. His talk is made especially for her, a custom job, impressive in its inventiveness, its volume. When she knew him casually he seemed bookish and flabby. Now he has shown her his brilliance! Fiery tongues! The frankincense and myrrh of the soul! If he were already Einstein she might be tempted. Einstein was a sexy man at fifty, it's the early stages of genius that are repulsive. Like wine, genius has to age properly. Still, she is moved by Brian's predicament, a man trapped in a fat kid's body. And no one else has offered her intimacy. She begins to understand that no one else has spoken seriously to her before.

Painful Paradox, Part I
She acknowledges to herself that they *are* intimate.

Painful Paradox, Part II
Precisely this intimacy makes their union impossible. Think about it: why shouldn't she go to bed with him, give him her present? She does with plenty of other men she's not in love with. She toys with them, they toy with her, and in the great scheme of things all parties are innocent, no one gets ripped off.

But to toy with this man would be an atrocity!

She must *not* go to bed with him, precisely because she isn't in love with him.

A party in the Palo Alto hills, somebody's parents' house, the parents gone. Evening in May, air soft, abundance of flora in the deepening dark. Nature doing the pants-off things. Increasingly black sky, increasingly star-studded. Radio sources in distant galaxies beaming their beams to the scene. The quarter moon, sharp as a die, this moon enough to make even Brian shut up.

They wander out to the flagstone terrace, Brian brings along a bottle of Scotch. She feels like she's in an ad for Chanel, a beige silk dress, understated, very classy. The future hasn't shown up, but she's ready. Goes out occasionally with some man who looks promising but isn't. This interlude is all right with her, though, everyone is required to put up with a certain amount of dead time. Meanwhile she's amused carrying on negotiations with Brian. Like two nations engaged in talks, they can't simply walk away, go about business. They must reach agreement on the issues, neither can face their constituencies without a treaty. They do not touch, but act as though they do (or do they act as though they don't but do?). They stand a little away from the others, they're at the party but not at the party. "You know I'm in love with you," Brian begins. A winning case begins with a summary of the basics. He continues casually, a bit methodically at first, but as he drinks he begins to extemporize, he begins to talk in earnest. "Listen, Laura, I've got this idea. It's really very simple: we lie down side by side on a bed, and what we do then is stare up at the ceiling. Nothing tricky about this at all, trust me. No strings attached, we don't even hold hands—unless of course you wanted to—but in my view the situation is basic. We lie completely still and stare at this ceiling. Absolutely no lust present, I swear it. I do not get hard, we stay chaste as brother and sister. Flat on our backs, we don't even look at each other. Don't turn your head! The point is this ceiling over both of us at once, and at which we are both of us staring up at the same time. We stare at this ceiling at the same time! Synchronicity, Laura! Think what I'm saying! It costs you nothing, you don't have to compromise your principles, you go right on believing in love as though nothing unusual is happening, I go right on not turning so much as the flickering of an eyelash in your direction . . . ."

His speech begins to slur, she listens patiently. She intends to perform her task to the best of her ability. He lurches on with this line of rhetoric, beginning to sway where he stands. She tries to see his eyes through the thick lenses, but what she sees is a seething mass of talk, a buzz of subatomic events emitting sound. She has the perception suddenly that he really has lost his boundaries, has become pure sound hovering about her. He has dispersed, and the drone of his talk is now just part of everything, that landscape that is everywhere around her.

"Christ," he says then, "I'm going to be sick."

Oh no. She's suddenly on call, slings his arm over her shoulder. André sees them and hurries over, slips under Brian's other arm.

"You should not dreenk, my friend," he admonishes, but Brian doesn't hear, is already deeply into misery. Inside and upstairs they find a bedroom, moonlit, stagger forward, lunge, lay him down. André motions to Laura to stay with Brian, says, "I veel geet a pan."

She stands over Brian, as though keeping watch. What is it she watches over? His ruined childhood? His stuttering soul? He moans and jerks. She touches his shoulder, but he is too far gone to notice her hand. Light from that moon pours a stream across the carpet, pure milk of the spiral arms. She observes this light as a sweet invitation to enter even further everything there is.

And she is about to kneel, intending to speak to him, bring him to his senses, when he twists up, and in one grand unmistakable arcing, leans over, throws up at her feet.

The sound of his retching, she feels, is more of her task, she listens to this patiently too.

Later, very late, when the party breaks up, she goes back to the bedroom, looks in. André washed the carpet with soapy water, but the room still smells faintly of vomit. The moon has moved on, leaving a trickle of itself thin as a length of string at the foot of the bed. Brian snores. She thinks she will wake him, then changes her mind, lies down beside him instead, takes his hand. She can feel his fingernails bitten to the quick, poor baby. Side by side, their bodies, impossibly cruel, oh very cruel, she thinks, the housings of souls. Who planned this, she wonders, who set us up? His snore reminds her of something large and reeking of itself, a woolly mammoth, maybe, or a Gaudi cathedral full of old pizza. She holds his hand, but after a moment he jerks in his sleep, and flops over, away from her.

She stays, looking up at the ceiling, memorizing the shadows, remembering for him.

Superluminal Speed

Before she publicly announces her engagement, Laura calls Brian one evening to tell him. "I've been expecting it," he manages. "Congratulations." Gets off the phone as fast as he can. Rushes out, gets behind the wheel, puts the key in the ignition.

He sits behind the wheel.

He knew someday he would have to marry Beth. Beth is the real world, and he has been mad. Destructive, crazy, romantic madness! His dreadful life rises up mocking, and he begins to fall—no, plunge—downward to depression. He who was going levelly about his business, memorizing theorems, plodding eastward across the tundra. But he can't get depressed, he can't stop studying, this would mess up his prospects, ruin what life he has. His life depends on maximum output, depression is a luxury he can't afford. His teeth clench, his jaw locks, his blood pressure shoots up, and he bursts into tears.

He sits behind the wheel, sobbing. Stars, one by one, come out above him.

Status Quo Update

Spring rains have given way to sunny days, bathing suits, magnolia-scented twilights. He tries doggedness to get back in the groove. He tries to get interested in Beth, goes through all the motions. He proposes, she accepts. Presto, he finds himself engaged. He even attempts to ravish her on the seat of his car, but in the process of getting himself ready he panics. What in God's name is he doing! He doesn't want her! "Listen, I'm sorry," he says. "We really should wait. I know you want to wait and you're right. We'll wait." Working at feeling affectionate, he kisses her hair. Actually Beth would like not to wait, but decides to go along with Brian. She's ready to leap out of blouse, bra, skirt, and panties, but she thinks it best, now, not to tell him. This decision should come from the man in her judgment. She pulls up short, and he is relieved, his penis soft, declining flesh. Maybe later, this infatuation with Laura passé, later when he and Beth are actually married.

Then, surely, he will rise.

Good-Bye Gang

He has not got over the mortification of having passed out in her presence. He determines to rise above this sordid event, to rise so high and so magnificently that the image of his disgrace will disappear so thoroughly it will actually never have existed. His wish is simple: to annihilate unflattering portions of the past. Such is his will in this matter that the impossible poses no obstacle. He intends to make an impressive final impression. She'll remember him as a man, dammit, a person with intelligence, dignity, sophistication. He has planned this final meeting, the aplomb with which he will conduct himself. He's even planned his parting words to her, the expression on his face when he delivers them. "Look," he says on the phone, "I want to say good-bye. But not on the phone. Let me take you out, we'll have a celebratory drink."

"Oh good," she *says,* enthusiastic, "I'd love to." She's relieved actually, he sounds sane, she hears him gathering himself into a semblance of poise. Not bleeding after all, no reason she need feel guilty. When André told her Brian and Beth were engaged, she envied them the simple curve of their lives. Only for a moment, though—after all, it wasn't her curve. She thinks hers is the one she will travel with John, and she is not completely full up with the fact of him—his handsome confidence, his position at HEW, his lust for her, his intention to run for high office. They'll move to the capital, she'll wield her French for profit, they'll make money and love, ascend and ascend. With this infusion of euphoria she has become even more attractive. Strangers who meet her on the street stare, wondering how she got that way. Now this one last loose end will be tied up: no ugly scene with Brian, no sad silence between them. He's measuring up, he's coming around. She sings to herself as she brushes her hair.

The patio of some bar or other. Laura's silk dress will survive the *Sturm und Drang* of fashion. She looks glittering, a scene out of *Breakfast at Tiffany's.* He orders champagne to mark the occasion. He wants to get just a tiny bit drunk, enough to enjoy to the bittersweet hilt this last cluster of moments with her. This after all is their last meeting, this is the meeting that will ring the change. They reminisce and laugh, they toast each other's engagements. She says she'll write, thinking he'll like that, but he waves this away, I can make it on my own, thanks. She's impressed by this savoir faire, and she wishes him well. She who has, at the moment, all the advantages.

They leave, sunniness of afternoon over them. She notices his hands on the wheel, remembers feeling the tips of his fingers. His fingernails have not grown out. She hasn't really looked at him, she has thrown her whole being into listening, dimming out his visual presence. It occurs to her to wonder if he's feeling so fine as he professes, and she begins to suspect that in fact he's making a heroic effort. He looks under strain, as though the thinnest of spines may at any moment fail to hold him upright. And then it hits her: she's been avoiding her feelings. How to dismiss their strange tenderness, their intimacy like no other event in the galaxy! To think that he actually wanted to marry her! The passion in him! The things he said! Marriage would be a disaster, she thinks, she'd go mad. And she never intended this, their being duped, led on by some force mocking them both, a great cosmic joke at their expense. But if nothing in this universe is casual, why in the hell did she suppose *she* could be? He's part of my history, she thinks, his dye in the cells of her memory attesting to his having been there. Like parents and kin, he is a chemical fact in her, in her blood, in her chromosomes, in her spiraling DNA. Well, she will not let him be ruined, she loves him! She cares about his goddamn soul!

He imagines the moment when he will leave the motor running, possibly a quick kiss on the cheek, then she will wave as he drives away waving. When he pulls up she says, "Turn off the motor." "I'll go on," he says, not wanting to lose the pretty illusion of having a grip. "Come in," she says, "I want to take you to bed with me. Yes," she says, "you heard me rightly." And she turns from him, slides toward the door. Water torture, needles under the fingernails. All right, he gets out, his body seems to be working. He can, after all, stand up, he can walk. He stands and walks, one foot in front of the other. And bringing to the moment as much grace as he can muster, he follows her up the steps, inside.

She pours Scotch into glasses. He's clumsy with the ice, but this is reassuring, he still has his quavering hold on things. And he observes his own clumsiness for the first time as benign: she doesn't mind it. She leans against the counter, calm, opening all his doors, letting the sun stream in. Whatever he does is all right—hasn't she been telling him this, hasn't she been agreeing to him for weeks now, for months?

He goes to her, kisses her on the mouth. She opens her mouth, inviting his tongue inside. He explores this mouth of hers, pulls her against him, discovers his prick already rising—what should the order of events be! He kisses her again, she seems to like it! His hand rhythmically squeezing her shoulders, one hand down her spine, slow trepidation, oh God the cheek of her ass in his hand!

When he pulls away to look at her she takes him into another room.

The bed. His consciousness catapults forward—will he survive the sight of this bed? The spread is white, he will never forget this. She squeezes his hand, letting him get used to things, and he's encouraged: he'll forge ahead! She has to help him a little with her buttons, but he steels his nerves and all by himself pulls away one strap of her brassiere, revealing her lovely tit, Kodacolor. He stares at her breast for seconds and more seconds, trying to go slowly and memorize the detail. The seconds tick and gather around them, steady and quiet, sparrows assembling. What, he wonders, can she be thinking, just as she leans, lifting her nipple to his mouth.

Take anything at all that's offered, anything! He closes his eyes and gently sucks, hears her breathing, listens to it change. Hears her fingernails growing, her hair humming, the sound of a struck tuning fork coming off her skin. He stops to draw breath, she takes off her dress, her skirt a blossom opening around her shoulders. Naked, gleaming like the gold of Tutankhamen, she kneels, begins to unlace his shoes. A voice in his head shouts: she's naked at your feet! Where did she learn such things, think up this devastating simplicity! He watches her perform the miraculous act of undoing the buttons of his shirt. The sordid details of undressing, he discovers, are practiced movements in an act of devotion. Her tiniest motions take on the weight of rite, and she proceeds to unbuckle his belt. Obediently he stands, and when she looks up he feels his knees go weak: SHE IS NOT DOING THIS OUT OF KINDNESS.

Adrenaline, buckets of it, racing around in him. He pulls her to her feet. She is at once so tensile and so pliable in his hands that he wants to weep. He lays her down, gets out of his pants and shorts, oh God to lie down naked beside her, that would be enough, can he stand more? Yes, but he is not going to be able to be slow, he's had no practice at controlling this careening feeling, and he climbs up and pushes his thickened penis into her—easily, gloriously—he knows what to do after all! Suddenly everything is pure physics—as she reaches up with her hips, as he delves, space-time expanding in every direction, Bell's Theorem proving and proving, and as it proves, the thought comes to him that he'll never need even a glass of water again.

Bell's Theorem suggests that what we think of as separate parts of the universe are intimately, immediately, connected. Brushing her hair one morning years later she thinks of him. An ordinary enough January day, elms leafless and black, the temperature dropping. Her husband (the second) has already left for his office. She hears her son running water in the bathroom, her daughter talking to the cat as she fills its bowl.

Laura stands in her slip at the full-length mirror, brushing her hair, considering this hair of hers critically. She is letting it grow long again, and as she brushes she admires the length, its fullness and color, a few strands of gray making their premiere appearance. *A gorgeous head of hair still,* she thinks, and flips backward to *then* and him, Brian: *what did my hair look like back then?* It wasn't curly, for one thing, this waviness set in after the birth of her daughter, her coming permanently altering her mother's chemistry. Back then, she realizes, we rang each other's changes. His talk not idle talk and her listening not lost on him. And his speeches still a part of him now, as her decision to act that sunny afternoon has been present ever since, a throbbing in sinew and bone. Only the particular curve of their tenderness—his talk and her listening, his drunken lack, her soft fullness—could have produced her as she is, here, now, before this mirror.

She supposes one day when she's an old woman she will open the newspaper and read the announcement of his prize.

And she brushes her hair and thinks very well of him. She brushes her hair and thinks very well of herself.

City Tag

J. Deborah Klein

"You know what man really desires? One of two things: to find someone who is so stupid that he can lie to her, or to love someone so much that she can lie to him."
—Djuna Barnes

Friday

At the Savvy tonight there is a man sitting at the bar. I had a class with him once, and tonight he is alone and looking interested. Allan heads to the other end of the bar and I sit down with this man. He looks only a little older than he did before; his hands show it but his face is still young and we drink rum and talk about that class we had, what we remember of it. He remembers me and my name and even some of the things I said in that class four years ago, when I was still trying to sound like I knew what I was talking about.

I want to say his hair is blonde, but it isn't, really. It's a plain color, more dishwatery than anything, and it isn't too long. His mouth is what gets me right off; his lips are dark and full and I remember noticing them across the room in a course on Tragedy. I remember his lips more than I remember the course itself.

Lowle and I talk about people we knew in college. These are the same conversations I end up in all the time, the "remember whens" which make me wonder if these people have had lives after college. Most of them still refer to their college years as "the good old days." Three years later we are still the same people we were in college. Allan and I lived on the same hall in college. Now Allan lives on the edge of Hell's Kitchen and I live down in Soho, but we still get together on Friday nights, and at bars in the West Village we find ourselves with all the same people we knew before.

To stop Lowle's reminiscing, I ask him to dance and we do, not too close at first and then quite close once we've gotten the feel of it. The bar is dark and loud, the dance floor is crowded, and I feel younger than my 25 years.

I didn't expect to kiss Lowle an hour later, standing close on the dance floor. Allan is dancing with a long-haired woman and the room is dark and I like the way Lowle kisses, and so we keep doing it.

"Why are you laughing?" he asks me.

"I'm not," I say, and laugh again.

"Why are you doing that?" he asks, pulling back a little.

"I do that when I'm pleased," I tell him. I do that when I'm nervous, but I don't tell him that.

"Oh," he says. "And you're pleased now?"

"Very," I say, kissing him again. Very pleased, I think. And very nervous. Because it's so sudden, and I'm a little drunk, and because anything that makes me feel good makes me afraid of when it will end.

At the end of the evening, I've left Allan behind at a bar with the long-haired woman, and Lowle and I are in bed together. I don't think about how we've gotten to my apartment. I remember that we passed Allan and the long-haired woman on the way out, and Allan said "see you" and for some reason I felt strange that he was seeing me take Lowle home on the very first night.

And now there are candles and music, soft music. We sit on my bed, sealed off from the harsh lights and city sounds. I've scraped my knee tripping on an uneven sidewalk and he watches me clean it, tries to distract me. There's a little blood and mostly it just stings and is raw. By the candle my bare legs are soft, sleek, and he sits curled around them, touching me. The bactine stings. He blows on it for me.

Lowle asks about a picture of Allan which hangs by my bed. In the photo Allan and I are eating sushi and smiling at each other. Allan, I tell him, is just a friend. Everyone in college might have thought we were an item, but it's not true, I tell Lowle. We were always just friends.

"He keeps me in line," I say. I like that Lowle is curious.

"This has to be casual," he says.

"Of course," I say. "I don't want to be in a relationship right now." What I mean is that I've stopped expecting relationships to be meaningful.

"I can't be monogamous," he tells me.

"Neither can I," I say.

"I want to have fun." He kisses my leg.

"I *am* fun," I say.

We have sex and he says things and touches me like I'm everything in the world. I've learned to distinguish: there are those who act like you're everything in the world, and there are those who act like you're everything in the room. Mostly I get the second kind, but both types have forgotten what they said by morning.

After we've had sex, Lowle says it *was* fun. Then he moves to the other side of the bed to fall asleep, and I wish I still had the skinny single mattress I had in college, so he'd have to hold me.

Saturday

Lowle wakes up earlier than I want him to.

"I have to go," he says. "I have things to do."

I don't answer, and don't say anything while he puts on his clothes. The room is bright with sun and I feel self-conscious, naked beneath the covers. I wish I'd thought to get up ahead of him, to get my hair to lie flat and my face to look less creased. I spit on my fingers and rub them under my eyes, in case there are dark smudges from last night's makeup.

"Want to have another one-night stand sometime?" I ask finally, when he is almost to the door. Lowle comes back to the bed, kneels down, and kisses me. He touches me, and smiles.

"I don't know how to answer that," he tells me. "I don't think of this as a one-night stand." I'm surprised.

"It needs to stay casual," I say, because I know it's what he wants to hear. *He's* surprised.

"Sure," he says. He writes his number on the pad by my phone and leaves.

That night I call, but I get his answering machine. I tell him to call me back. He does, but it's late, and he doesn't feel like getting together. He suggests that we start a game of answering machine tag. He says he'll see me around, and I go to sleep feeling stupid for having expected another night together.

Sunday

I want to call Lowle, but don't. We don't run into each other.

Monday

Lowle calls and leaves a message on my machine. He asks that I call him later. I do.

"It has to be casual," he tells me. I look out my window at the fire escape across the street. The neighbors are planting flowers in little boxes, and they are kissing and getting dirt on each other.

"I know that," I say. "I want it to be casual too. I just want it to be consistent."

"I'm not sure I can be consistent," he says.

"Do the best you can," I say. It isn't what I mean, and he doesn't want to come over. My apartment is huge, silent and empty, and I go to bed feeling stupid again. Allan told me today that someone said Lowle's been burning his bridges; he's broken off with two women since Saturday. Thinking about him makes me nervous. I don't want a relationship right now. At least, I don't want him to think that I do.

Tuesday

I don't call Lowle, and he doesn't call me. We are being casual.

I run into him at a cafe midtown during my lunchbreak. He is sitting with a large group of friends, and I recognize all of them from college. Lowle and I say "hello" and "how are you." He acts nervous, and we have nothing to say to each other. A blonde-haired girl appears and sits down in the empty chair next to him, and he stops talking with me to talk to her. This must be what casual means to him.

I call Lowle late in the evening, expecting to get his machine. He picks up.

"Are you seeing other women?" I ask.

"Not right now," he says.

"So I'm the only one," I say. I look at the rain outside my window, trace the patterns as the water runs down the panes.

"Right now you're the only one," he tells me.

"I think you should be seeing other people," I say. I like saying what he wants to hear.

"Oh?" he says.

"Yes," I reply. "I wouldn't want you to be disappointed."

What I mean is that I'd rather entice him by his own rules than go back to being alone.

Wednesday

I don't call him. I want to handle this well. Coming home late I think there might be a message from him on my machine, but he isn't playing tag today.

I remember when the kids in elementary and junior high "went together," which only meant holding hands and the occasional awkward kiss, I was always alone. I know that sounds typical enough, but I don't mean it to. It never *felt* typical; I was never as lucky as the other girls and I was always quite convinced that I was cursed with bad luck. I also wondered if I might be inferior in some way, and no one would tell me the truth. Sometimes in truth or dare the boys kissed me, but only on a dare. I didn't like playing; being kissed terrified me, the clumsy gestures so wet and startling. I wondered whether I was supposed to wipe my mouth afterwards, or if it wasn't cool, and I know I always blushed. So by the time I reached college, I was ready to say yes to any man who was interested. And there were plenty who were, and I said yes to all of them, but it never meant anything, at least not to them.

I have lunch with Allan. We sit at the window and watch a man playing harmonica on the sidewalk, a cello case open on the ground in front of him.

"You don't really think this is working, do you?" Allan asks. "It's not exactly a healthy understanding you have going with Lowle."

"It's not so bad," I say. Allan has a way of laughing at me which makes me notice myself. It's a tender laugh, and he does it now.

"It's pretty bad," he says.

"It's casual," I tell him. "I don't have any expectations, and neither does he. It's better that way."

"Like that's really what you want," he says.
"It's not so bad," I repeat.
"No pressure," Allan says.
"Right," I reply.
"No monogamy," he says.
"Right," I reply.
"Remind me never to get involved with you," he tells me. I don't know why he always says that. He has never needed reminding.

Thursday
I call Lowle to say that I'm not calling anymore.
"Let's go out for pizza," he says. I go.
The pizza place is one I've never been to, in his neighborhood in the Village. The air is thick with smells and loud with music, and the tables are crowded with high school students. We talk about our parents, and it's nice; we can actually talk to each other. I don't put garlic on my pizza in case he wants to kiss me later.
He doesn't kiss me later. We walk to his apartment a few blocks away and he holds the doorknob like he's planning on going in alone. He has work to do, he says.
"Call me later if you get tired of working," I say, knowing I shouldn't say things like that. It sounds too friendly. I don't want him to think I'm getting attached.
"I probably won't call," Lowle says.
"OK," I say.
He goes into his building, it begins to rain, and I walk back to Soho alone.
Later, Allan comes over and we sit on my bed, talking, and there is that friendly intimacy between us which always helps to make me feel that I don't need another man in my life, a romantic man who is ready to fall in love with me. We're talking about our lives and feeling like friendship is all we need, and then Lowle calls.
"I'm tired of working," he says.
"Oh?" I'm casual.
"Mind if I come over?" he asks.
It's the end of the week, I think. He only wants to be with me at the end of the week. He doesn't want to see me too often. Otherwise it might seem like we're serious. People might see us talking at cafes, might notice we've been together a lot lately, might think we're more than just friends.
"Sure," I say. "Come over."
I tell Allan, and he thinks it's all very funny. He wants to stay until Lowle arrives, to see how he acts toward me with another man in the room. I don't care, or at least I try not to. The lighting is golden and Allan looks very beautiful to me, as he always has, but then Lowle arrives and is surprised to see

him, and Allan and Lowle talk about their work, act interested, and I sit and watch.

As soon as Allan leaves, Lowle asks me about him.

"I thought you two were just friends," he says.

"We *are* just friends," I say.

He doesn't look like he believes me.

"Did he know I was coming over?" Lowle asks.

"Sure," I say.

"So he knows about us?" he asks.

"Kind of," I say, and know it's the wrong answer. Lowle cringes. He's so bothered by anyone knowing, even someone who went to college with us, who he knows would have found out eventually.

"What a bad triangle," he says. I'd like to tell him that it's really not such a triangle; that actually, if he was paying attention, he'd see that it's all very simple. But I don't tell him that. Instead I lie and say, "I didn't tell him details," which I did. And I say, "he doesn't mind," which I think he actually does, but of course he wouldn't tell me that.

Lowle's on the bed beside me. We read stories to each other, and there's something playful between us now. He kisses me, acts a little silly, and then all of a sudden it's hot and heavy, we're getting naked, and he's saying things about sex.

"We'd better not," he says. "I have more work to do tonight."

"OK," I say. "Whatever," I say.

"We should wait until tomorrow," he says. "Then we'll have plenty of time. Now it would be rushed."

So much for casual, I think. Now we're planning in advance.

"And let's keep it quiet," he says. "Private relationships are more intimate." Private relationships are secrets you don't want to tell, and secrets have reasons behind them. I know this is what he means.

"See you tomorrow," he says as he leaves. I'm naked and in bed, and I want him to be staying, but he's ignoring my signals.

Now Lowle shuts the door behind him, and all I can think is that at least there's tomorrow. He wants to be together tomorrow.

Friday

Allan and I drink together at my apartment after work. I stay home so that I won't miss Lowle's call.

"It's not worth it," Allan tells me. "It's not like you're in college anymore. You can do better than that now."

"It's not so bad," I say.

"He's not being fair to you," he says.

Why is it that men who aren't involved with you always know how to treat you? It's the men who are glad to get involved, even casually, who don't know what they're doing. When I was in college I always called them boys; boys you could catch, while men had learned to see you coming. That was college, though, and now I try to think of them as men and to see it as more than just a game of tag.

Then it's evening, late, and I'm drunk. I didn't intend to be drunk, though of course I never intend to. Allan has left and I've gotten drunk waiting for Lowle, and so in addition to being drunk I find I'm angry. It's late, and I've called him, but he wasn't home. I left a nice, casual message, saying how he can call me if he wants to when he gets in, since I'll be up late. I don't mention that he was the one who said we might end up together tonight. I don't mention that I hate waiting. I don't say that I planned my evening around spending the night with him, or that I'm getting sick of being disappointed. I keep drinking. I go to sleep very late, very drunk, knowing for certain that it's over between us.

Saturday
I don't call him. I spend the evening with Allan, who reminds me that it isn't worth it, that I don't need this, and that Lowle's not being fair to me. I know these things.

Very late I get back to my apartment, and there's a message from Lowle stuck into my mailbox in the entryway. It says, "I stopped by—call me later, and maybe come by if I'm up to it, which I probably will be." He actually stopped by. Funny that I'm so surprised. I call.

"I'd like to be with you," he says.

"Really." I don't act enthusiastic.

"Sorry about last night; I got in too late."

"Sure," I say. "No problem," I say.

"So will you come over?" he asks. "I'd really like to see you."

"I don't want to see you anymore," I say, and believe it.

"Why?" he asks. I don't have a good answer.

"I just need a definition for our relationship," I say. "I don't understand whether it's just a series of flings, or if it's something more. I want to know what it is we're doing."

"But I thought that *was* what we were doing," he says. "I think of it as a series of flings. Isn't that what you thought?"

"In a way," I tell him.

"Maybe we *should* stop having sex if it isn't what you want," he says.

"That's not what I meant," I say. I don't know what I meant. "I guess I just wanted to know that we were both thinking the same thing." I've always been good at compromising. "This was what I needed; now we have a definition. That's all I wanted."

Ten minutes later Lowle is unlocking his door for me. The tv is on, and he doesn't waste any time. I've had a little to drink but he's had plenty, and he's more encouraging than usual. The room has a blue glow from the tv, and I can't help being ready for him.

With him on top of me and inside of me, I start to tremble. His face is close to mine, his breathing touching my skin.

"Are you shaking?" he asks. I nod.

"Why?" he asks.

"I shake when my body is tired," I tell him. I shake when I've had anything to drink, and then have an emotional moment. I'm having an emotional moment, but I don't tell him that. It's the beer and the way his mouth looks and the way he touches me, the way I want so much to be here, but that's not what I tell him.

"Are you tired?" he asks.

"Not *so* tired," I say, moving against him, sexual. I bite my tongue to stop the shaking. His face is very beautiful right now.

Then it's later, we're still having sex and I'm on Lowle's lap, and without meaning to I find I'm looking at the tv over his shoulder. I wonder why he chose to leave it on, or if he thought about it at all. I can't tell what's happening on the screen, and the sound is very low. He doesn't know that I'm doing it; he is facing the window behind me. I wonder about the plot of the show, am curious about what the characters are thinking. He's moving below me, there's sex between us, but I've caught myself watching tv. I laugh when I realize it.

"Pleased?" he asks.

"Yes," I lie. Moments ago I felt so touched that I trembled. Now I feel so distant that I'm watching tv and lying about it.

Sunday

I stay at his apartment until late morning, on purpose. I want to see if daylight scares him away.

It doesn't, and we're sexual in the morning, and when I leave he's kissing me at the door. It feels different; I imagine it might be, but I don't ask.

"See you later," I say.

"Sure," he says. "I'm having dinner with friends at the Cherry House. Maybe you could stop by."

I spend the day wondering whether things have changed. I might have told Lowle why I trembled. I might have told him right then about my fears, my anger, even about how I've been betrayed and how sex makes me feel it could happen again, so easily. It would have scared him away, if I had told him these things. I knew he would have said "I needed this to stay casual, and now you're getting emotional. It means too much to you." And he might have asked me to leave. So I didn't say why I trembled. I didn't explain anything more than what he wanted to hear.

Allan and I go to the Cherry House for dinner, but I don't tell him why. Over our table is a painting of a man and a woman holding each other. The embrace is so close and tight that they are one form and the woman is lost in the picture; all we can see are her eyes and the top of her forehead. I have never been held like that.

Lowle comes into the restaurant with his friends. They sit at a table nearby, but he walks past without looking at me. He's being casual. Allan thinks he's being stupid, and reminds me again that I'd be better off without this.

Allan leaves to take the long-haired woman to a movie, and I sit alone for a few minutes more. Lowle doesn't come over. I get up to go.

Lowle comes out of the restaurant and onto the sidewalk right behind me. The evening is crisp, the air smells like meat and exhaust but there is a pleasant stillness.

"Hey," Lowle says. "How's life?"

"Fine," I say. I hate talking about stupid things.

"I enjoyed last night," I say. He looks uncomfortable.

"I have to get going," he says. "I have a lot of work to do."

"Then I won't ask you to call me," I say.

"Yeah, I probably won't have time," he says. "See you later."

He turns and goes, and for a minute I stand in front of the restaurant, angry and immobilized. "I won't call you again," I say to the air around me. "It's over for good now," I say, but he is already blocks away; I can't even make out the color of his jacket in the dim light.

I walk home alone. The streets are oddly empty, and the city feels still. I think about my shaking, my laughing, and how glad I am that I didn't tell him the truth. I think about Lowle and his tv and the word *casual*. Maybe it means waiting until Thursday. Maybe it means realizing that it's not worth it, that I'd just as soon communicate and get close and chance it if I'm going to bother at all. When I get home my bed is big and empty and I'd like to call Lowle, but I don't have anything to say. I won't call him tomorrow.

Hole in the Wind

Janice Levy

"Can I tell you a secret?" Brandon Bryan asks. In the dark I twirl the hair on his chest. I run my teeth down his ribs and shake my head.

"No, really," he insists and turns on the light. I notice the bits of crust in the corners of his eyes.

"Where are you going?" he calls. In the bathroom, I run the shower so it sounds like a rainstorm.

I have always had trouble with secrets. Later, when he has finished sulking, I will cover his mouth and shove his secrets back down his throat with my tongue. I will be hot-eyed and driven.

I stretched out in the back seat, my toes scratching pictures in the dusty side windows. My father drove his taxi back to Guatemala City from Lake Atitlán, down the highway through Antigua. I was six, maybe seven.

We stopped to watch a woman who stirred blue enamel pots of food on a charcoal grill. The woman's skin was so dark she looked like she had swallowed her shadow. My father bought a little of everything she cooked. He pointed to his taxi and told her he had taken many beautiful women for rides. He'd take her too, he said. *"Gratis,"* he said and spread out his empty palms.

The woman looked like one of my stuffed dolls, her eyes unblinking, her face stiff. She fingered the red and purple material of her skirt and tapped her fingers on the patterns like they were game board pieces and she was planning her next move.

My father turned off the Callejon de San José and parked his taxi under a shady tree. He pulled his cap over his eyes and tapped at his watch. He gave me a handful of *quetzales* and told me to come back with two cold *cervezas.* He told me to go very, very slowly so I wouldn't spill them. Carry them like you are walking on hot coals, he said.

When I came back, the woman had moved to the front seat. Her blouse clung to her back like wet tissue paper. My father's lips moved from her ear to her throat.

I sat in her kitchen and watched "El Chapulin Colorado" on a black and white T.V. Just when the hero swept his cape over his shoulder, shouted, *"Sigame los buenos,"* and bumped into a wall, my father bounced into the kitchen with a silly grin on his face. *"Ya,"* he said and banged the top of the T.V. set so hard it shook.

"Making love with your father is like gulping down steamy *cafecito,"* Doña Lupita said in my ear. She brushed my hair gently, undoing the knots with her fingers. "He is darker and sweeter than any of the others, but shhh," she whispered and put her finger to her lips. *"Este es un secreto entre señoritas."* Then laughter spilled out of her hands, poured down her body and washed over me. It was hard to breathe.

At the Mercado de San Sebastian, my father bought me wooden earrings, quetzal birds painted pink and green. "Your mother must not know about our visits to Doña Lupita," he said. "Doña Lupita lost her husband and is very lonely. Your mother will get sad and she needs to rest and not worry so much." My father kissed my forehead and swung me in the air. He gave my mother flowers and ate with the appetite of several men. Once, I remember he came home wearing only one sock.

My mother never asked. She held my chin in her hand, stared into my eyes and popped the secrets from my skin as if piercing a boil with a steaming cloth. She snatched at them and curled her fingers, one by one, squeezing, squeezing, her eyes dark knots in her face. Then slowly she stretched out her fingers and rubbed her palm down her thigh. Her eyes became calm and empty, like the unblinking stare of a cow. Stripped of my secrets, I became weak and chilled. My mother sat by my bed, covered me with blankets and smoothed the hair off my face.

The *curandera* came to our house with a small black box filled with things that smelled and rattled. She sprinkled sawdust around my mother's feet and made a sucking noise with her teeth. She held my mother's hands, swayed and mumbled. Then the *curandera* placed her thumbnail against my lips. She said if the wrong words slipped out, my tongue would grow until it rolled out of my mouth like a carpet. She counted her money out loud and left.

"How can I trust you?" Brandon Bryan demands. "How can I trust you if you won't let me tell you anything?"

Brandon Bryan argues with his biceps. They tense and strain against his veins. I bend to kiss the part where the top of his leg meets his hip. Soon he is still.

I am often quiet. Quiet women are tempting, like the undisturbed surface of a lake. Few can walk by without tossing in a pebble to see how the ripples spread.

I think that if I were beautiful I could be myself.

I am a bartender. The room lies in cool, brick-red shadows. In the chipped glass mirror behind the counter, I look almost pretty.

Dark red makes people forget about time passing. That's why the walls of the bar are painted this color. Brandon Bryan tells me this and much more as he leans on the counter. I watch his biceps press against the cuffs of his short sleeve shirt. I crush ice with my teeth and stare.

Later, he plucks at the straps of my dress as if playing a tune, then questions with his chin. He says my silence makes him want me more.

Brandon Bryan looks like his name. If you colored him in, you would use burnt orange. He has come to Guatemala to negotiate the building of a MacDonalds. I remember that my last lover had flabby arms and his skin hung down like the wings of a bat.

My mother left little plates with burning candles around the house and a figure carved in soap on the dashboard of my father's taxi. My father complained of bad headaches. He drove his cab in circles with a wet bandanna tied around his forehead. He squeezed his temples and moaned that it was like scorching his fingers in hot oil. Then we caught my mother holding a photograph over a candle. There was a hole where my father's head used to be.

My father threw money on the kitchen table, more than he usually did. My mother tucked the *quetzal* notes in the waistband of her skirt. Then she pinched out the candle's flame with her fingers and put her wet lips to my father's forehead to extinguish his terrible pain.

When my father left that last time, I remember running, just running down the street until the lights of his taxi disappeared. I think I made a hole in the wind.

Brandon Bryan rolls up his sleeves and dips his hands in a bowl of hot bubbles. He lifts my arms up and massages my hips, moving me this way and that. I am a candlestick, then a flower vase. He makes the water hotter and spreads my thighs. I am a teapot; tipping, dripping, but I know the rules. He fingers himself. Behind me I feel the cool bite of a zipper. In five minutes he has showered and gone.

This is his favorite game.

"I am a winner. I have the power." Ten times Brandon Bryan says this as he combs his hair and bares his teeth in the mirror. He is careful not to eat carrots or beets. They will stain his fake front tooth.

"Some people walk in the rain. Other people just get wet," he says, snapping on his tie clip with the golden arches.

In the morning Brandon Bryan's biceps look like tight pincushions. I see that someone has monogrammed his socks in green thread.

My mother sat rigid in a chair and rubbed her gums with her thumbs, her eyes half closed. Sometimes when I called her, she wouldn't answer. She wrote letters to *Tia* Magda in Arizona and stopped cleaning the house.

"You can follow the coins," my mother whispered in the midnight air, when she left me on the steps of the Orfanato de Jesús. "When I come for you, I'll have so much money the coins will fall out of my pockets. Anything, I'll buy you anything. *Hijita mia,* what will you want?"

I said a monkey. When my mother came for me, she should bring a monkey.

Brandon Bryan is still talking. He is up to his third ex-wife. She painted the bedroom two shades of green. The kitchen always smelled of broccoli.

You trust too easily, I say.

And you?

Only once. He drove a taxi in circles. His hair was dark and straight like mine.

And? he asks.

And, I reply.

I lean my head out the window and close my eyes against the wind.

"People clap for the loser, but nobody stays to shake his hand," Brandon Bryan says.

He lies on his back and spreads his legs. He lets me clean him like a cat.

The phone rings. Brandon lights a cigarette, turns his back to me, his words graying the nighttime air. I have never heard him giggle before.

Brandon Bryan snuggles back under my arm. "I like you here. You feel like a baby monkey."

His third ex-wife makes the nights grow shorter. Her voice slides up and down the scale.

She has nothing over you, he says. She just calls me to cry. What do you do with your pain?

In the pub Brandon dances with a woman who is round and spilling out of her green dress. Her head shakes slightly all the time. His third ex-wife looks like lime jello.

I look at her so she knows I am sleeping with the man who has his tongue in her ear.

I take Brandon Bryan's sock and stuff it with two *bolillos* I have gotten from the bakery. I tie a knot at the end and attach his tie clip with the golden arches.

Outside I watch the birds peck at the sock, their beaks breaking through to the hard rolls inside. The ants carry bits of its soft middle dough away.

Feel my forehead, he says the next morning.

His lower lip quivers in the mirror.

His dumbbells feel too heavy to lift.

Brandon Bryan twists his head like a pigeon and picks at the shirt collar that bunches around his neck.

Drink this, I say. I pour him a glass of amber mescál.

I run my finger over the veins in his biceps. I pinch the loose skin.

Eat the worm in the bottom of the bottle, I say. I have seen it done.

"Follow the coins," Brandon Bryan says as he makes the money disappear in his hand and then reappear behind my ear. We lie on a blanket outside the Mercado de San Sebastian. My pink and green wooden earrings dangle.

I slide my hands under his clothes. Everywhere he is soft.

Fix me, he pleads.

You are the magician, I say.

And you? he asks.

I am only magic.

Brandon Bryan speaks in torrents. Whole paragraphs come out as if one word.

But he packs his clothes slowly, gently, as if tucking in a child.

I twist the bedsheets around my body. I can feel his arms pulse across the room.

"I have always had trouble with secrets," I say, all the rest sinking like quicksand in my throat.

Brandon Bryan waits, but only until his taxi honks twice.

I lie alone and the monkey comes again in my dreams. She wears pink and green wooden earrings and dances at the edge of my bed. Her tail forms a question mark and teases me like a beckoning finger. Through the open window a taxi honks its horn. The monkey stands over my face and screeches.

Chicken

Lisa Vice

I saw him this morning, pawing through a garbage can for empty bottles and cans, his torn shirt thick with dirt and sweat. His hair matted and grey. He paused for a moment in his search, looking around as if I had called to him and he was about to answer, but he didn't know who I was and I didn't stop to offer an explanation. It had been nearly twenty years, after all. Twenty years. A lifetime, I thought, hurrying toward my job, my heart pounding. Now all day long I've been remembering. All day long, I've been wondering. Has he ever seen his daughter walk by him on her way to school, laughing with her friends? Or walking alone, head down, in that determined young woman way, her hands clutching her books? Would he recognize his own eyes staring back at him out of her young face?

All day long, while the cursor on my computer blinks. While the phone rings and my office mates walk up and down the carpeted corridor, laughing in front of the xerox machine, I am not really there. I am somewhere else, remembering. It was three a.m. when the two of them came to the door. I'd been up late trying to bring on my period with epsom salts and a bottle of Humphrey's, swallowing the bitter liquid and praying for blood the way Carmen downstairs had advised me to do in her broken English. I slid open the chains, first one, then the other, my finger pressed to my lips signaling them to be quiet so as not to wake the baby. She was blond, her large moon face flushed, a tattered backpack dangling from her shoulder. She followed him in, wordlessly. I went out to the toilet at the end of the hallway. The toilet that had a pull chain, a wooden box over my head, that sometimes leaked so bad I had to hold an umbrella open over me when I used it.

When I came back into the apartment, he was making up the bed in the kitchen. A fold-up cot we found on the street and kept leaning against the wall in the corner in case we ever needed it, which we never had before. He took the pillow from my bed and one of the blankets, which he tucked carefully under the end of the mattress. He was almost whistling, so industrious were his movements. He was so sure of himself. His excitement almost palpable in the small room.

She was heavier than I was and her blond hair was thick and wavy where mine was straight. She wanted to know if I had a hair dryer. She took her sweater off and washed her hair, bending over the sink, using the baby's shampoo. She took my blue towel off the doorknob and wrapped it around her head. She sat in the chair beside my bed and took a bag of rollers from her backpack and began to comb and part her hair carefully. She rolled the wet strands slowly around the pink foam cylinders, snapping them into place. She never looked up. She didn't say a word. She sat in the corner as if she were alone, at home in her own apartment. He sat on the end of my bed watching her every move. I stood in the kitchen doorway, hugging my belly, which ached as if someone had punched me over and over with a hard fist. The need for sleep rested like a dead weight between my shoulders.

When she finished rolling her hair, she put the puffy plastic cap around her head and slipped the nozzle into the hair dryer. This was in the days before we had blow driers. This was a long time ago. A time I have tried to forget. But now, just as if it happened yesterday, I can see him leap up and plug the hair dryer in for her. I can see him, how he stood at the mirror in the morning, that last morning, his blue velvet coat on, his shoes polished, his black eyes glistening. His parents had been sharecroppers, he told me. They brushed their teeth with twigs, he said, shaking his head in disbelief. This was all I knew from his past. This and one story. How he was whipped for wanting to wash his face in warm water. His grandfather took off his belt to do it. Called him a sissy. He said it made him grow up hungry for luxury.

What I remember most when I think about him now was the night we met. It was an evening at the end of April, unusually hot, the air thick and heavy, clinging to my skin like a web. I was sixteen years old, alone in the city, a runaway. A casualty of the sixties, I sometimes say when I have too much to drink at a party. I can't begin to explain how lonely I was as I trudged up that street to buy the newspaper. And there he was, coming in my direction. A tall black man with a halo of black hair, a beautiful smile aimed at me.

Once a woman I met at my daughter's day care center told me I must have been very angry at my mother. She was studying psychology at the time. She said it like having my daughter was a way of thumbing my nose at the world. I couldn't begin to explain why I had her then any more than I can explain it now except to say I had this dream, this fantasy, that babies of mixed color might save the human race.

That night when he brought this other woman home with him, finding her on the street much the same way he'd found me, what I remember most clearly is how much I wanted to lie down. I felt as if I'd been forced to walk twenty miles under a hot sun, barefoot, and I was so tired I could have slept in the middle of the road. I wanted my bed. The thought of it, of lying curled up in the worn sheets, was enough to bring tears to my eyes. But I didn't know how to make them leave. I kept thinking, maybe I am asleep already and soon I will wake up. Maybe this is all a dream, I thought, blinking my gritty eyes.

He sat on the bed, smoking and looking from his clean shiny nails to her blue eyes, smiling with pleasure. Two women at last. He'd been wanting this for so long, telling me how much better life would be if we had another woman with us. How she'd help with the baby and we could go out sometimes. Sometimes when we were making love, his chest pressed against mine, his breath hot on my neck, he would say how he loved me but it just wasn't enough. He would whisper that what I had was so good I ought to sell it. It was this or another woman. Like those were my two choices. Pick one. I loved him so much I pretended I didn't hear what he said. That I'd misunderstood. He couldn't really mean that. I pulled him close. I am happy to say I have never loved that way again. So reckless and blind. It is a relief to know I never will.

They met in the park, he said, where he went every afternoon, looking. Her name was Wanda and she didn't have a place to live. She broke up with her boyfriend and didn't want to go back to Kentucky. She'd be living with us now.

I was too tired to argue. I prayed for them to just hurry up and go into the kitchen so I could fold myself into the bed and close my eyes and stroke away the pain in my stomach. The dingy morning light was already coming up over the air shaft. Soon the woman next door would climb the stairs to let her dog shit on the roof. Windows would scrape open. Voices would call across the narrow space. Julio, Julio. Pots would clang. Radios blare. And the baby would wake up. Would cry, kicking her legs and waving her tiny fists to be picked up.

Wanda reached up under the bonnet to check her hair and when it was dry she combed it out all soft and fluffy around her shoulders. She painted her lips a pale pink, watching herself in a round mirror she held in one palm. Then they went into the kitchen and closed the door. I made a kind of nest out of the blanket they'd left me and curled into it. I could hear their gasps, her soft voice and his deeper one while the cot thumped on the linoleum floor. I concentrated on my own breathing and began to build a wall around me, fixing my mind on the cement I plastered between the red bricks, feeling the rough surfaces scrape my hands as I stacked them higher and higher until I was completely enclosed.

In the morning, I brought the baby out to the hallway toilet. Held her close while thick clots of blood spilled into the stained bowl. She made her da da da sounds and tangled her little fingers into my hair. The pain felt good. It felt good knowing the life that had tried to root itself inside me was gone. A baby that would never cry for my arms. The whole mess flushed so easily down the six flights of stairs.

When they got up, he went downstairs to buy food. They weren't happy with the bread and juice I had. They wanted coffee. A real meal, he said, his fingers closing around the money she handed him. While he was gone, she ran a bath. The tub was in the kitchen and while I made the baby's cereal she washed herself, lifting her long white arms and rubbing the bar of soap into her skin, as if she had done this every morning of her life. We didn't say anything to each other. What was there to say?

He brought home chicken. Chicken for breakfast. I'm hungry, he said, grinning, flashing his perfect white teeth. She put flour and salt into a brown paper bag and shook the pieces carefully, frying them in hot grease while he held the baby in his arms and talked baby talk, something he'd never done before. When the baby began to fret he handed her to me like she was a sack of soggy diapers. I changed her and put her down in her crib, still crying. I went back into the kitchen, stood at the door, my arms folded, determined. As if I had suddenly woken up. You have to leave, I said. They both looked up at me. Her mouth a thin pink circle of surprise, as if she were just then noticing me for the first time. He paced up and down the kitchen. We're not going anywhere, he said. He laughed. I live here too, he said. This is as much my place as yours.

Leave. I'll call the cops, I said, my voice all thin and shaky, like it was floating into the room from the cracks in the plaster. He began to yell at me in clear, clipped tones, calling me bitch and slut and she kept frying the chicken, reaching to lift it from the pan with the tongs my mother had used when I was a child.

It's ready, she announced. Her voice was soft, apologetic. He turned his back on me and took down two plates from the cupboard. I shut the door and began to dial the telephone. He jerked it from my hands, prying my fingers off the black plastic, but I kept grabbing at it anyway. I felt if I could just hold on to that phone I could make everything all right somehow. Then he hit me over the head with it.

I lay on the bed listening to the sounds of their lips slipping against the chicken skin and their teeth sucking at the meat between the bones. Then they went out. As if they did this every day, they slipped out the door, their leather-soled feet clattering down the stairs. When I heard the door downstairs slam, echoing up the stairwell to where I stood, I took the plate of leftover chicken and put it in front of my door. Let the cockroaches feast, I thought.

That night, I didn't go to the door. He opened it with his keys. He did have keys. But I had both chains on. One that was guaranteed to hold back anything. He screamed and called me names, kicked at the door and reached in trying to unlatch the chains, cursing. Then he whispered please. He spoke my name. He was almost crooning, his soft words telling me I was the best one. I'll sleep with you tonight, just let me in.

Blood oozed into the pad between my legs. I was in bed with the baby beside me and I held her close, looked down at her astounded by the miracle that she was, her breath wet and milky on my cheek. She is a young woman now. This all happened a long time ago. I tell myself I built a life on the scars. But I worry. What if she makes the same mistakes I did? I worry when she goes out at night and comes home late. When she talks to young men I have never met on the telephone. I worry about the parties she goes to. But she is a good kid. She doesn't ask a lot of questions. She accepts that her father isn't even a photograph.

When she was young, she would make up stories about him. They all ended with an airplane that fell crashing to the ground. There were no survivors. Boo hoo hoo, the end, she would say and go on to another game. She was a sturdy child, climbed those six flights of stairs before she even walked. She is a beautiful woman now.

Why didn't you have an abortion, someone once asked me, shaking her head all surprised I would have a baby so young. That question took my breath away. My daughter, I thought, nearly weeping. My daughter. I patiently explained how back then, even getting birth control was pretty near impossible. I tried to get the pill, I said. It was the only thing I'd ever heard of. I went to a doctor. He asked me if I was married. I didn't have the sense to lie. Then I was pregnant. Sixteen years old and pregnant. What did I know? I thought love was songs on the radio. But I am not sorry I had her. I can't imagine my life any other way.

The strangest things are passed down. Through the blood. Not just hair color and height. Not just the shape of one's feet, hers are wide and sturdy, peasant feet like mine. Or the eyes, how she has his huge dark eyes. What's amazing to me is the way she moves across a room in just the same way I do. How on the telephone, people mistake us for each other, our voices are so much the same. Strangers always stare, draw to us like iron to a magnet, the look back and forth, sensing the deep bond between us, looking from her soft brown face with its halo of dark curls to my pale one framed with blond hair. They try to figure it out. But what always startles me most is how when I see her eating chicken, when her long thin fingers pick into the meat and she leans over her plate to suck the flesh from the bone, every move she makes is a mirror image of him.

Divorce Story

Ellen Treen

He is there, right where I knew he would be, parked in front of my apartment, waiting. As soon as he spots me he opens the car door, and by the time I angle my Bug into place he is out of his Camaro, limping towards me. The limp surprises me, but then I realize a month is hardly enough time to heal a broken ankle. I haven't seen him since we met with Martha to sign the agreement. When we left her office he slipped on the curb; that was a month ago but I knew he would be here today. It's the real reason I declined a fancy lunch with a lawyer and a judge, came straight home instead. He wants to know what happened and I need to tell him.

When I don't immediately jump out of the car, he slows, comes to a halt and watches me from behind mirror sunglasses. They seem to blank out the top of his face, hiding those restless hazel eyes, their relentless curiosity. Now he is sizing up my mood, second-guessing my state of mind, so I spring out of my car, pull the strap of my purse up on the shoulder of my white jacket and step briskly forward. Relaxation flows over him like a warm shower, softening every line down to the silver bristles of his mustache. He comes closer, explaining himself:

"I just thought I'd stop by and get the papers from you. Save you the trouble."

I slide my purse in front of me, and pull out identical sheets of legal-size paper, official with state seals and flowing signatures. Fresh copies, they curl and stick together and I fumble, struggling to separate them so I can hand one to him. He snaps it straight and looks it over.

"Is this all I get? Just this? One lousy piece of paper?"

"That's it."

Deliberately, I widen my eyes, and we face each other in the Atlanta heat. It is only May and not quite noon, but the sun is settled overhead as hot and yellow as a child's drawing. I see myself doubled and distorted in his glasses and withdraw a step. We both shrug.

"So, what happened?" he asks. "Did it go all right? Were there any problems?"

The heat is suffocating, glaring down from above, rising up from the cement, the kind of weather that invigorates him, and wilts me.

"Come in where it's cool and I'll tell you about it." Without waiting for an answer I shoot past him. He hops aside, letting me lead the way up the narrow path between overgrown bushes and low branching dogwoods. Ahead there is real shade delivered by a stand of pines rising above us like plumed fans. In the steady crunch of gravel behind me I hear him rushing to catch up: he wants to hear the whole story. It's his reason for coming. Other salesmen collect jokes, but he likes family anecdotes and has a story to sell everything from frozen foods to cameras. Whenever I complained about being a commercial, he said family stories put his customers at ease, off guard. "I only tell the good stuff," he claimed. "Good" is not the word I would use.

"You look nice," he calls out as we move into the shade. "I don't remember that dress."

"Thanks," I reply without turning around. It took a lot of shopping to find this outfit, a sleeveless navy blue dress with a deep V neckline and a loose white jacket. The back fits well, a smooth stretch over the hips. "It's new," I call back. "I got it just to get divorced in. Most likely I'll never wear it again." A pleasurable glow fills me when I find that perfect combination of pride and spite, like a direct hit with a well-formed spitball.

He moves up, just a step behind me. "Remind me to give you my new address," he says. "I'm moving next week."

"Quite a butterfly!" This is his third move since we sold the house.

"I'm going to share a house," he says. "I can't get used to apartments. I'm not as adaptable as you."

Moving is something I've practiced regularly in twenty years of marriage, and I do it well, but that doesn't mean I ever grew to like it. Thinking of the garden I just left behind, I feel a rush of nostalgia. The bearded iris would be blooming now, covering a shallow hill in gold, bronze and mauve.

We round the path and come to a red brick complex curling around a swimming pool, more like an overgrown motel than a home. Sets of curved cement steps, bolstered by wrought iron railings, lead to carved wooden doors. I unlock the one that is mine and hurry inside to turn on the air-conditioning. The temperature drops quickly, as though the air were hosed down.

"Coffee?" I step into the kitchen and fill my copper kettle. He waggles "no" with his hand, then swings his head like a searchlight, over the walnut cabinets, formica counters covered with cookbooks and cannisters, to the refrigerator, back to the sink, the stove and me.

"Have you got anything to drink?"

"Only wine. There's a bottle in the refrigerator."

He opens the door and bends to peer inside while I reach up in the cupboard beside me for a glass. Automatically, my mouth opens, ready with the words to remind him that it is too early to drink, that he is already unsteady on his feet, to recall the cause of one broken ankle and how easily he could break the other. Then I remember. I shut my mouth and hand him the glass, letting my shoulders loosen, lighten with relief. While I measure out instant coffee he busies himself with the corkscrew. The kettle whistles and I fill my mug and lean back against the sink.

"You haven't learned to live without your coffee," he says. His disapproving expression is underlined by concern. I raise my mug and blow across the steam. He raises his wine, for a long sniff and a quick taste.

"Do you like working in a library as much as you always thought you would?" he asks after a quiet minute.

"It's interesting, but kind of tiring." Discouraging and disappointing, I could add. "Mostly it's shelving books."

"You'll be running the whole system in six months," he predicts in a tone that dismisses any facts to the contrary. I know he believes what he says, so I save myself the aggravation of presenting him with a reality he won't accept. The fact that I haven't held a job in twenty years and don't have the education to be a librarian, let alone an administrator, he sees as my handicap, the opportunity for others to have an even chance. I ask him how the camera business is going, his newest job.

"Great, fabulous," he says, slouching along the green counter, favoring his right leg, the one in the fiberglass cast. He gloats over a deal in Florida, and while he talks I am seeing him as he was twenty-two years ago when we met at a college party in Connecticut. Leaning on the porch railing of his fraternity house, he was a medley of long bones, hollow cheeks and dark straight hair blowing in his eyes. Now his hair is disappearing on either side of a delicate widow's peak, and his high forehead is tanned to match his jacket, which matches the dark strips in his saddle shoes. He seems to have thickened and shrunk while I have become thin and sharp-edged. Regret seizes me like a hard cramp and I want to ask if he remembers an earlier me, a compact shapely girl whose picture he carried in his billfold. That picture!

He had a down home spiel sales pitch and when the conversation was comfortable and everyone got out the family pictures, he pulled that crinkled snapshot out of his wallet and shoved it under a prospective customer's nose. It showed me in a white two-piece bathing suit, perched like a bathing beauty on the hull of a speedboat, squinting into an unseen sun. "Your wife?" they would ask, surprised as they were supposed to be.

"Yeah, that's the girl I had to marry. I owed her, so I married her," he'd say, wagging his head sadly. "She saved my life." Caught, the customer would have to hear the whole story of how I fished him out of the lake, more dead than alive.

More drunk than drowning was nearer the truth. It was true I towed him in, but it was all a joke, college party stuff. So was posing for the picture. Even now I squirm thinking of that picture passed around in every bar up and down the Eastern seaboard. And that silly story growing larger with every telling. Over the years he added sequels in which I shine as heroine, superwoman, a person of strength and daring, whose exploits amaze me more than anyone.

There is a hard slam of the refrigerator door and he stands back to gaze at the three pictures attached to the door. The kids all have his wide-set hazel eyes; I think it must be like looking in a three-way mirror.

"Do they know today is the day?" he asks.

"They do. But they don't know what to do or say." I know he wants news of them but won't ask.

"Holly is probably into finals," I say. Her first year away at college has been tough and her letters are terse and bitter. How, she asks, can she concentrate on literature, or write a paper when everything she took for granted is subject to court order. At first she wanted to come back, be with me, but her last letter announced her intention to spend the summer working at a camp in the Berkshires.

"Paul travels so much in his new job he hardly has time to sleep. You should understand that." It has been a while since he lived at home, but he resents his home disappearing. He feels set adrift before he has had time to establish his own homestead, one big enough to hold all the stuff he cherished. When he does write it is a postcard, asking what happened to his electric train or the darkroom equipment, his model airplane collection. All the things he left in his room.

"Seems like they could send cards or notes, or something . . . Paul at least. He's old enough . . . on his own . . ."

Words fade into head-shaking and I can see he is only sips away from reminiscing about the day Paul was born, one of his favorite stories. In his version, he dropped me off at the front door of the hospital, went to park the car and came back to find he was a father of an eight-pound boy. The way he tells it I have babies the way magicians produce coins: so fast you can't see it happen. He never explains that the hospital was in downtown Philadelphia where parking is neither simple nor quick in a neighborhood populated with old-fashioned bars. For each child there is a different story, a different city, different heroics and he loves to tell them all, but I am not in the mood. I sigh, a loud and practiced sound.

"It's hard for them," I say. "Even Mark can't talk about it and he's here, living through it." Instead of talking, he acts, aggravating his teachers, defying the principal. Two suspensions this spring. There are only three more weeks of school but the summer could be worse. Mark has seen the worst years of a marriage in decline, and he worries about his father, as though their positions were reversed. Some days he thinks he is abandoning him, the next he feels himself to be abandoned. He cannot settle any issues yet. "Thirteen is a hard age even without your parents getting a divorce," I add by way of defense.

"It's hard on everyone," he says, taking off his dark glasses so I can see the hurt in his eyes. My coffee mug clatters as I set it on the counter. Carefully, I arrange my face into a smile.

"Do you or don't you want to hear how you got divorced this morning?" I ask.

"I do," he pronounces, sulky but proud of his joke. "Seeing as how I was considered unnecessary to the proceedings."

"I'm not sure I needed to be there either," I tell him. "Martha could have handled it all alone."

He frowns at the mention of our lawyer. "No doubt," he mutters. "All she ever wanted to hear from me was the scratch of my pen writing out her check. Her idea of no fault is women are faultless no matter what."

He has told all our friends, anyone who will listen, that he came home from a business trip to find not only his wife moved out but his bed too. "No arguing, no crying, no warning," he says. "She just picked up her bed and left." Inside the bitterness is that strange kernel of pride.

It's true I left, but not without months, years of threats and ultimatums. When the promises of fidelity and temperance wore thin from repetition, thin enough to see through, I took enough furniture to fill an apartment and left. Then I found Martha and she saved me from a desperate inclination to walk away from everything with nothing.

"Well, what happened?" he asks, impatient for the details. "Was the judge satisfied with the agreement?"

"He didn't even read it."

"He didn't read it? None of it?" He is disappointed, suddenly and openly depressed. We look at each other, the letdown flowing between us like a trough of dark water. Over time and many moves we became increasingly isolated. Only we two know the damage twenty-two years of marriage have done to both of us, how serious the wounds, our need to confess everything and admit nothing. Working out the hard compromises, reaching agreement was a feat demanding some kind of recognition: an award, a speech, at least one sharp crack of the gavel.

"Then what *did* the Judge judge?" he wants to know.

For a moment I am blank, remembering only the long walk through the grey halls of the courthouse, following Martha down corridors familiar to her and strange to me. Above us Confederate generals and long-dead judges peered out of gilt frames, their eyes on vistas far removed from the petty squabbles settled in these courtrooms. Shivering, I sat down on one of the granite benches and Martha quickly dropped beside me, ready with smelling salts and sympathy. She knew I wanted to change my mind, rush back to any misery rather than face this change. While I shook and chattered she rubbed my icy hands. "Lots of people get the jitters at the last minute," she said.

Inside the judge's chambers, smothered in leather and dark draperies it was different. We all sank into cushioned armchairs.

"What he did," I say, in a poor imitation of a southern drawl, "was thumb through that big ol' agreement, and ask Martha if it took care of me and the chillun. When she said it did, he just rapped it with the back of his knuckles." I roll my knuckles over the edge of the sink to demonstrate. "Then he signed, I signed, Martha signed, and the judge said we were just about the best-looking lawyer and client he'd seen all year. And he kissed us both and invited us to lunch."

"He kissed you?" He laughs, holding back a little, sniggering the way he does over a dirty joke. "The old letch." He laughs a bit more, savoring the idea, kneading it around in his mind, shaping it up, creating a new story, the Divorce Story. It's hard to know what he can do with such slim material but he has often made more out of less. By the time I hear this story again, I won't recognize it, nor my own mythic role in it. The distance between my real self, the real events and his creations grows with every version until I am only a speck in the distance. It is the shrinkage that hurts.

Again the cork is squeaking loose from the bottle and he is refilling his wine glass. I turn to the sink and rinse out my coffee mug. Between us we make a lot of noise. I look down, astonished to see tears falling into the sink; fat, hot drops that ought to sizzle on the stainless steel. I try to turn them off, cleanly, as a faucet and when I think I have succeeded I face him.

"Was that it? Was that all that happened?" he asks. There are careful little pauses between his words, like moss between stepping-stones.

"What did you want? A full orchestra and a fanfare?" Laughing starts the tears again, seeping out as though I had sprung a leak.

The way he stares I can't tell if he is surprised or frightened and he quickly replaces the sunglasses and gulps down the last of the wine. Hitching his stiff ankle along, he backs out of the kitchen, the white paper standing in his jacket pocket like a rolled manuscript.

"Are you all right?" he wants to know. "Maybe you shouldn't be alone right now. Do you want me to call Tilly or Mary Sue?"

I can't answer him; I can only shake my head and jab my finger at the door.

"Okay, all right, I'm going." He takes a few more steps backwards and bumps into the coffee table knocking over a picture and toppling a candle, coming close to falling himself. My hands clutch the sink as I watch him try to right the picture, set the candle back in its silver cup, pick it up when it falls again. Finally he leaves it rolling on the table and limps to the door.

"I didn't mean to upset you," he says, and opens the door. "I just wanted to know what happened. Call me when you feel better."

He means he will call when he thinks I feel better, but I nod and wave him off. After the door clicks I keep on waving, until I realize I am alone. In a few moments the tears stop and I reach for my purse, take out my divorce paper and read it. There is no story, no heroics or derring do, only a plain statement of dissolution and separation, irretrievable loss. The big story just went out the door, leaving me half glad, half sad. I hated those stories but I loved the heroine, the person I always wanted to be. She's the one I will miss.

Alone, I'm not sure who I am. But I know it's time to find out, time to write my own story.

Rosalie's Cuisine

Maria Bruno

I had been separated six months from my husband, Guido, who had left me for someone he termed a "culinary genius," a woman named Kristie with a Cuisinart, a Tuscan oven crock, and, he said, "a white sauce that was a cream lover's dream." Besides the white sauce, she served him pork roasts capped in paper crowns, King Crab Louis, and a macrobiotic dish with garbanzos and sauteéd peas that was fit for the Dalai Lama. He said when it came to cooking, Kristie was a cool vichyssoise served with chilled chablis, and I was, at best, a styrofoam bowl of Chili Mac seasoned with Durkee's washed down with a Big Gulp from the 7-11. "She's perfection, Rosalie," he told me his last day in the house.

But then Kristie cut her hair with lasers, waxed her legs, had breasts like iced cupcakes, and even though she worked at being as thin as a Victoria Secret's model, she had decided, out of deference to Guido, to swallow one highly caloric ejaculation daily (a whopping 130 calories according to *Playgirl* magazine), while some women, he reminded me, "still spit into the sheet."

My need for revenge grew as I began to date a succession of men. Men like Leon Spivinsky, a laboratory biologist, who performed two finger Pap smears on adolescent monkeys for his IUD research grant. He joked during the appetizer on our first and only date that he called his little patients his "Rhesus Pieces." "You know," he said, " like the candy." And I tried to laugh. But after that, I just kept staring at his spatulate fingers wondering how many simian cervixes he had dilated that day. And I wondered, during the main course, if he even bothered to wear surgical gloves during the procedure. By dessert, I could hear my mother's voice emerging from the back of my mind saying the same thing she had warned about my eleventh grade boyfriend who often helped his mortician father on weekends: "God only knows where those hands have been, Rosalie."

Then there was Clifton DeBork, the psychoanalytic critic from the English Department where I taught who chased Freud across the pages of Modernist literature. At lunch, on our first and only date, he said the house specialty, the "Big Mama Burger," smothered in sliced zucchini and dill spears, was obviously concocted by a woman, "a Tooth Mother" was the precise term he used, who had a latent desire to castrate all men and claim their masculine appendages as her own. Keeping this in mind, I scrutinized the menu, and immediately dismissed the Tuna Torpedo and the Baby Bratwurst as simply too risky, and settled finally on an endive salad with a lemon dressing. Later, he told me the fact that I cut my salad into tiny bits instead of eating it passionately whole was symptomatic of an anal retentive personality and before I lifted the rim of my wine goblet to my own lips I made a quick exit to the bathroom, and sat in a closed stall for several minutes before I decided to leave the restaurant without saying goodbye.

After Leon and Clifton, I decided to date a younger graduate student, hoping this new generation of men could offer a more optimistic approach to establishing a relationship. But Hugh McHugh, or "Baby Huey" as I later referred to him, called me "Mommy" in bed, and pummelled my flesh like a nursing kitten.

"Mommy's a yum-yum," he slurped at my breast, kitty-fisting my stomach on our first and only sexual encounter. "It's twoo, it's twoo," he said in his best baby falsetto.

"Could I please get up?" I asked, wincing at the word yum-yum, and half afraid he'd start to groom himself with his tongue.

"But I'm not done yet!" he wailed.

"Yes, you are," I said, pushing at his doughy freckled shoulder.

For a while, celibacy began to take on a certain appeal. I remembered reading an article in *Cosmopolitan* on how celibacy could clean your pores, make you more creative, increase your earning potential. I decided *Cosmopolitan* couldn't be all wrong. Hadn't they featured those definitive articles entitled "Know Your Own Orgasm" and "Fight For Your Orgasm" which my college roommates and I read diligently after hours, as if they were some lost torn pages from the Bible?

But a year after my aborted encounter with Hugh McHugh, my celibate pores seemed less than cleansed. My creativity hadn't extended beyond two modest academic papers on Sylvia Plath and a fiery letter to my mother explaining the reason Guido left me had nothing to do with the fact I couldn't keep house, sew from a Butterick pattern, or find all his lost socks. And my earning potential had not increased significantly since the department was still paying me per course instead of a salaried position.

So I invited a man named Theo to my house for dinner, much to the amusement of Guido, who, I'm sure, after I made him pick up our daughter Francesca that evening, had thought I had given up on men forever.

"Ma, things don't have to be perfect," Frankie said, as she watched me scurry around the kitchen preparing for Theo's arrival. "Times have changed," she continued, running her plum-lacquered nails through her spiked hair.

That's easy for her to say, I thought. Her idea of getting ready for a date is tie-dyeing her bangs fuchsia and donning a Day-Glo T-shirt that says, "Mutants From Hell."

After sixteen years of training in perfection with Guido and after a few more of not even remotely fighting for my own orgasm, I did want things to be perfect. And Theo seemed almost golden to me, tall, blonde, gentle, and he laughed out loud—three times, I counted—when I read my short story to my creative writing workshop.

So for Theo I had decided to make my grandmother's old-world spaghetti recipe. I hand crushed each clove of garlic, added fresh minced parsley, sweet basil and oregano to my sauce of individually steamed and hand-peeled plum tomatoes. I rolled the meatballs in my hands, balancing them on my open palm, spinning them into perfect spheres, like I remembered my Grandma D'Angelo doing in her kitchen when I was a child. I sprinkled grated parmesan into the steaming sauce, dropped the meatballs in with a wooden spoon, and said like my grandmother, who would first smell the sauce, then taste it: "Madonna. A little bit of heaven!"

My spaghetti sauce was the only thing that Guido didn't complain about. "It's near perfection, Rosalie," he always told me. Every other meal was his idea. Ever since he went to work as a lawyer for a corporate firm, he had a sudden interest in WASP food, as my mother called it, always frowning, as if she were talking about animal waste or PCB contaminants. He left me a mini-menu magneted to the refrigerator. Every day he would suggest meals that would take me hours to prepare; meals that would send me to the store searching for shallots or coconut milk or baby goose livers and I'd spend my late afternoons in my kitchen nurturing pans of beef or stews or pots of fish soup and lentils. And he would tell me, after taking a calculated sip from a wooden spoon, that something wasn't right; it was a little off, too much salt, too little salt, too much sherry, too little sherry—then he'd proceed to fix it, make it over, make it his.

So it was my sauce for Theo.

I bought a new musk cologne made out of crushed pig scrotum, that was guaranteed to provide an attraction, according to the shop clerk at Griswald's, that would have me dusting off those cobwebs on my diaphragm. I hung for an hour in my inversion boots to bring a subtle flush to my skin, checked my teeth for plaque, spreading my lips as if I was a prized race horse. Then I moussed, dried, and pinch-fluffed my hair like I saw Jose Eber do on Donahue. Then there was the silk dress, the cinch belt, the textured panty hose, and some four-inch strapless black heels.

And while I was thinking about what women go through for men, I began to wonder if Guido made Kristie view his bowel movements like he made me. Guido always made me look, then do an impromptu tarantella on the bathroom tiles, to recreate the childhood toilet training scene where his mother, suitably impressed with the contents of the miniature bowl, would feed him an M&M, squeal with delight, then do a barefoot jig. I can picture Kristie in her basic black and pearls, her waxed legs cold against the toilet bowl, a lacquered nail brushing a strand of bottled East Hampton Blonde away from her forehead. She glances down at Guido's bizarre flotilla, perhaps for a moment wondering how she ever got herself into this, and perfunctorily smiles. Of course, Kristie cannot do the tarantella in four-inch Bandolinos, so she does something classier, like one of those carefully placed Juliet Prowse kicks to the ceiling to show her approval.

Frankie entered the room wearing an off-the-shoulder sweatshirt, a miniskirt, and little suede boots that wrinkled at the ankles. Her hair was tangerine.

Her father's going to hate that, I thought, as I knelt and looked at my reflection in the black glass of the oven door. My fluffed hair spread across the glass like a swirl of cotton candy. I pouted at the alien reflection. Frankie hunched besides me, steadying me, as my spike heels began to wobble.

"Mom," she said, gently helping me to stand. "You've got to relax. Theo isn't Dad. No one is. You'll see. You'll be perfectly fine."

"Will I?" I asked.

But then it happened. Something simple really. Frankie and I both looked at the same moment. A mouse, all saw-toothed and pink-eared, did a platform dive off the refrigerator ("Pike position, 8.1 degree of difficulty," Frankie later said.) into my plum tomatoes, and hung for a brief moment on one of my meatballs, shredding flecks of hot beef into the waiting sauce before it steamed to its untimely death.

I saw three little air bubbles pop open and then there was nothing but a rise of heat that pinked my nose. I looked at Frankie, who stood with her hand over her mouth. I looked at my Origami napkin holders, my tapered candles, the woven mats imported from Ecuador, and my Lucinda's Beauty Boutique acrylic nails. I bit into a meatball and spat it on the floor. My mind was a jumble of images: hog scrotum, a rhesus monkey in gynecological stirrups, Johnny Petapinto in ninth grade who told me my home ec project tasted like marinated elk pies. I thought of what I had in the freezer to serve Theo: some Koegel Viennas, an open bag of shoestring potatoes, two Scooter pies. I smelled my sauce and it filled the room. It smelled so good.

Frankie giggled, then mascara tears fell down her cheeks.

"Are you serving Theo *mouse*teciolli? she asked, wiping the tears away from her face. "How about *vermin*celli? Better yet, *rat*atouille?" She was on a roll and she knew it when she howled, "Are you serving the noodles al dente or *ro dente*?"

"Out, Francesca Philomena!" I snapped, still mooning over my spoiled cuisine.

But all I could think of was how you'd never find a disabled swimmer in Kristie's Tuscan oven crock. No Mark Spitz breast-stroking through her garbanzos and sautéed peas. No siree.

"Anything wrong?" It was Guido. He had walked in on his own. He still felt that somehow this was his house.

"Nothing," I said.

"Ahhhhh . . . marinara," he sniffed. I could see his nostril hairs. I had never noticed them before. He looked at me and smiled, all dapper in his $500.00 suit and spit-polished shoes. He wore a hand-painted silk tie. "That's about the only thing Kristikins doesn't do better than you."

"Really?" I asked, pretending to be pleased.

I thought of Grandma D'Angelo cutting thin triangles of yellow dough in her windowless kitchen. I heard the white ball of cheese rasping against the grater, her floured hands mixing in the rich ingredients of the imported bowl. She sipped lambrusco from a thumbprinted glass, then wiped her hands on the white butcher's apron. She tells how she scouted Grandpa's lover in 1918, tackled her on Second Avenue, pulling the long pins from her blonde Gibson Girl hairdo. But, she explains, that is not the Sicilian way. It's too overt. Too open. And besides, the girl pressed charges and Grandma D'Angelo went to jail for two days. Sicilian revenge is when she sent an ailing messenger to the girl's house, and in turn the girl contracted the flu so severely that the carts used to carry the dead stopped at her door every day. My grandpa vowed never again to mix with Anglo-Saxons because they are a weaker stock, had bad teeth, and contracted the flu so easily. It had only cost Grandma D'Angelo $2.00 for the messenger and fifty cents extra for the sneeze.

I thought about Kristie's Betty Crocker breasts and how I was going to have to buy the newest copy of *Cosmopolitan* with its CLIP-OUT-AND-SAVE "Guide to Self Orgasm" and how Leon Spivinsky flashes the "Victory" sign to his rhesus pieces. And then I thought what Clifton DeBork would say when he found out I was serving Theo Koegel Viennas for supper. Somewhere in the back of my mind Hugh McHugh was pummeling Goddess flesh in some vain attempt to learn her secrets. And when I looked at Guido standing there in my kitchen, straightening the polo pony tie Kristikins purchased for him at Neiman Marcus, I decided that I would still, in the final analysis, spit into the sheet.

I stirred the thick sauce deep, feeling the balls of meat thud heavily against the swirling wooden spoon. I stared into the pot and scooped up the hairy mound.

"Close your eyes," I said smiling and lifted the spoon to his waiting lips, "and take a bite."

Going Through the House

Claire Braz-Valentine

I don't care
really I don't.
I can remove you from my life
throw you out
like last year's calendar.

So you want another woman.
So fine.
I'll start with the refrigerator,
remove your peanut butter,
your hot sauce,
that stupid stuff you put on your steaks,
and the last piece of the cake I made for your birthday
I'll put them,
no I'll throw them,
I will smash them to smithereens in the garbage can.

I'll go through the closet,
grab that shirt of yours
that I used to wear in the garden
the sock you forgot in the corner
wad them up
tear them up
shred them
take them into the street and
drive my car over them
get them out of my sight.

I'll yank that smart ass teddy bear
you bought me for Christmas
right off of my bed pillow
rip its seedy little eyes out
wipe that wise ass grin off its face
hang its skin from a nail
on the tree you planted
Then I'll kill the tree.

I'll take every card you ever gave me
not read those dumb sappy lies anymore
about how you'll love me forever,
burn them up,
pulverize them into cat litter.
I can do it with my eyes closed.

I'll get that picture from the living room
that you bought at the flea market
and rip it up
flush it down the toilet.
You always had rotten taste anyway.

I'll yank clothes that you liked me to wear
off of their hangers,
go to Goodwill.
Go to hell.
Give them to her, the new woman,
but as you say
she's so much smaller than I.
Who gives a shit?
I sure don't.

I'll get all my cleaning supplies
scrub the whole house
get your prints off.
Take a hot bath,
no a scalding one,
get your prints off me,
cut my hair,
paint my fingernails.
You always hated that,
wear the big earrings you said are flashy,
and lots of the perfume that made you sneeze,
get your smug scumsucking voice off my answering machine,
not forward your mail,
return it to sender,
tell them you died.

I'll do these things
I really will.
I don't care
really I don't.

Falling

Lynn Luria-Sukenick

Laura pulled awake, breathing hard, but the dream was gone. At the window crystals flung rainbows onto the wall; little fish of light swam searching for a stable place. The day was going to be hot. She dragged the blanket up to her chin, hearing his voice, as cool as wine, saying, "Do you really need all those covers?"

For a minute she dozed, then she boiled awake. The space for his clock radio still startled her. Her clock was round, everything there on its open face. On his digital clock one moment had tapped the next on the shoulder and told it to get lost, the used-up minutes dropping into oblivion, disposable, like the music he woke to, music like styrofoam. He could use it, he said, his serious music fed on what was in the air. Laura wanted the rock and roll they had listened to in Los Angeles in the Seventies, when everyone was happy, when they cruised the freeways between Porsches and shiny trucks, listening to music so rhythmic it could keep you in your lane even if you forgot to steer.

A rapid knocking on the wall made her sit up. For weeks the woodpeckers had awakened her, pecking holes in her sleep. Every night she put ear plugs in, the way the woodpeckers tucked acorns under the shingles of her house, but then she heard her heartbeats as if they were someone's footsteps coming to find her. *Get out of your nightgown.* A sock she hadn't noticed clinging to the flannel crackled as she peeled it off. He was supposed to call the day before, about shipping the piano to New York. He was always late, he thought time was his, was only where he was.

In the mirror her eyes looked shallow, the eyes of an animal hit by a car. *Soon you'll start looking old then you'll always be in a bad mood.* The clothes in her closet seemed dead. She knew she dressed sanely every day, though how she couldn't remember. Pride was like fat—everyone had it in a different place. At least there were no moths flying out of her dresses this year. She washed her face, opened a compact and absentmindedly dusted rouge onto the small mirror. *Not* again, This week she had stopped for a stop sign in her rearview mirror, a stop sign on a side road a block behind her.

The cat sat on the other side of the bedroom door, his black paws drawn in, his posture courteous, his meowing importunate. "I'm up now," she said to him. "Now what do I do?" He trotted ahead of her to the kitchen, throwing a look over his shoulder, as if to suggest a gourmet breakfast. She was too tired to know what to eat these days. Since Nick had left, her sleep had been full of dark and sudden drops. At four in the morning she would panic awake as if falling from a trapeze. "I'm halfway between wheelchair and trapeze," she had told her divorced women's group, and they had nodded sympathetically. She could go back to bed and satisfy herself, fitful fantasies drifting into relief, but there was no point, it was worse than nothing. *Get moving.*

She had been making two cups of coffee every morning since she had asked Nick to leave, homeopathy against bitterness. In California people did not like to hear anything bad. She had told no one that one day she couldn't remember how the receiver was connected to the body of the phone, on another she couldn't remember how steering wheels were attached to cars.

She shut her eyes and tried to visualize the refrigerator handle a few feet away from her: was it vertical or horizontal? She could picture a refrigerator, but it was the rundown one in the house in New Hampshire the first summer of their marriage, humming with the secret privileges of vacation houses. She saw herself reaching for the handle in order to get the lemonade she made every afternoon while he composed. He sat loose-limbed at an old Baldwin working out the song cycle he later dedicated to her, based on the colors of her voice, he said. She pruned the image of him until it was perfect, the lamplight a halo around his face and shoulders. Her voice had disappeared after their first couple of years together, although before they were married she could sing for hours into her solitude, lost in the drowsy confections by Fauré and the faceted jewels by Mozart she knew by heart. After he'd left she had tried her voice out with the radio, the last live Metropolitan Opera broadcast of the season, but it was a badly caulked voice that could hold no breath, energy leaking out of it like wind under a door.

If he had been there he would have put on music by now. In the past year it had been his own music most of the time. He had stopped writing for instruments, silver, ebony, spruce, mahogany, brass, pressed directly by hands and mouths, to composing with synthesizers, pieces committed to endless repetitions, morose and unedifying. His new music had made her jumpy, had made all his previous work seem innocent as sunlight. After a while you find sunlight boring, he had said, as his trips away from California increased, concerts and lectures swallowing him up. She had continued with her teaching job at the university until her contract was up, had made do with the redwoods and windy beaches, attached to pleasures she no longer enjoyed. She had saved enough for a year, for getting her bearings, if she could bear them.

The craziest she had been was in the three days after Nick had left, three months ago. She had listened to the Four Tops singing "Seven Rooms of Gloom" a dozen times and calculated four times seven equals twenty-eight times twelve and so what; she, divided by him, was nothing. Now she lost things, unpaid bills, sweaters, ballpoint pens. They eluded her, whereas he had been a finder; things jumped into his hand, eager to be near someone who had math and music in him, who would not be unnerved by an x or a y. She had lived on cottage cheese and tequila and soundless TV for three days, then she had abandoned the tequila and allowed the TV to fill her mornings, afternoons, evenings, had let a machine keep her alive.

A year ago she had been visible and had asked Nick to take some pictures of her. He was an expert photographer, at home in a confident medium, but that day the only frames he didn't blur were the frames in which he chopped off her head, leaving a closeup of her full breasts in her Roy's Market T-shirt. He had always been bothered by that edge in her face where character interfered with prettiness. No one liked to be reminded of thought or conscience in the middle of making love, especially if he was a liar.

As his lies had multiplied, her amnesia had increased. Now her memory was slipping away so quickly that when she remembered the past it felt only slightly familiar, like a premonition of the future. "I have seen the future," she said to the cat, "and it's the past. Don't worry, though. In California here to there is more important than then to now. Memory isn't essential, but you really have to have a car."

She knew the amnesia was protecting her, too, from recent shocks, the flash flood arguments, the gasp of his suitcase zippers as he packed to leave. Some loss of memory was natural, a shedding, but caterpillars and all liminal things must intuit the next stage, their moulting like fresh clothing, not like sacrifice. While Nick lived with her there would always be more of everything, but now that he was gone none of it would happen again. And if he lied and if she had no memory, she would have no history, and if you had no history, time became heavy, like a machine that runs all day and manufactures nothing. Like television. Most mornings she sat there absorbing the game shows as if they were sunlight, waiting for *All My Children*.

"Soap operas are realer than novels," she said to the cat. "They go on and on." He chewed mental cud, mulched her words, emanated consolation. "On television nothing lasts more than a second; you can hardly remember what remembering is. And color TV is using up all the color in the world. People barely notice that for the past twenty-five years everything around them has been fading. Things have been going faster, too, but of course you've noticed that, haven't you noticed?"

Eat something. She'd had only brown rice yesterday and the day before. When she opened the refrigerator and lifted a block of tofu out of the greenish water, the tofu crumbled into three pieces and fell on the floor. *You lost him: butterfingers.* She took out a bag of Pepperidge Farm cookies and tore open the package, leafing through the nutrition magazine she'd left on the counter. In California food was the site of big conversions: I was sick but now am well. *When plants are exposed to stress they emit poisons.* She opened the closet where she kept cookbooks, earthquake supplies, onions and potatoes. The smallest potato, veiled with green, looked sick. She poured out some Crystal Springs: there were unacceptable traces of everything in the local drinking water. *Some pesticides, when combined with others, are fifty times more toxic than when used alone*. Could the hints for healing keep up with the catastrophes? *After she had eliminated tomatoes from her diet her pain was entirely gone and she beamed with gratitude and joy.*

She had never seen so many doctors. She would talk to the divorcees' group about what it felt like to go to a doctor when you no longer have a husband, someone who has been inside your body three thousand times. You needed to go to a doctor because you needed someone to tell you you were all right. Maybe she was going to be touched. In order to be touched.

She disliked being part of the flight pattern of divorced women. She objected to them referring to themselves as survivors. True, they were learning to live without love, money, safety, grace. But there had been no holocaust, they had not been tortured or blasted with radiation or left for dead. They were not even like Scarlett eating radishes at Tara, everything burned down around her. And all of them seemed to be resentfully, permanently, celibate. But how, without sex, could you get to the wisdom on the other side of the world?

The cat sat with determination at the sliding glass door. She let him out, then followed him onto the deck. She lay on the chaise and aimed her face at the sky, her mind jumping. She knew she shouldn't be lying out there like that, the ozone shield torn away. What did you do when your source of energy turned against you? a) hide; b) compromise; c) give up and die.

The cat lay down under the chaise in the cool shadow made by her body. He had come to their door eleven years ago, one night when they were cooking fish in the cottage in the Hollywood Hills and feeling happier than she could remember. Now he was too old to recapture the territories he had lost to the younger toms. They had argued about getting him fixed and then stopped arguing. Slowness won most of their arguments, Nick's slowness, especially: fighting with him was like walking through sand dunes in a dream. His ritardando, a friend of theirs had said, was different from hers; his was to make people wait, whereas hers was to let people catch up.

Laura lifted her face to the sun; it would heal the small wound on her brow that had scabbed over once and opened again. She fingered the rough spot and saw that her fingertip was streaked with red. In what opera was there a wound that didn't heal, a symbolic wound? She liked the quizzes that came on during the intermissions of the live Met broadcasts. Nick had taken her to dozens of operas before he had stopped liking opera. Mozart, Puccini, Verdi, all replaced now. Evenings in red satin and thrift store rhinestones, Nick handsome in a dark suit, their feelings moved huge distances by the music.

She sat up. The hummingbird was dipping its bill deep into the red-hot-poker again, bleaching it of its red nectar from the bottom up. The *chip* sound after it sipped was like children's scissors going *snip snip.* The tiny berries on the rosemary hedge were a dusty blue. A hawk hovered over the arroyo; in his placid eye his prey was already jelly. The matilija poppies—white crinolines with gold knobs at their centers—drooped against their props and strings. Someone would have to tie them up: put it on the list. She was sure that if you went long enough without sex you forgot the names of flowers. She almost had it: there had been wind in the dream, not a nice wind. The sun slid out and reached for her face and she let it hold her, hungry for the feeling of immortality a suntan brings.

The valley was already an oven, the heat like a curfew maintaining quiet. Over the narrow highway that led to town the redwood trees cast their long-legged gloom. She did not look at the scenery now; to do that you had to be in the passenger seat. In front of her was a black Chevy pickup truck with six letters painted out so that it said CHE. Steve liked to talk about politics but she didn't feel up to it today. She had known him since she was in college and he was in law school. He had given her a lift to New York at Thanksgiving and in the settling November dark had described his childhood in hiding in the south of France. He had told her about the sympathetic *concierge,* the Christian family in the country, how he was hidden under potatoes in a wheelbarrow, someone moving him out of new danger into a safe place at the monastery. His father had been shot in the back. His mother, an opera singer, had died shortly after she got to the camp but had not escaped being forced to sing with the concentration camp orchestra.

Now Steve was a lawyer in Cambridge, visiting California to interview victims of industrial sickness in Silicon Valley and to see a young cousin in Santa Cruz. In their few visits together Nick had pretended Steve was a rival, even though he thought him merely dull and decent, because there was only one kind of intimacy Nick understood. She had never taken that seriously but now there was a wisp of hope in her. She wondered if Steve would think it odd that she hadn't invited him to her house. Whenever she could, these days, she ate in restaurants because they made sequence so clear: you ordered, you waited, you ate, you paid, then it was over, as if one gesture were fastened to the next, as if something were really happening.

As she entered the café she heard the first notes of "I Fall to Pieces," Patsy Cline. The café's air conditioning seemed to be broken. The chintz curtains, the poinsettia, looked tackier in the heat. At the back was a large poster that said CHOKING. Steve was already there and he rose to hug her, the first time she had been touched in three months. She was surprised by her embarrassment. He looked different. He wasn't wearing his glasses, his eyes soft and dark behind contact lenses. Confronted with his angular serious looks, his new gaze, she felt like confetti.

"How are you? You look a little shaky."

"I'm okay, it's just hot."

"It's all fog downtown. I took the bus and hiked a river trail and it was fairly cool, but it's suffocating up here." He'd been perspiring, dark circles at the armpits of his blue Oxford shirt. She looked at the lovely stretch and curve of his chest. His voice sounded deeper now that he wasn't wearing glasses. He had always had a rich mahogany voice, the ghost of a European accent, reliable and agreeable.

Even so, she couldn't hear him very well. Lately people's voices seeped back into them as they spoke rather than coming toward her. Nick had developed a hearing problem in the last months, really a listening problem. She had had to repeat herself. He of all people knew how things became either ridiculous or sublime through repetition, how you could make a fool of someone just by forcing them to repeat themselves.

"Heard from Nick?"

"He's in New York, on the verge of being famous." She didn't want to talk about it, not yet. She forced herself to notice the menu, its delicate calligraphy like alfalfa sprouts.

"Are you okay? When I saw you last year you looked like you were going to get a divorce the way a woman looks like she's going to have a baby."

"I couldn't trust him anymore."

"I always thought you had an arrangement."

"It was a bad arrangement. And on top of that he rearranged it."

He smiled wryly. "Who can trust anyone completely? Not that you didn't do right."

"What's trust if it's not complete?" she said.

"Laura, in California you can't even trust that the ground won't give way under your feet." He patted her cold hand. She wanted to grab his hand, hold it a long time.

"There's a best way to trust everyone," Steve said. "You just have to find the right way. Are you anxious about the future?"

"I'm anxious about the future because I'm losing my memory," Laura said.

"Of course you're losing your memory, you're living in a place that doesn't have any history."

"No, it's me. I can't remember anything." She felt as if she were confessing to a drinking problem. Everything seemed too heavy to lift to speech.

"But tell me how *you* are," she said, after they had ordered.

"I'm very good. Seeing someone new. Very new. That is, very young and very recent." He pushed the bridge of his nose as if he expected to find his glasses there. "Melanie's a teacher. I went to her class to lecture on the Holocaust. I've been doing this in public schools, a program called Never Forget. The kids ask questions like, did the Jews wear gold stars because they were good, did you see Hitler, if you had a number on your arm would you wear long sleeves after the war?

She had seen someone with a number on her arm, months ago, where had it been? No, she'd just had her hand stamped with a blue saxophone at the jazz club, that was all. No, now she remembered. A short woman in her sixties on the stationary bike on her right at the spa, pedaling hard, breathing hard. She had disappeared before Laura could talk to her. Laura had been busy talking to Willow, on her other side, Willow who had given her a few massages, read her Tarot cards, who was tall and blonde, a gentle California beauty. Laura felt split apart as she panted on her bike: on her right was a woman who had fallen through the huge crack of Auschwitz or Dachau or Birkenau and had landed in wonderland; on her left was Willow, pedaling gracefully, her casual tranquility so distant from the specifics of the sequence of numbers on the woman's arm. The numbers sewed the woman into her place in time, irrevocably, while Willow floated above hers, playing with consciousness, with the body.

Steve was looking out the window, his gaze soft-focussed, and Laura followed it to a figure in a long white dress moving lightly, like snowfall in a paperweight, toward the café. The woman wore a white turban and an amethyst pendant that flashed back at the sun. Willow. Laura remembered Willow's gentle hands spreading eucalyptus oil over her back and felt a retroactive gratitude. Then the screen door wheezed, a warm breeze floated into the hot café, and Willow sat down. She put her hand over Laura's, the second time in an hour that Laura had been touched. Sanity was a matter of knowing whom you're allowed to touch.

Willow flashed a blond smile at Steve and Laura introduced them. "Laura, I dreamed about you last night. Some kind of wind." Laura felt a *frisson* scissor down her spine. It made her want to take a nap.

"I can't believe this heat. Do you suppose I have skin cancer?" Willow leaned closer to show Laura a scaly patch at the juncture of cheek and nostril. Why hadn't Willow asked if she could sit down?

"All this skin cancer means sun worship is finished. Forget Apollo. We have to return to loving the moon, our mother. Cancer is our national punishment for not believing in the invisible."

Laura looked at Steve, expecting raised eyebrows, but his eyes were relaxed and consenting, the pupils large. In her white dress and turban Willow looked alluringly lunar. Laura felt a triangle forming, felt a metallic edge around her body and a prickling in her hands, like when strange dogs barked at her.

The table shook for ten seconds.

"Subway?" Steve laughed. Laura scanned the room to see if there was a table big enough for the three of them to hide under. "There've been a lot of tremors lately," Willow said, "but we won't have a big one soon. Cats and dogs aren't running away, the way they do before an earthquake. I always check the classifieds for missing pets." Steve looked impressed. "Trust me. I'm psychic. Everyone in my family is. It's our way of being polite."

Nick had thought Willow was beautiful, had flirted with her the one time they met. Willow, on a somnambulist's plane that day, had seemed not to notice. It was during a stretch of time when Laura felt that he hated her, had finally told him that. He had flatly denied it, looking bored with the idea. "Don't *lie* to me about *hate,*" she had shouted, rushing toward him, raking four tracks of blood onto his wrist. He had grabbed her, held her hands so that they blossomed from his grip like flowers.

"What will I tell people?" he said later and she said, "Tell them you were attacked by a rose bush."

She excused herself and headed for the bathrooms marked THEM and US, next to the CHOKING poster. She chose THEM and leaned over the sink, splashing her face with cold water. Their anger had not been the clearing anger that brings a second chance. In this small space she could hear his pacing, a pacing he, in his repressed fury at her, would extend beyond his study, as if she were not sitting in the living room reading, or standing in the kitchen cooking dinner. A certain number of measures one way, then the same the other way, then back again.

One day when she came back early from the store she thought he had extended his pacing to the garden, but then she saw that he was leaning against the fence, talking into the cordless phone that had nine memories. He was murmuring, but her listening was so refined and urgent that she could hear him through the screen door, her hands pressing against the doorjamb, her head down, as if she were praying her way through an earthquake.

"I will *certainly* call you," he said in a voice full of tenderness. A spot on the top of her head burned. He was supposed to tell her if there was anyone; that was their arrangement. They would rebuild their Eden out of honesty, even if other people snaked through their lives. She was sure the woman on the phone had something to do with the sharp changes in his music recently. When he had played his first electronic piece for her, a piece in which he undermined memory by eliminating melody, she had said of the withholdings and repetitions whose incessantness pressed her against a wall, had blurted out in her first disobedience as a muse, "Isn't this just a case of the emperor's clothes?" And he had responded without missing a beat, "In California the emperor doesn't need any clothes," and had walked out of the room.

She ran the water again and patted its coolness onto the back of her neck. A week after the murmuring he was back in New York again. He called one morning at nine his time, six hers. "Sorry, I forgot," he said. He needed a phone number from his revolving file. She stumbled sleepily into his studio but couldn't find the file anywhere on his desk.

"Try the top drawer," he said, when she came back to the phone. In front of the file in the drawer was a stack of snapshots, the top one a double exposure of three people. She recognized Lincoln Center, the stony plaza. Winter light brought his handsomeness to full pitch and definition. Whoever had held the camera had inspired his happy boast in the lens. Laura had not been to Lincoln Center in four years; yet she saw her own bony sculpted face, with brown hair that looked like shreds of confetti, posing under a floating geranium. Plastered to her face in a double exposure was the face of a woman with electric black hair, half of the woman's features lost in Laura's, the other half unblending. Nick had taken a whole roll of Laura to make up for the blurred pictures and had unthinkingly reused the film; she had wondered where it had gone. After the argument, the day he came back—anger melting them together like records on a hot day, so annealed that no free joining could ever take place again—she had learned that the woman was a cellist, someone he had been seeing for six months, although at first he said he barely remembered her, his eyes blinking wildly. She had always thought of cellists as dowdy and sad, their legs spread for only one thing, the music, but this one wired her cello for duets with her own amplified breathing and had been on the cover of a magazine.

She rinsed her face again, avoiding the mirror, feeling stuffed with heat and sadness. She was glad Willow was there, to do the work of talking; she realized she had been depending on Willow from the minute she sat down.

They didn't look up when she returned. "This net of conceptualization, that's what's making the world sick," Willow was saying as she ate her crumbly muffin with boarding school composure.

"The world is sick because people don't think *enough,*" Steve replied, their eyes locking.

Laura felt as if a piece of her back were falling away; nowhere in the world was there anything that was hers. Willow's eyes looked like flowers being fed by water, and hers must look like lumps of clay.

The waitress came with the bill. "How did you like the eggs? The cook wanted to know because the recipe came to her in a dream."

"Perfect," Willow said.

The waitress turned the sign in the window to CLOSED and they went out to the car. Laura slid behind the wheel; it was too hot to touch and she put Kleenex under her hands. Across the street in front of Valley Discs Used and New, six records had been set out to warp and twist in the heat, local humor.

Once they were driving under the redwoods it was cooler. The bumper sticker on the car ahead of her said GIVE PLACE A CHANGE. No—GIVE PEACE A CHANCE. Steve sat between the two women, close enough for Laura to smell the graininess of his sweat, his sweet near-vanished aftershave. Up ahead a man in khaki stood next to a wooden barrier, a car stopped in front of it. Had there been an earthquake? Laura surreptitiously extended two fingers, hexing the stop sign. She knew that Steve got uneasy at borders. The man in khaki peered into the car. "Do you have any fruit?" he asked. A small insignia showed that he was with the agricultural service.

"No," Laura said. "Have they moved the state line? Are we entering Nevada?"

"They found a pregnant medfly in Boulder Creek," he said, unsmiling. "Strawberries are okay." He gave them a copy of the afternoon paper.

Two helicopters arrived at 10 a.m., circled the periphery of the nine-mile spray zone and then began to spray.

As the helicopters were first seen, residents and store owners ran into the street to watch. "This is really exciting!" said Page Smegmer. "It's too bad they aren't spraying at night," said Lompico resident Helene Hoglen. "It's beautiful over in San Jose when the helicopters light up the sky, like fireworks."

The water district fears the valley's open streams could get a toxic level of malathion because of the dripping from trees and the runoff into streams.

The entire county is now part of the emergency area and may be sprayed up to eight times.

"But they said they wouldn't spray here," Laura said faintly. She thought of the way lies had smeared Nick's voice. He had gone, but now the lies were coming from elsewhere and fog would drip malathion into the open streams and make a toxic mist over her world. People had run out in it. Soon they would have beauty pageants for Miss Sun Damage, Miss Black Lung, Miss Acid Rain. Whereas other people would develop a dread of the future and a loathing of the past that had contaminated it.

"Have a nice day," the agriculture man said to them, waving them on.

When they stopped at the red light in Felton a young man came over and handed Laura a lime-colored flyer. It said MALATHION at the top. Willow asked to be let out, and Laura turned south onto Graham Hill Road, climbing out of the Valley, where blue sky slowly faded to gray, the redwoods reaching up into the fog. The sore on her brow stung a little. She decided not to touch it. The somber trees whizzed past, spokes of light flashing through the branches in a strobe effect. *That can cause epilepsy. Don't look.* Who had told her that? She had no idea. Loss of memory was like fine china breaking. Sip. *Crash.* Sip. Crash. Was amnesia a form of clairvoyance, the memory of a foreordained extinction, soon to come? Maybe her memory was leaving her to give her a sense of possibility, as one of the women in the group had said. Laura had tried to tell her that she thought it was more serious than that, something close to real amnesia, but she had forgotten the word for it: "You know, whatever that is when you forget something."

At Main Beach Laura shivered in the foggy chill. The CASINO sign pumped red to green to red in the bleached afternoon light. She and Nick had gone to a Halloween Ball at the Coconut Grove. What had he gone as? Something false, a cape and mustache. She had been a salad, a seamless green, without dressing.

She and Steve went down the concrete steps to the beach, the calliope's music drowned out in the ocean's roar. Shorebirds skimmed the edge of the surf, almost touching the breaking waves. The fog brought out the harlequin colors of the rides and the long arcade. Willow had said that auras were easy to see near the ocean. Laura thought she sensed a whiteness around the crown of Steve's head, like white fuzz on a strawberry, moving fast. His aura was gathering mold. Out of boredom with her. Or it was a vitamin deficiency, hers.

"I'm fascinated by water," Steve said, as if it were orchids, a hobby. He seemed like a stranger to Laura, lighter, changed, not on her side of misery.

"It took me four years to get over the breakup with Rachel. And we weren't married as long as you were."

Laura tried to remember what Rachel looked like, a quiet person, a round face. How long ago had it been, the four of them at a party, Nick flirting in every direction, drunk, Steve's awareness of it an unintended gilding of her humiliation? Steve had hinted that Nick loved her unhappy watching because it spooned manna into his narcissus pool. She had taken his chivalric concern for granted then; it was surplus, mere friendship. Now she wanted to pay attention, but if you paid attention only after you needed people this much were you merely using them? The women's group hadn't discussed this.

They stepped over a tangle of olive-colored kelp, a cloud of gnats flying around the ridged leaves and rubbery bulbs. Insects collected near people who were angry or frightened, someone had told her. She stamped on the kelp to feel it pop, then listed into Steve's tallness and almost tripped. He didn't reach for her.

"Of course now it seems long ago," he said.

Maybe he would help her with her history over dinner, when she had the courage to talk about it. They would have turkey burritos in the old Mexican café across from the boardwalk or clam chowder on the pier where sea lions with whiskered faces lay on the rafters barking.

"You seem brave," he said. She shivered. That's what people told you when they meant *don't ask me for anything*, even if they liked you. A few feet away a lone seagull was tearing a fish apart. She could feel Steve thinking about leaving.

Let's just walk as far as the pier, then I should go," he said. She sensed space widening around her as if she weren't sure where anything was coming from. Steve put his arm lightly over her shoulder. "Take care of yourself. I wish we'd had more time. I'll be in touch soon."

She let him hug her, the third touch of the day, and then walked quickly, blindly, in the other direction. Somewhere there was a vocabulary she hadn't learned, a vocabulary that made other people act the way you wanted them to.

She did not want to go home to the poisoned valley, the malathion wafting in from Boulder Creek, moist, ammoniac, punitive. She did not want to buy food for dinner, because when you were alone the supermarket muzak went straight into your bones, the grinding buzz of refrigerator cases, the smell of locked-up frozen dinners, the brand names jumping under the fluorescence on the bright stacked-up packages. She would have to pilfer her earthquake supplies or stop at Kentucky Fried Chicken and buy little broken legs and breasts. The cat had food; the room would darken around him until it was the same color as his fur.

She sat down on a bench facing the ocean. *Think.* There were certain minutes on earth when nothing was right, as if time were scarred and stuck in its conveyor belt. She took out the malathion flyer. Information could help you out or do you in. She had asked very little about the cellist. It was easier, after all the years of candor melting into silences into lying, simply to leave.

She skimmed:

No warning to pregnant women bees should be taken away for seven days put cars in garage the bait is not supposed to drip from the trees but heat inversion twilight fine chemical mist over the valley highly toxic when inhaled and sprayed into the air discovered malathion is the same company developed gas used by the Nazis in the

She looked out at the ocean.

gas chambers

There was an extremist group now that insisted the Holocaust had never happened, the unspeakable attempting to replace the unthinkable, assassins of memory.

uncontrollable coughing chest pains extreme fatigue paralysis conjunctivitis rare diseases He told me to go to hell in heavy amounts uphill the wind blowing from that direction no longer able to do much loss of memory before I was in excellent health

She noticed that she was walking toward the car.

Farther north, every once in a while, there was something, a rape, a murder; the nearer beaches were safer. She had to think of that now that she was alone. If she drove up Route 1 just so far she would be fine. She would do that for herself. That would be something.

The nude beach was the most beautiful, with acres of leafy brussels sprouts spreading right up to the edge of the cliff, but she would avoid it because she might run into a student there. She already had, once. She had been wearing pants and a shirt and had kept her eyes on his face but he had looked down at her body twice as if a second glance might make her clothes disappear. He had been in the Humanities class, the author of a paper on Kafka that began *Gregor Samsa awoke one morning to find himself in a no-win situation.* Pascal, with his infinite spaces, had given him trouble too. Incredibly, for a moment, she could remember some of the famous passage, *Man is only a reed . . . a puff of smoke, a drop of water is enough to kill him . . . . All our dignity, then, consists in thought. It is upon this that we must depend, not on space and time, which we would not in any case be able to fill.*

She had forgotten to fill the gas tank. The gauge read close to empty, and she passed up the detour through the stand of eucalyptus she and Nick had always visited on the way to San Francisco. Long strips of pink and gray bark peeled down the trees in narrow maps of damage. The young eucalyptus were fragile in a storm. The best thing to be in an earthquake was flexible. Had she wanted to be hurt? No, but after years of hurt she had wanted his guilt made evident, justice served. There had to be justice; if there were no justice, how had anyone thought of it in the first place?

She turned into a small parking area and got out of the car, breathing in the large pungent smell of the ocean. Before last year's 5.2 there had been an arch at this beach. Now there was only a cliff, the surf smashing out a hundred paintings, the colors of cameo, nicotine, mahogany, rich and wet, in the wall of the rock.

Laura saw only two people on the beach at the end of the trail. Two girls, their bodies firm as bombs, spoke in Los Angeles accents. Their vowels seemed to have irrigation ditches inside them.

"I feel real gude now," one was saying. "But like I was going out with him for three months, okay? And so I go, basically, I don't think I want to go out with you anymore. I mean, he just said like, 'Really' in a totally nasty way."

Laura took off her sandals and scrunched through the cool sand. A woman partly draped in a towel was posing for photographs next to the pampas grass growing out of the cliff, her blondness matched to the feathery platinum blooms, her skin shockingly smooth against the protruding textures of rock. Somewhere a bird Laura couldn't identify was crying *rigid digit rigid digit*. On this side of the beach the sea sounded, tiny, distant, and cozy; back near the path it had been a flat roar. If Nick lied and she didn't remember, could it matter? Was her forgetting a kind of forgiving?

Laura felt a presence on the empty beach. A man sat crosslegged on the sand in a deep niche in the cliff; he was bearded and wore swimming trunks, his eyes closed, his fingers curved in a *mudra*. Often people came to the beach to do yoga, tai chi, meditation; there were organized classes on the beaches closer to town. The man looked pale and spiritual. He was uttering a low nasal drone—Laura couldn't make out the words—a mantra, a way of getting sound on your side.

She found herself breathing more deeply as she walked past. A small waterfall glistened down copper-streaked rock into a shallow pool, a waterfall she had thought was on a different beach where there were rocks with fossils as extinct as memory. Growing out of the cliffside next to the waterfall were snapdragons stippled red on their yellow tongues, like dots on the delicate flesh of a lobster. Laura stared at the waterfall until the rocks next to it seemed to flow upward. Underneath the hushed cascade of the waterfall were the reassuring explosions of surf, the waves breathing into spray. She felt herself loosening as she listened to the indrawn roaring breath of the ocean, the push of breath out again. All she needed was to hear the breathing of the ocean and to see another person occasionally, doing something wholesome and attentive, and she would be fine. The cave might be empty by now, made warm by the contemplative, and she could sit there, safe and breathing, the sound coming from the back of the cave and from the sea all at once.

As she approached she saw that the man was still there, his eyes closed, his position changed slightly. He had made a zero with his thumb and middle finger. Now he lengthened the zero, made it with a loose fist, his hand a rhythm pumping up and down at the center of his body, his swim trunks gone. She was sick before she realized, then the shock sent the blood rushing to her face. She walked fast, not seeing, a dizzy feeling traveling across her heart. She sat down as close as she could to the Los Angeles girls. A Labrador, heavy with health, frisked around them. Laura had looked like the girls one hundred years ago. Firm, as if she belonged on *terra firma*. If Nick had been with her he would have looked and looked at the girls, and she would have looked away from his looking. How could someone be right for you but not good for you? Nothing supported her now except mother earth, and how quickly that was giving way—nitrates, formaldehyde, malathion, DBCB, EDB, DDT, PCB's, CFC's. The earth was still the place where you buried your dead but now it was also one of the dying. Were the choppers overhead at this very minute, stuttering 100 feet above her garden, spraying poison, the garden withering backward to a time before Eden? Eve's first disobedience and the fruit, you don't make a mistake like that twice. The wind came up suddenly, scattering birds as if they were leaves. The northern beaches grew cold in the late afternoons. Laura's blouse flapped and sand stung her face. She had read somewhere that air anywhere could be from over 200 miles away, a stranger.

Her legs were shaky on the uphill path. Twice she looked over her shoulder. When she slammed herself shut in the car, panting hard, the silence seemed unnatural after the roar of ocean and wind. She smoothed her hair, and in the rearview mirror saw, on a station wagon across the lot, a license plate that said TOUCH ME. A woman was in the station wagon, adjusting a baby seat; then she went around to the driver's side.

The wind stopped for a moment; the trees outside were still. Now she could hear it. Her dream last night had been about a wind that didn't belong to her. She saw her antique dresser with the lace runner on top, and on the lace runner were a small turquoise bear, a rock with a fossil snail iced into it, and pink pebbles from a distant ocean. Nick was there, looming over the dresser, and with enormous force he blew all the objects onto the floor, the lace crumpled and blown off too. The top of her dresser was blank and bare and she could feel the powerful wind of his breath as bitter and frightened sounds came from her throat, separate from any voice she knew in herself.

"What am I doing?" he said to her, his voice huge in the dream, and she replied timidly—she could hear the words muffle and blow as if she were in a big wind—"You're blowing on me," the flat taste of her obedience in her mouth. Her hand shook on the ignition key. To remember is to put back together, then you fall apart, amnesia's valium gone.

She stared straight ahead and saw the Los Angeles girls, who had reached the crest of the path from the beach. At a party years ago, not her kind of party, she had glimpsed Nick in strobe light on a sofa between two girls in shiny dresses, hems high on the thigh that year. Her memory clicked shut like a camera finished with a picture, but she forced it open and found the cellist embedded in a transparency over the girls. Hindsight gave the clarity of second sight. There was only one thing worse than the end and that was the beginning of the end.

And yet he had loved her many days of her life after that, as if they existed in a strobe effect of separate gestures, no continuity, no consequence. The last good day together had been only two years ago. They had gone to visit the house in New Hampshire. The few houses that had once been there, wooden houses, had melted into the trees, pine against pine in the midst of the light and shade and stone walls. Now the house was no longer there and the road wound through tract houses set into the landscape like potted plants. They drove ten miles to their old swimming pond, where insects played a game of jacks on the water and trees tossed their reflections onto the surface like flowers. She held his hand and let the sun shine on her face, her loose blouse lifted by the wind. She wore nothing underneath and the sun was warm on her breasts. He kissed her neck and lifted her blouse, their minds clear and peaceful together; he spread a blanket on the ground.

She released the handbrake, pulled out of her space and saw, guiltily, the yellow wheelchair painted on the asphalt; had she imagined, unconsciously, that she was entitled to it? TOUCH ME was in front of her as she turned out of the lot. She wanted to put her head on the woman's shoulder and go to sleep. You had to pretend that here and there people were caring for you, blessed seconds of comfort, because where was the softness of mother earth? She and Nick had made love quietly for hours in a grove of birches next to the pond, needly pines exhaling into their skin and hair, the soft water of sunlight on their skin, a scattering of tiny bluets under them, a blessing from the sky as it rushed through green leaves. Better not to remember the Chinese boxes of greater and greater happiness. TOUCH ME pulled out and passed the car in front of it; Laura, for a split second, felt abandoned.

She drove slowly, watching out of the corner of her eye how the wind dragged the dark water into wavelets and cut it up into small pieces of white. She had to get home. She didn't want to see the changeable desires of sunset, pinks and mauves straining for climax until moonlight shattered on the breakers. She felt a long shiver when she thought of the man in the cave, the image of him like larvae in the seams of her clothes.

She glanced down at the pretty yellow cotton dress she had worn for Steve. When would Nick call about the piano? Her dashboard clock would tell her nothing; it gave the same time always. Her gas tank read empty; she knew that with her car that was also a lie, but she didn't know where the truth began.

A helicopter smacked its *whop whop* into the air over the beach, but the ocean was calmer now. The evenness of the waves slipping slowly into the night reminded her of her old voice. You can live a new way if you sing a new song, Willow had told her as she hummed at the spa, upside down on one of the machines, the humming blowing her blond hair forward.

Laura drove past the stand of eucalyptus. The small ones were fragile but the big ones, once they were well established, were strong enough to withstand the wind. The good was as true as the bad, if you waited. A turn of the light, a temperature change, hope comes out of nowhere, where was the justice in that? Willow's voice wandered into her mind. *The best thing to do, if you have amnesia, is to become clairvoyant*. She laughed, her laughter sounding unfamiliar to her. She imagined the phone ringing, Steve calling, concerned, to check on how she was, her shaky voice telling him.

She turned on her lights, twin beams pulling the darkening road toward her. She saw, distinctly, a day in autumn, season of acceptable little deaths, the leaves red on the maple and liquidambar, a day when there would finally be a change, something in balance inside her. She would be in the living room, the piano gone, listening to the Saturday opera live from the Met, the music that was passé for Nick now, music he had tossed away like Kleenex. The members of the audience would be roaring for curtain calls as if they were in pain. Singers in elaborate costumes she couldn't see would come out and take bow after bow until the diva was left alone in applauded solitude under the lights, the tears streaming down her cheeks and flowers filling her flawless arms. Laura would be petting the cat. And amnesia would be part of it: she could see that one Saturday in October, her body filled with music, her eyes clear, she would not remember that, right now, at the edge of her mind and exhausted, she was sure she was driving into the empty summer nights of the rest of her life.

Our Lady Examines Her Anger

Nita Penfold

like a foreign object
turning it over, looking for cracks
flaws in the obsidian surface.
She is angry at him
for going on with his life
as if she were not maimed
as if she had not lost an arm to him,
a foot, hobbling around now
trying to grow them back.
Each memory of their life together
an obstacle to trip over:
the little boy who wanted approval
from his father, the little girl who needed
her mother's love, two artists attempting
support through the hardness,
holding each other's tears in the night.
She loved the soul of this man who
reflected back her own undetected strengths,
who could transform himself into roles
with rich masks, who played like
a gleeful boy, who showed her
that happiness was indeed possible
but must be made, joy
could be found if you are open
to the moment. So she opened,
and he closed to her.
But most of all, as she catches
her distorted face in the shiny whorls,
she is angry because
loving him was
the closest she had ever come
to loving herself.

Letter

Elaine Romaine

This is Mary Joy, hello, hello! Is Greg there? Oh. Well, tell him Mary Joy called. From Ohio. Let me spell that for you. M-A-R-Y J-O-Y. J as in joyful. We went to high school together. When he was here, he said, I mean, is Greg alright? Oh? I see . . . . thank you.

Did I hear her? I heard her. M-A-R
J as in joyful. J as in stupid.
I wax unkind. I do.
In fact, she *was* joyful.

At 47, his age, my age, here in the East Bronx where I live now, where I was born, and where no one called Mary Joy lives. Only me, Anna. And Carmen, Maria, Rose.

Saturdays I lean out the second floor window into gasoline air, the rumble of buses over old trolley tracks, eight-year olds smoking cigarettes below the window, the fruit man selling overripe bananas from the back of his truck. Sitting on the tenement stoop, Maria is rocking her baby to salsa while Carmen yells up to me that her husband's gone again, fuck him. Rose sidles up to the fruit man, grinning. She wants some grapes. She's out of money.

And what of Joy? Mary.

I imagine a place, Alliance, Ohio where a voice that lilts is possible, probable. Her voice is the America of crew cuts, church bazaars, the local football game on Saturday, the brick-faced building where my husband went to high school, with a girl named Joy, who at forty-seven wears rose-colored lens she painted slowly over the years, who is safe (is she?) within a picket fence. She lives in the house where she was born, a porch shaded by elms, windows washed, frilled white curtains, looking out from the window seat on which she sits with morning coffee, warm in a quilted bathrobe, fluffy mules.

Mary Joy, her husband fucks her once a week. Quietly. After which she showers right away, washes the sheets, certainly changes her panties. Her bras are still pointy. She wears high heels to town to pick up groceries. Her husband does not want her to work. Does she still practice cheerleading in front of a bedroom mirror in the late afternoon when she's alone?

Maybe she lifted her skirt with a whirl for her old high school friend when he, the man I married, visited her for old times and delivered his sad tale: What a bitch he married, a mistake, she's nothing like you. You remember, don't you, Mary Joy? That time in high school when . . . .

Imagine high school. And joyful Mary Joy cheering:

Go guys go, I will yes.

I will not open my legs, no!

And Mary Joy smiles at the team as if to say it's a joke, I might, I just might spread them. But she never does.

Too simple a portrait of Alliance, Ohio? Of America? How can the Mary Joys believe the tired tale of the misunderstood husband?

Consider her telephone call. "Is Greg alright?"

She got hooked by his sad tale.

And if hooked, then she had her mouth open to be hooked.

Me, I carry a knife in my jeans, Mary Joy. I lived with the object of your concern. Is he alright? What could be wrong with a man who plays the violin? Who won the state championship, playing Bach? Who got a scholarship to Harvard? Who was born in Cleveland, America. What could be wrong with a man who went to high school with girls named Betsy, Laurie, and Mary J-O-Y. Who had a paper route, won the Latin medal, had a mother called Bea who baked endless pies for her church? Who lived in a brick and stone house on a street with oaks, elms, beeches, O America the Beautiful.

This knife's not for the streets. Not for the tenements. I grew up here. When I go outside, I know how to walk, I know how to see and pretend not to see. I know how to look and not move my ass any faster than I should.

The knife came later. After college, graduate school, the living room stacked with books, after my daughter, after she grew up and left, after his fists.

I am in a two-room apartment. I carry my knife to remind me not to get sucked in, not to believe that intelligence breeds understanding or that love includes kindness. A knife reminds me not to open my legs one more time. My ass is my own.

I don't know Mary Joy. She is America, the small town I have never seen but which I want to be out there. She is a woman who walks any time at night down to the store for ice cream. She trusts the hero who comes to visit his old town, believes the tall boy who read all those books, got his Ph.D, who tells her she is different, she is not like other women.

Consider this woman who called, imagine her when she is listening to him: she bends forward in a Queen Anne chair, covered in flowered chintz, her hand on his knee, her eyes sorrowful for his tragic figure. There is no one home to break their privacy, to break his tale of loss and loneliness. Does she understand that he calculated the precise time to ring the bell to her house: when her husband left for work?

It is six a.m. I get up for work. I dress. I lock my door with three locks. I remember to put my money in my sneakers. Sitting on the bus, I think about how America sounded in Joy's voice. A lightness that never knew of two bucks in the pocket, a part-time job, sitting at a kitchen table, honing an old knife.

When she looked at his hands, did she see how large, how strong? Did she ask, Do you still play the violin? Did she think he was still the boy she knew? The articulate intellectual, the musician, how different he was from the others.

Dear Joy,

Violin hands beat up women. Violin hands are not soft. There are callouses on the tips of each finger of the left hand, close to the top of the nail, hardened after long practice. The right hand, best for hitting, is particularly strong, needed as it is for bowing. The left wrist is quite flexible, kept loose so the fingers do not press heavily on certain notes. The left hand has a peculiar strength, a force with precise direction: the mouth and teeth, then blood and bits of teeth, swallowed.

My skin is not the pink skin of America but the skin of Southern Italy. My name does not lilt: two a's, and two n's. This Anna disappeared into the America of books and degrees, writing about Woolf and Austen, grand ladies all. This Anna remembers (in the middle of blood vomited in a library) Mary Cassatt alone in Paris, Colette locked in a room, I remember my mouth and gums raw from stitches. And I remember an old Sicilian rule: If you can't break his knees, get a knife.

I apologize. When you called, I should have said:

Maybe he's dead.

Or I hope he is.

Or look, sweets (in my best tough New York voice), my ribs are healed, my lips are down to normal size, and I walk into my lousy apartment and I am not scared.

I live, I should have said, in a neighborhood where if you get beat up, you know it's coming. I live where it is brutal and clear. I am not in a place I once called my home, the place I thought safe but never was, where he said I love you, only to beat my ass.

Let me soften it a bit; let me permit you to wear the rosecolored lens.

He *did* stop. Surely yes he did.

That is, his hands stopped.

Can you imagine with your once a week fuck what was next? The bed linen is clean; it is cold. The double bed spreads white, two pillows gridded by sunlight reaching through the blinds. It is quiet. I think I am safe; I am asleep.

A hand moves over my mouth. My arms are pushed above my head, my wrists clamped by his other hand. I am turned over. I become a dog for his cock. I am nothing, he says, but a hole. My insides are scraped out. He tunnels in so far, he is a hook grabbing at my ribs, reaching into my throat until my entire body is silent.

Do married women get raped? Yes, over and over, until they bleed. I bled, days it seemed, weeks. There was blood on my pants, my skirt. I stood in the lecture hall, speaking of writers who in the end drowned themselves, gassed themselves, all of them bleeding.

I am them.

I am someone else.

We are all the same.

In my lecture I tell the students of the room one must have: the money one must have. Only with the word money do their eyes open. They know power; they know what it is, what it allows: a man with balls and money can beat his wife, his children. I imagine hiring toughs to shatter his knees, but I keep going. I say, I will smash that violin; I will earn money to bribe and threaten until he leaves.

And goes back to Alliance, Ohio. To you, Joy.

Regards.

This is my letter.

I understand now, on the bus home, books under my arm, repeating lectures in my head, real words about dead ladies, I understand something about Mary Joy, the cheerleaders, married after high school, their clean lives. I understand how they can ask in all innocence, call another woman and ask, How is Greg? Is he alright?

She knows what I do not know.

She knows how to open her legs just so wide.

So nobody really gets in.

She learned what I never learned. You got to open your legs just so wide. And no wider. Did her mother tell her that? Did her mother say, open too wide and he won't respect you? And even when you're married, not too wide either because that is worse, because they know you then, and then you've got no hold. How do the Mary Joys learn that?

I learned that from a book too late: a week ago: Woman has mystery, mystery is power, sex destroys mystery.

I take out my knife. I hone it back and forth. I listen to it hiss. Anything could happen anytime. I listen to my neighbors Carmen and Rose yell at the fruit man, I remember my daughter on the other coast who says the word shit like it's a comma. When the noise dies, I lie on the bed and spread my legs out to an inverted V, so wide it seems impossible to spread them further without breaking my hips. I spread them every night like this, knowing no one is here to put a fist up my gut. I spread them, remembering how sweet it was once, how I spread myself open, how I trusted: Do you need? I will give. Do you want? I am here. I believed his words: always, plight, commitment, love, trust.

I hear you, Mary Joy. I am crazy. Perhaps. Never too wide. I lean on the windowsill like my mother and grandmother before me. I walk to classes, my shoulders no longer sloped in pain. I do not have to lie about a swollen mouth, sores on my lips, bruises on my legs. I no longer wear sunglasses to hide bruised eyes. When there was blood on my pants and skirt, the drycleaner did not ask. He did not want to know. My daughter comes home. She sees; she knows. It is not a tired tale. Nor a moral fable. It is for Mary Joy from Anna, the one he lived with, the woman you called, spelling your name. I hear you, I see you lean over and say, disbelieving, you say to him, She carries a knife? You say, Are you alright?

Getting Rid of Randall

A.D. Ross

I pushed him down the stairs, Polly was thinking as she guided her grocery cart past the fish counter. He broke both his legs and both his arms. No, just his legs. But he could get to the bathroom without my help. He had to sleep in the house, on the living room couch, and he got in everyone's way. Soon he was driving me and the boys crazy.

Polly was shopping at the Co-op and getting more and more depressed. She looked at her list and then at the deli case. Could she get away with buying deli desserts for tomorrow's party? She decided to try. Into her cart went pink bakery boxes containing an Amaretto cheesecake, a chocolate almond torte, and lemon cookies.

Polly then bought leeks and zucchini for Randall's dinner and gruyère for the boys. After she stowed her groceries in the car, she did not drive directly home. Instead she took a route over the bridge to Coralville, 20 minutes away. She went to Wittski's Gun Shop, which she had previously looked up in the yellow pages, and bought a handgun. The man who sold it to her was wearing a yellow necktie and a white short-sleeved shirt. He had Daffy Duck tattooed on his forearm. "You can pick it up in 14 days," he said. She paid in cash. Then she drove home.

Polly's position in Randall's house was still uncertain. They had fallen in love ten years ago, just before Polly's bead business failed. She was at that time making good money. There was a big demand for handcrafted beads. Randall, who taught sociology at Columbia, had come to Berkeley to attend a conference. They met at a party. While their friends shouted and drank and danced, Randall and Polly walked around the block, then around the neighborhood, and finally to Polly's car. Polly sent the baby-sitter home. In the morning Randall was captivated by Polly as she fed her boys and drove them off to school. She came back with fresh bagels, and made Randall the best cup of coffee he'd ever had. He had already given his paper, and found he was able to skip the rest of the conference. A few days later he left for New York.

Polly couldn't understand why she stopped getting orders. She fired fewer and fewer batches of hand-rolled porcelain beads in her kiln. She ground fewer and fewer bone and soapstone beads. Still the boxes of beads, packed in cotton, piled up in the corner of her bedroom. She thought about Randall constantly. She had trouble paying the rent. It became clear to her that she had to visit Randall in New York. Her sister loaned her the plane fare and agreed to take the boys, then four and six years old, for a week.

They were happy together in New York. Randall gave a big party and Polly prepared the food. She made dozens of intricately decorated deviled eggs, and a lavish green California-type salad. Randall's friends and colleagues loved her. She was an asset. Randall thought they should live together, in New York of course.

"I have no money," she told him, "no one's buying beads any more." "It doesn't matter." Randall was uncharacteristically passionate. "Come anyway. I can afford to support you, and Theo and Mikie. I need you, Polly. Love is more important than money." Polly too felt that love was more important than money. During the Christmas vacation, in Berkeley, they discussed conditions and made agreements. This time when Randall went back to teach, Polly stayed on only to pack up her things and consider what she could salvage from her sinking business. Not much, as it turned out. But Randall had said he would support them. Randall had lots of money.

I told him I would drive him to the doctor, Polly thought as she left Coralville and drove back over the bridge. I parked in a deserted mall and got out of the car. Where are you going? he asked. His voice had that same executive tone he uses when he says, "Polly, haven't I told you I hate mushrooms in my food?" I walked away from the car without answering. I turned to look at him. He had already opened a book and was reading it, sitting in the passenger seat. I left him in the car for hours. However, he continued to nag. The next day I crumbled four valiums and dissolved them in his favorite low-sodium French-style salad dressing. He complained all the more, although in a distinctly calmer, even somewhat satisfied, voice. I had to do something final about Randall. I hung him from a tree with his green-striped necktie.

Home from Coralville, Polly unloaded her groceries, and was soon making a quiche out of leeks, zucchini, and two kinds of parsley. The custard was composed of nonfat milk and fake eggs, and the crust contained whole wheat flour and toasted sesame seeds. Polly loved leeks, and as she sauteéd the cut-up pieces in a little corn oil and wine, she couldn't help tasting a bit here and there.

Polly was cooking dinner in the kitchen of an old framehouse in Iowa City. Ten years had passed since Randall announced that love was more important than money. The boys had become huge, heavy-footed, croaking-voiced teenagers. Randall slept and worked in a two-room cottage in the back. Love had gotten sparser and harder to come by through the years, but Polly vigorously filled the void. The big house was crammed with yard sale chairs and rugs and lamps, and heavy coats and boots from the Goodwill.

Randall's quiche was in the oven. Polly began two other quiches, using real eggs, and ordinary low-fat milk, and gruyère cheese. These were for her boys. Before they went in the oven, she sprinkled over them all the leftover shreds of leek and parsley she hadn't been able to use in Randall's quiche. Then she added little strips of red pepper laid on top to form a T on one quiche and an M on the other. The quiches for the boys looked much more attractive, she thought.

Polly sliced tomato and cucumber. She was apprehensive,a familiar feeling. She did not look forward to Randall's coming home. The house was so cheerful without him, especially when she sat in the kitchen with her boys and their friends. The young people, whose posture was uniformly terrible, slouched over the table or stood like wading birds on one immense Reeboked foot, pulling little pieces of leftover lasagna out of a platter in the refrigerator. She listened to stories they told her with their mouths full. In fact she dreaded Randall's arrival. When six or seven kids lay around the living room, the TV their only illumination, listening to their loathsome punk rock music and eating chips crumbling from garish bags, Polly sometimes sat with them and laughed at their silly cryptic jokes. No such gatherings could occur when Randall, busy and serious, was present. Polly felt continually inadequate. The money that Randall gave her to run the house, admittedly a large amount, wasn't meant to be spent on the boys' friends. Was it? He glared at the kids, studied the contents of the refrigerator, tore her monthly checks out of his checkbook with a snap and examined them carefully before handing them over. All his entertaining, including the departmental reception on which she'd splurged buying fancy desserts, was of course included. In spite of her budget she was generous with food for the boys and their pals. It was hard to feel physically close to her sons these days, they were so tall, they took up so much space, they left so many dirty socks on the floor. But when they gathered with their friends on the living room floor or in the kitchen with the refrigerator open, their shouts and guffaws and dirty words echoing through the house, she felt happy that they were at home, had brought their social life home, accepted her attendance, and ate up the cold lasagna.

The boys played their terrible music over their powerful stereos and Polly heard it clearly in the kitchen. Their favorite band, which Polly had learned to identify, was Galen Doom and The Dregs. To her ears this group sounded like a heavy pre-typhoon surf pounding behind the splintering of smashing furniture and young men crying out in pain. "The Dregs," she would murmur as the boys came through the kitchen to snatch a round of carrot from beneath her knife. "Mom likes Galen Doom," they told their friends.

If Randall walked in, everything changed. It was magic the way Randall weighted the vibes in the room, brought them down suddenly to the floor, so that even the young high-school faces with their fresh fuzzy jaws sagged with the heaviness of Randall's presence. "Hello," he said briefly, pausing for a minute with his briefcase in his hand before going out to his cottage to do his mysterious and important work at his desk there. He didn't look around him or comment on the general state of the house, but Polly knew he perceived its deep chaos through his pores, and if he stayed within it too long he would absorb it and fall sick from its toxic clutter.

That the house was messy was undeniable, but Polly felt comfortable with heaps and stacks of papers on all horizontal surfaces. She could usually find what she wanted. She didn't see the need for the kind of swivel-hipped broken-field walking that the boys did to get from front door to kitchen and from there to the stairs. They avoided the little forests of tables, floor lamps, tiny rugs, circles of chairs and baskets of tree-like house plants; they headed unerringly for what they wanted. Into the open refrigerator they reached long arms and without looking pulled out gallon jugs of milk.

This semester Polly was heavily involved in the details of Theo's graduation. She met with a group of the other seniors' parents to discuss safe driving on prom night, consumption of alcohol on graduation night, storage of perishable salads at the senior picnic, and other topics of concern. Mikie meanwhile was entering the Science Fair and thought he might run for class president. Days went by during which Polly and Randall brushed past each other in the kitchen with only a few words, Polly's polite and diffident, Randall's cold and abrupt. He was always working. The lights in the cottage burned late. Yet, whenever Polly sat in the kitchen at night drinking tea with a few seniors' parents, or helping the teenagers make pizza, Randall invariably came through on swift, hostile errands of his own. All conversation stopped as he came in to pull his carton of nonfat yogurt from the refrigerator. "Polly," he demanded, "Did you buy Ivory soap? Polly, will you please pick up The New York Times? Polly, please write down the Dean's Dinner in your book." Polly was beyond embarrassment. She began to find his lordly manner a little comic, as though it were a kind of retaliation that backfired, like Wiley Coyote in the Roadrunner cartoons.

While he slept, Polly thought as she poured a bit of Randall's low-calorie dressing on the salad, while he slept I released mosquitoes into his cottage. I thought perhaps he would move to a hotel. It did not work as I planned. None of these things worked. Indeed they affected him not at all. I began to concentrate on shutting him up for good.

Polly heard the cottage door slam and then the sound of Randall's shower. The feeling of anxiety was stronger now. His tiny bathroom was only three or four yards from the kitchen door. He would have arrived all sweaty after his run. He liked to eat after he was cleaned up.

Her mood slowly became recognizable as the confused dismay with which she routinely contemplated her relationship with Randall. She checked the oven and pulled her hair into a knot with a chopstick.

Polly's long straight coarse black hair had bright threads of white, and was of a texture which resisted attempts to smooth it. Unless it was braided in a few skinny tails, it seemed too heavy for her short, slim frame. Her very dark eyes still had the softness and sweetness with which she had attracted Randall. For his benefit she had always dressed in long flowered skirts and bright silk shirts, under which she wore little, if any, underwear. Her taste in clothes had not changed over the years, and now Randall, who was next in line for department chairman, sometimes frowned when he saw her.

He came in the door with his hair still wet. Randall was a small well-shaped man, and although he was going bald on top he didn't look his age, which was 45. He wore black-wire-rimmed aviator-style glasses. Polly could see the defined muscles in his arms. He had equally impressive sinewy muscles in his legs. Jogger's legs. Randall ran on the track four times a week, Sunday and Monday, Wednesday and Thursday. In addition to this unalterable schedule, he jogged home from work, when weather permitted, with his work in a backpack.

"Polly," Randall said, crunching his salad and washing it down with swallows of white wine, "You haven't forgotten our reception tomorrow night, have you?"

"No, Randall. I'm getting everything ready."

I ran over him with the car. He was loading up the trunk with his list in his hand, standing in the driveway. On the pretext of looking for the map I got into the driver's seat. Quick as a wink I gunned the engine and threw her into reverse. Randall's legs made a satisfying crunch as the tires bumped over them. But why do I keep breaking his legs?

Then I knocked him down and jumped on him and smashed him in the face. I was getting meaner and more violent. He rose, blood like in the movies trickling out of his torn and cut mouth, staggering a little on his fractured legs, but unhurt in that deep protected way that babies are unhurt in their mother's wombs and careless drivers in expensive Nader-approved cars are unhurt in their billowing airbags.

Randall pointed to the pink bakery boxes. "What's in there?"

"Desserts for the reception."

"Oh?" Randall was wary of bakery-made cakes. They had too much butter for him, too many eggs. They had cream and custard and sugar in abundance. He loathed and feared anything containing cholesterol. Ordinarily Polly baked fruit crisps for parties, and bought store cakes only when Randall was at a conference, out of town. However, Randall did not follow up his concerns about the deli desserts. With his special pencil he checked items off his list. Wine. Coffee maker. They'd never yet run out of anything, but this was Randall's way of participating in the preparation. Napkins. Wine glasses. Dish soap. When people thanked him and Polly for the lovely party, Randall smiled his closemouthed stretched smile and said, "I'm glad you came," somehow taking at least part of the credit. Flowers. Mineral water. Randall looked at her over the rims of his glasses to make sure she was checking her list too.

On the morning following the party, Polly woke up exhausted. Immediately after their reception, several of the junior people, some of them distinctly older than Randall, had invited him and Polly out for a drink. Polly couldn't refuse. They had got home rather late, and together cleaned up from the party, murmuring sentence fragments to each other. "Big chair." "Tablecloth." "McGuire's jacket." "Outrageous." "Flowers?" "Margaret's boyfriend." "Couldn't be over 20." "Saran wrap." Then, Randall had mysteriously elected to sleep with her in the big bedroom upstairs instead of in his cottage. When she realized his intention, she swept clothes off chairs and quickly straightened objects on bureaus. She put a new cake of soap in the bathroom and threw the slivers away. Her books, shoes, dirty underwear, clean underwear, all the heaps on the floor, got kicked into her closet. With a swoop she made the bed. There was no time for clean sheets.

In the morning she left the neat, compact lump of Randall still asleep, and went downstairs in her black silk kimono to make coffee. It was Sunday, her easy day, but she was groggy, her shoulders and neck were stiff, her eyes were slits, and from inside she felt frown lines in her forehead. She had been unable to respond to Randall, whose sexual ardor seemed to her more calculating, more attentive than it had before. What was he looking for? Did he find it? What did it mean? She brushed her teeth in the downstairs bathroom and put handful after handful of cold water on her face. When her coffee was filtered, she drank it standing up and began to feel a little better. As she put a slice of leftover quiche into the microwave, her tall son Theo came down the stairs.

"Yo, Poll," he said. He kissed his mom on her jawbone. "Any more coffee? We still on for this afternoon?"

"This afternoon?"

"Stanford reception, remember? You wrote it in your book."

"Reception, of course. For incoming Stanford freshmen and their moms. *Parents*. Of course."

"Hey, if you'd rather not go—It's not, strictly speaking, necessary. Just a lot of propaganda about how great the school is and how lucky we are to go there—Probably eat some boring cheese with really weird foreign crackers. You know."

"I wouldn't miss it." Theo would be gone next year, and then, in a couple of years, Mikie. And then what? Could she revive her old bead business? Maybe she could set herself up as a caterer and hostess so that single faculty members could entertain as expertly and graciously as Randall. There might be money in that if she could ever organize it. It seemed like a brilliant idea to housekeep on a freelance basis as she now did on an indentured basis for Randall. She slowly tried to pursue this new and grownup line of thought but more engrossing images took its place.

Before I pushed him down the stairs I put ground glass in the biscotti dough. I chose biscottis because they're naturally crunchy. On reflection, I also cooked up some walnut brittle, and threw half a cup of ground glass in there, too. He ate three biscottis over a period of two days. They didn't seem to bother him. That's when I pushed him down the stairs.

Mikie entered the kitchen, scrambled four eggs, and ate them while telling Polly in detail the plot and special effects of Alien which, she forbore to remind him, she herself had seen. Car horns honked and both boys left. As she rinsed the last dish Randall came in. He was carrying his desk calendar and his special pencil.

"Good morning!" Polly said, her mood greatly improved.

"Let's do some scheduling," Randall said. He wasn't meeting her eye. She sat with her calendar in front of her, poised to make lists. "I'm going to Chicago next week." What this meant for Polly was a vacation. When Randall was out of town there were no receptions to prepare or attend. She could cook meat, and let the errands slide. She didn't have to pick up *The New York Times*. She wrote down Randall's instructions for hours, it seemed, until he had to leave for a meeting.

Later that afternoon Polly, back from the Stanford reception, sat with another Stanford mother drinking tea and discussing S.A.T. scores. Randall walked through with his brisk angry walk, and she forgot to introduce him. She felt a moment of extreme disorientation when she realized what she had done. The other mom did not seem to notice, and left without commenting in any way on Randall's existence. Polly, slightly frightened, began to wash up the teacups. She heard Randall returning to the house, and then, louder than his footsteps, the music of Galen Doom over Theo's stereo.

Randall entered the kitchen. "Polly," he said, "we've got to talk." Polly could think of nothing to talk about. "Polly, I really believe we can work this out."

"Work what out? What are you talking about? What do you mean?"

He came into the kitchen while I was washing the teacups, Polly thought as she listened to the agonized cries of Galen Doom coming through Theo's door. The pounding of the surf was actually soothing, in a way. She could see why the kids liked it. He spoke to me. Polly, he said, we have to talk. Did you write down the Dean's Dinner for Saturday in your calendar? Did you write it down, Polly? I wiped my hands on a paper towel. In the pocket of my apron was the gun. I took it out and cocked it in the way I'd learned at the police department class. I pointed it at him and held it steady with both hands. Randall was still looking in his calendar, holding his special pencil, when I shot him. He dropped the calendar, which fell onto the counter and slid into the sink, but continued to hold his pencil in his hand. He looked at me impassively as he fell to the floor. His glasses slipped from one ear. He jabbed or gestured with the pencil and then dropped it and I knew he was dead. Then I had to get rid of the body. Later I cut my hair off short. After an appropriate interval I got all of Randall's money, and the boys and I just went on with our lives.

Polly smiled at Randall as he went on talking, telling her what he wanted her to know.

The Last Mr. Wrong

Sherrie Tucker

I wasn't looking for Mr. Wrong when I walked into his used books and records store. I was looking for a clean copy of Johnny Smith's *Man With a Blue Guitar*. But men, right or wrong, are most often found when you are not looking for them.

So there I was, innocently flipping through the jazz "S" section, when I felt his hot, dangerous eyes on my back. Without even looking up, I knew he was the next Mr. Wrong. He would be the Mr. Wrong to follow the drunken, bongo-crazed Mr. Wrong who called me a "zero" and lusted after local teenagers, who in turn had followed the reality-impaired Mr. Wrong who thought he loved me while simultaneously thinking I was somebody else. What I didn't know, was that this Mr. Wrong would turn out to be the last Mr. Wrong, the Mr. Wrong to spoil me for all future Mr. Wrongs, the Mr. Wrong who would change my standards to—well, not Mr. Right, actually—but to Mr. Years-Of-Therapy.

"Wanna go to a movie or something?" asked Mr. Wrong. I turned to see him towering over me, a gaunt, trembling, hungry-looking New Yorker with hair that looked like it had been cut by a lawn mower or prison warden. His eyes looked straight over me so that all I saw was their pulsating, vein-streaked whites. At the time, he was my type.

"Okay," I said.

"Good," he said. "I would have asked earlier, but I'm shy."

If he had asked any earlier, I wouldn't have even been there.

Not only was the last Mr. Wrong far from shy, but he was big trouble. Right off the bat, he told me about an intravenous drug habit which made him moody and erratic. I accepted the news with the glaze of politeness so common in early dates. Although I am an organic vegetarian who believes chemicals are unhealthy, I secretly found his drug-induced unpredictability extremely attractive. The suspense of whether Mr. Wrong would be happy to see me or whether he would cruelly rip into my personality with criticism and loathing carried a sick thrill I couldn't resist.

If Mr. Wrong had been a household appliance, he would have been a potato peeler. Somehow, I fell under his spell and cooperated as his complimentary vegetable.

"I hate your gestures and inflections," he said, leering at me one day when I dropped by to visit him at the store. "They annoy me. I often want to strangle you."

I stayed away for several days, trying to rid myself of my annoying habits. I studied myself in the mirror and, because I didn't have a clue which particular gestures he despised, I tried to lose them all.

The next time I saw him he said, "Why don't you ever visit me in the store?"

I said I would drop by. I used no inflection in my voice.

We continued to see each other and despite my efforts to improve my personality, his criticisms of me snowballed. I learned that I was "too nice," "too phony," "too aloof," "too shy," and "too gentle."

"You are too critical of me!" I sobbed one dark night at the far end of his couch.

"I know," he answered, matter-of-factly. "I'm a son-of-a-bitch."

I couldn't argue with him there. He was cruel and impossible by his own admission. And I was hooked. I couldn't wait to hear what else was wrong with me.

Had Mr. Wrong been a vegetable, he would have been a toadstool. As household utensil, I would have been a ladle scooping up big second and third helpings of toxic soup.

One day, Mr. Wrong told me my voice was "too mellifluous." I cried and promised I would try to change. He suggested we take some time off to think about, and then have a serious discussion on, our differences.

I thought about our differences. They excited me. I imagined our life together: him as the severe taskmaster, me as the end product of his teaching, world-weary but sultry, a truly mesmerizing lover. I imagined him through the years, smoking the characteristic Pall Malls after our hot, erotic episodes in Parisian pensions, our naughty antics on off-season Spanish beaches. I looked up the word "mellifluous" and dialed his number.

"I'm calling for dialogue," I said in a tough monotone. It's a wonder he knew who it was.

When he arrived, I was already pacing with a shot of Scotch in my fist. I was not nice, not shy, not gentle and *certainly* not mellifluous. The drink in my hand would prevent gestures. My husky new way of speaking would prevent inflections.

"I've decided it won't work," said Mr. Wrong.

"And why not?" I demanded. I was prepared. My response was cool, but firm.

"You're too . . . too—" He paused. I chugged my drink into the back of my throat, confident that I had finally become his perfect match. "You're too West Coast," he said.

"I'm too what?" I cried.

"I can't explain it," he said. "It's a sensibility I can't stand. You're too West Coast and it annoys me. I'd better go."

He was gone before I could think of a witty retort like, "West Coast? You mean like Chet Baker? And who do you think you are—Miles Davis?" or "We are an important experiment in cross-cultural relations. We owe it to our coasts to continue this study." Over the next few days, I thought of other reactions I could have had, including rational responses like "If the West Coast annoys you, why have you lived here fifteen years?"

Then I crumbled and asked my friends if *they* thought I was too West Coast.

"Dump that guy," they said.

But I couldn't dump him; he was everything I had ever hoped for in a man: moody, critical, impossible to please. With self-esteem like mine, you can't fall for someone who thinks you're great all the time. You can have nothing in common with those people. What you look for is someone who hates you most of the time and then, when you least expect it, jumps you while you're loading the dishwasher. It's the excitement of thinking you blew it with too much cilantro in the salad or stupid jokes at dinner and suddenly he's pulling at your jeans, shoving it in from behind and slapping your hips, going, "Fuck me, baby, dance with me, squeeze it, suck it, fuck me all up . . . ." Then your naked breasts press start the wash cycle and he's shooting like a fire hose and you didn't even think you were pretty that night.

And the next time? You'd just never know. I might annoy him with a gesture or nuance, in which case he'd either glare at me with such hatred it would heat the building or, worse, he'd leave and I'd go crazy with self-recriminations and wanting. The main thing was he would never always like me—something I had always found a major turn-off. In this respect, he was perfect. A veritable master of suspense.

But he dumped me. I could tell I was being dumped because he turned bland and friendly, even losing interest in pointing out my flaws when we bumped into each other on the street. He acted weird, smiling a lot and asking how I was. Finally, I accepted the truth. Mr. Wrong didn't want me. Period. He had tried to give me reasons, but there was nothing I could change to make myself his match. I was his Ms. Wrong. I wrote him a teary manifesto telling him that although I still desired him, I'd decided to leave him alone. I told him that he had lost a very good customer.

And so I began the painful cooling-out period in which I made a silent vow to avoid the four-block radius of Mr. Wrong's used books and records store. My detours were laborious and planned hours in advance. A trip to the grocery store which was once a pleasant jaunt through the neighborhood became a strenuous hilly hike with a couple of weedy side streets and a chaotic convenience store parking lot. Once, with a full double bag of groceries in my arms, I felt angry that I had become a fugitive on my own turf and walked dangerously near the store. My bags broke and goods rattled and rolled all over the sidewalk. Tears formed behind my bad-ass shades and I scrambled around, feeling pathetic and stupid. I was still excited by Mr. Wrong, even in his absence. I would remain excited until someone even worse came along to take his place.

That's when it occurred to me to quit. Snap out of it, as my mother would say. Wake up and smell the coffee, in the words of Ann Landers (or is it Abby?). I began seeing a therapist and turned into one of those people who thinks everyone should be taken apart and rebuilt. When men asked me out, I now replied with a question of my own, "How many years of therapy have you had?" It seemed to me that a desire to work on one's own problems is a good quality in a companion. This may not rule out the Mr. Nothing-in-Commons, the Mr. Borings, or the Mr. Close-but-Not-Quites, but it did effectively prevent further relationships with Mr. Wrongs.

I feel safe in saying now that the last Mr. Wrong was the final Mr. Wrong, not just the most current in a continuing series. Which is not to say that when dining with a man who is a good listener, who knows what he wants, and who is sensitive to my feelings, I do not yearn to be with the man across the room who is throwing his drink at his date.

It only means that my sweater is dry. Which is a start.

17 Reasons Why You Should Never See Him Again

Barbara Louise Ungar

1. You can't trust him.
2. AIDS
3. He's incapable of love.
4. His dick has a mind of its own, and it's an evil genius.
5. He makes you come seven times, and then talks about other women.
6. He's already repeating his stories.
7. Right after the first time, he told you you could lose some weight.
8. You like his girlfriend more than you like him.
9. All the horror stories she tells you about him you know are true.
10. Sooner or later she'll find out and hate your guts.
11. He says things like: Who would you rather be, the one I was making love to when I said the wrong name, or the one I was thinking of but not making love to? You say, I'd rather be you.
12. You quit playing second violin in Jr. Orchestra.
13. Sex is his junk, and he's a pusher, and he's the monkey on your back, and you're not an addictive personality. Repeat: you are *not* an addictive personality.
14. He says, you're never safe when I'm around.
15. He should be castrated.
16. He's the best lay, but he doesn't know the first thing about making love.
17. You think you can change him.

Wanda the Rug Woman Catches Her Freedom Bus

Vicky Phillips

He is leaning every which way in my kitchen door, his fat hands slapped around his thick old neck and his big brown eyes going bug-a-boo bug-a-boo like maybe if he does not do something and quick his angry old head is going to pop off and roll a bloody path right across my clean kitchen floor.

I am standing at the stove stirring his lunch soup and not looking right at him either though I see him all right, right there in the very corner of my eye. I see him and the way he is looking at me and this makes that voice inside my head start to screaming, "Oh boy, Wanda, time for you to be getting your sorry old ass out of here!"

His looking and acting like that means only one thing and I surely ought to know about that by now. It means he is still as mad as the crazies at me. It means some ugly part of him would like to run across my kitchen and beat me silly or smash me up the side of my head. Every since he got back from that prison he has been hoping to beat me good one more time, just like he used to all the time.

But maybe Wanda is too smart now for the likes of him cause I am not getting beat again this time around. No more beating for me cause I done decided this before he ever got his prison walking papers and came on back promising he was going to be a good man like I have always wanted if only I would take him back like nothing bad ever happened between us or with him even, like when he got sent off to prison for robbing that store and beating that old man to death in the first place. The beating was an accident, he says, like I am supposed to believe that and keep right on loving him, like that is God's only truth or something.

"Soup's done, honey," I call out loud like I don't know he is standing right there in my door getting as mad as ever at me and for no reason at all just like always. I drop my spoon into the kettle and slide along the wall dancing and fading backward like a quick little shadow when the sun slips away in the winter and everything goes black SNAP! SNAP! just like that. When my hip-bone hits that screen door I ease on out. I ease on out and wipe my hands on my britches as I slide along the back stairs and on out into my own backyard. "Soup's all ready!" I holler at him. "Be back later, honey. I am going to the grocery now for your supper!"

I run lickety-split like I run real-real fast with my feet and with my hands. I am pumping my elbows like bird wings to get across that yard real fast. "Run, Wanda, run!" screams some part of my good brain as it pants inside my head trying to keep up with me and give me some common sense encouragement. "Get out of here for a while till he cools off again!"

I pump myself up and run all the way to the corner bus stop where I sit on the curb and look over my shoulder. He is not there cause I know he is eating his hot lunch soup in my kitchen. Sometimes he follows me across the back-yard dragging his one bad leg in circles with his giant hands. He drags that bum leg like it is a special club he has been saving to beat me, but he is not following me this day cause he is too busy eating my good soup instead so I relax and suck some cloudy daylight into my aching lungs. This is one day Wanda the rug woman ran off so fast that he sure never got a chance to beat her good.

"Where are you off to now, Wanda?" That is my good brain asking me what we might be up to now and where in the dickens we are going for real cause it knows we are not going to the grocery store cause we do not need nothing like that at all. "I guess we had better go for a bus ride," I tell my good brain. "Go on for a bus ride till he cools off, so you climb onto the first bus that pulls up and you be quick about it!"

My legs climb inside the number 43 bus and I take a seat up front behind the driver cause I really like riding up front where the whole world comes smashing at my eyes through that big front window. World all curved and shiny. World goes bouncing like a crazy blue snake all around my eyes. Watching the neighborhood go by like this makes me feel good inside behind my belly button. Makes me feel little-girl-good like I have got no problems when I go riding that old number 43 up and down my neighborhood just like I did all the time twenty years ago when I was still my momma's baby. Just like I did before I ever did meet the likes of him.

I ride the number 43 up and down Bryant Avenue. See people going out shopping. See people going out to find a job. See people going out to visit other good people and this makes me think about my friend Felicity and how I have not seen her like forever or at least since she got back from Santa Rita, the women's jail up north. Maybe I think I should be seeing her again and finding out how she is doing now that she is back home making it on her own again. Thinking like this makes me pull the stop cord on that bus and then I get off at the new Windlewood project apartments where Felicity is staying now till the rehab people get her a permanent place over at the Washington Square.

I walk through the playground where all the tiny little kids are screaming and squalling cause they are hanging upside down and sideways from those red and orange pipes the new woman mayor put up so those kids would have someplace to play besides the tar roof, where they like to play a lot but always go falling off and getting hurt bad or killed all the way. Little bitty kids hanging ever which way and upside down so their eyes go bug-a-boo bug-a-boo like their brains about to pop out their ears and their hair hanging down like parade flags flapping from their pointed heads. I like them kids. They look so funny they make me feel like maybe the world is not so bad after all. I wave at them little bitty kids and they wave at me. They flap their little hands like seals I seen once at the zoo so I flap my big hands right back so they know I am meaning to be friendly with them.

I go on over to Felicity's door and wad up my hand and knock so hard it hurts my knuckles. "Felicity!" I call. "Open up! It's Wanda looking for good company." When nobody comes to the door I wad up both hands and beat at it some more thinking maybe Felicity is there but asleep like she is sometimes an awful lot cause she sleeps whenever she likes. Felicity loves her sleep and I know this about her since we started being friends a long time ago.

Then the door opens a crack like maybe about as big as the side of my finger. I see gold chains shining in that crack and I see one little green eye rolling between them gold chains like it popped out from somebody's head and got stuck up in them chains so now it must roll up and down between them chains all day long. I know this is not Felicity's eye cause I know her eyes and they are big and blue like rain puddles trapped up inside a pretty pink china saucer. Felicity has movie star eyes, no doubt about it, just ask anyone.

"Felicity ain't here," the green eye says while it rolls around and around taking a good look at all of me.

"Well," I say. "Well, I am Wanda from the old neighborhood. Felicity and I are friends so can you tell me when she is maybe coming back here so maybe I can see if I should wait for her to come on back or just go on back to my place across town? Maybe you could tell me that?" I ask trying to sound nice like I am most of the time with people I don't know all that well and I don't think I know this green eye at all.

"Wait a minute then," that green eye says. "I can let you in if I can get all the chains tore off this damn door. Damn chains will not let anybody go in or go out. Felicity got all these damn chains I got to deal with everytime somebody like you comes looking for her." Green eye says this like she is tired as everything and would rather knock down that door than have to look at it again.

After a bit the door swings open like I should walk on in so I walk on in but have to blink a bit before I can really see where my feet are taking me and then I can all of a sudden see a body that maybe goes with that green eye. "Nice to see you," I say to that body with the green eyes and I say it meaning it too cause now I see a skinny young woman right there in front of me and she looks friendly enough to speak with a bit.

"Hi," green eye says to me. She says I can call her Tommy cause even though that is not her real name that is the name she likes well enough to ask people if they would please call her that anyway. I say okay by me whatever she wants to be called. I will call her whatever she likes since what she gets called ought to be up to her anyway. No one should be stuck with their baby name if it does not suit them is what I tell her, and she really agrees with that.

Tommy steps back in the room which is dark as dark can get and starts motioning for me to have a seat somewhere as she scoops up magazines from the sofa and throws them onto the floor like she's too tired to stop and stack them up nice and neat. The magazines fly open all over the floor like they are paper birds getting spooked and maybe even getting their heads knocked off to boot. "Sit down," Tommy tells me. "Felicity ain't here right now. She went out to get us some smokes."

I say okay I will have a seat for just awhile. I plop down in Felicity's big red chair the one that has those cute little white lace things pinned onto the arms. Felicity's place is always like this cause she likes lace things stuck around the house wherever there is room. Felicity loves pretty things and this is something I have always admired about her the way she decorates her house so nice. I tell Tommy the place is looking good and I hope this means Felicity is doing good now that she is back from up north.

Tommy looks at me like maybe she's not sure how to start talking to me since she does not know me from the mailman. "Felicity expecting you?" she asks. I don't think so I tell her cause I was not really expecting myself. We both get a good laugh out of that one and this laughing makes Tommy ease up and smile a bit. When Tommy smiles I can see she has not got most of her teeth, with a couple missing right at the corner of her lips. I do not know this Tommy like I said but what I see makes me think maybe she is Felicity's new girl cause she is surely a lot like Felicity likes them, young and kind of boyish and all. Felicity likes them like this, says you have to get them real-real young if you want them sweet at all nowadays.

Tommy sits up and grinds her little fists into her thighs so maybe I think she is hurting for a cigarette. "Felicity is okay and doing good," Tommy lets me know. "She is off the stuff for good now so she can keep her head straight most of the time. She is in recovery good this time."

I tell Tommy I am sure glad to hear this cause I know how Felicity loves her stuff like the pills and the needles and all of it, and how that stuff may make the world pretty like Felicity says but it can make life awful ugly before you even have the time to see what has happened to you, and Tommy rolls her eyes and says ain't that the truth or something like that anyway.

Then Tommy starts fishing through a glass jelly jar on the table looking for cigarette butts that maybe can be smoked down a bit more and her tiny fingers look just like claws on a crab as they walk through all them butts pinching at any that feel long enough to draw up and smoke. "You smoke?" Tommy asks as she pulls a couple of bent butts up and lays them on the tabletop and starts ironing them out with the side of her little hand. "You can have one of these if you do and if you want."

No thanks I tell her cause I do not smoke, not that I have not tried it cause it looks nice the way some people flip around their cigarettes like they are magic swords or something special for their lips, but every time I ever tried I ended up in the toilet on my knees praying to the porcelain goddess which as you might know is another more polite name for the toilet.

Tommy is sucking on one of her butts her eyes all squinty cause I guess she cannot get it to draw worth a dang when Felicity comes bursting in the door like a wad of light and wind. Felicity comes in talking a mile a minute about why are the shades still down and why are the lights not on and why the you-know-what and #*@# is she slipping over all those slick magazines that are now spread out all over her floor.

Felicity is carrying a brown grocery bag up to her face so she cannot see me as she is hollering for Tommy to come and give her a hand. Tommy is up and hopping around like she means to give Felicity some help but before she can get a hold on that big paper bag Felicity has plopped down on the sofa and is pawing through the bag till she gets hold of a pack of cigarettes and has them ripped open and is sucking on one of them while she is frisking herself for a light of any kind. Tommy is right at her in a flash with a match struck up so Felicity bends down and takes the light from Tommy with a nod and a thank you honey.

Felicity does not see me till she looks up from her smoke and shakes the long blonde hair away from her eyes then she jumps up and runs over to me and gives me a peck on each cheek and says Lord she hasn't seen me in such a long time and isn't it nice that I stopped by for a visit and how am I anyway? Felicity is all over me like water gushing and she sure is excited that I have dropped in to pay my respects for just a little while.

Felicity takes my hand and squeezes it a good bit as she steps back and eyes me up and down. Then she laughs and tells me I have not changed not one little bit. I tell her ain't that the truth, oh ain't it though? Then Felicity winks at me and points over at Tommy and says, "You met my new girl? You met my little Tommy? She nice to you? She behave all right while I was out and you were coming in to see me?" I say Tommy was as nice as anybody could be since she never met me before and could have just told me to go away cause she did not want to be bothered entertaining somebody she did not know at all.

Tommy is standing up between me and Felicity and is all smiles now as she is leaning every which way with the grocery bag sagging in her arms and a cigarette in her mouth and she is leaning down to kiss Felicity a big one right on the lips.

Felicity takes the cigarette out of Tommy's mouth and kisses Tommy right back hard with her tongue cause I can see this all right from where I am sitting so now I know I was right this is Felicity's new girl and every bit as nice as the last one she had living with her. When they are done kissing Felicity slides me a look and smacks her lips in the air which tells me she liked Tommy's big kiss a whole lot. Then she tells Tommy we are all thirsty women so how about Tommy pulling some beer out of that grocery bag and passing it around so we do not feel like we have got the dry mouth and there is nothing to be done about it.

I take a beer from Tommy and say thanks a lot and pop it open and swallow a big fist of bubbles and wetness. Ah it tastes so good like maybe I am swimming in the bathtub with my mouth open and it is rushing all the way through me like I am some kind of big-mouthed sea creature.

Felicity smiles when she sees me smile and raises her can of beer like maybe she wants to make a toast and she says, "Wanda you are looking so good. Are you feeling as good as you look?"

I tell her that things are good and getting better since he came back from jail where he was most of the last few months anyway.

"Just like me," laughs Felicity.

"Yeah," I say. "The very same." Except I explain that he went up for robbing these video stores with this smart-butt guy named Jimmie Johnson who I told him was no good to be hanging around with at all. But of course he would not listen to me, would rather have died than listened to any words I had for him, so that all he could say to me was you shut up Wanda cause you are always ruining chances for me and this thing with Jimmie is my one big chance, the one big chance you are sure as hell not taking away from me this time. I explained to Felicity how he and Jimmie went to these stores and memorized the lock make and numbers they were using to screw down the display models and then how they came back later in store uniforms and picked these locks and carried off all the display models just like they were store employees and that was what they were paid to do.

Felicity and Tommy shake their heads. Felicity asks me how long those Einsteins—Einsteins that is her word for them—got away with that kind of stuff and I tell her about two months and they would have been okay but they got the greed and started thinking they were invisible or something. That was when they got caught leaving a store and he had to pull out one of those videos and hit this old man over the head with it and he told me he only tapped him once or twice but that is not what all the lawyers said in court. They said he hit that old man maybe twenty times like maybe he went crazy and kept hitting him even though that old man was dead maybe the second or third blow.

Felicity shakes her head and points at me with a cigarette she is about to light with this table lighter which is shaped like a dragon made so that fire comes out his nose if you flick his tail just so-so. Felicity tells me that she hopes this teaches me that I do not need to be staying around with the likes of him that I do not need to be standing in line waiting for his hand to accidentally slip and smash my head to pieces too.

Tommy sits up and rolls her wet beer can back and forth, back and forth between her palms. She stares at her beer can. Then she stares at me. Then she stares at that can. Then still looking at the lip of that can she says something like, "You mean to tell me you let him beat you?"

Now I do feel like a fool all ashamed because I know Tommy does not know me or him and I do not want her thinking that he is all that bad so I explain to her that he has never ever meant to hurt me, that he just cannot control his own hands sometimes and that besides he has stopped all that once and for all and all I have to do is help him by getting away for a while if I see him getting too upset by something.

Like I did today for example.

Tommy looks at me. Then Felicity. Then me all over again. Her face twists up like maybe she would like to spit on something like maybe even me. Tommy makes a fist with one hand and strikes it down in her own palm so that a big SMACK! pops out all of a sudden and almost scares us all to death. Tommy says, "Hit him back. You need to hit him back."

This thing that Tommy is doing—SMACK! SMACK! she does it a few more times—scares me a little so I have to take a swallow of my beer to wash down this little knot of stuff which has somehow got stuck in my throat just behind my Adam's apple.

Felicity is looking at Tommy and shaking her head like Tommy has got it all wrong all right. Felicity starts talking to Tommy leaning over close to her and touching her little shoulder as she tells her that the world does not work that way when it comes to this kind of stuff. Felicity explains that if I was to start hitting on him then maybe we would just kill each other and that is about all we could expect to happen if we both start in on each other. And I agree with Felicity that these things happen in life and that Felicity knows about this and how these things have got to be handled real delicate or else.

Tommy sits up real-real straight and takes a cigarette in her hand and starts to play with it by poking it in and out of an "O" she has made with her thumb and forefinger. "The world works just how you make it work," Tommy says at last. "The nicer she is to him, helping him and all, the meaner he is going to get till one day she wakes up and discovers that she is long dead. She had better kill him first, that is the choice she has now if she is not about to leave him. Her choice is she can kill him up front or wait for him to kill her."

"Tommy, oh honey," says Felicity. "You are too young to know about this kind of stuff." Felicity turns to me and says, "She is too young to know this stuff at all so never mind her crazy ideas on stuff she does not know much about at all."

But Tommy is not happy with this polite way that Felicity has of telling her to shut up and mind her own business and she tells us so right out by jumping up between us and knocking her beer across the table so the can spins like a top and beer foams out like the can is spitting at us all.

Felicity is up and waving her hands and reaching out for Tommy with one hand and reaching out to grab the can and stop it from spinning with the other. "Honey," she is calling a lot over and over again. "Settle down," she adds at last like maybe this will be something Tommy can hear.

But Tommy is not happy and not about to shut up, not at all. "I am young! I am young!" she keeps yelling, "but I am not ignorant not at all ignorant like this woman who is going to get herself killed because by not saying a word or fighting back she is as good as acting dead for him and everyone. She is digging her own grave, digging her own grave, digging her own grave, digging it deep and somebody should be telling her this because it is the honest truth, pure and plain."

I can see that Felicity is not happy at all with Tommy acting like this and not listening to her or me or anything. Felicity is trying to keep her voice calm like you hear mothers doing all the time when their kids are screaming and screaming and screaming, like they will surely die that very instant if somebody does not give them some kind of relief. Felicity stays calm like a mother as she tells Tommy she has got to stop acting like that in front of company cause it is not polite to act like she is acting, even if you are acting like that in front of your own flesh and blood.

I would like to drink some more beer, like maybe five or six more all at once, cause that thing is back in my throat, and now I see that I have just upset everything with Tommy and Felicity like they really needed me and my problems landing at their front door. Something is hurting in my head like maybe there are a lot of needles sticking through my eyes and I think I had better get on back to my place cause it must be past supper time and I need to be there if he gets hungry or else I don't know or else what but I feel like I had better be going cause all I have done with Felicity and Tommy is make trouble.

So I stand up and say I have really got to be going now that it is getting dark outside or else he will not have any supper and how I enjoyed talking with them and thanks so much for the beer and could they maybe come over next week some time that was good for the both of them?

I am going for their door but I think I am going too slow cause it seems like I am walking under water and that my feet are heavy like someone stole them and stuck flat wide rocks at the ends of my legs instead. I do not seem to be getting to their door all that fast if you can imagine what I am talking about.

Felicity is helping me, I know cause I can feel her hand on my arm and I can tell that she is saying things to me like okay then Wanda, and that would be nice, and it was surely good as everything seeing you again, and she would call me about when she could come over, and then maybe we could catch up on all the gossip, and that I should be careful on the bus ride home cause there is so much crime everywhere nowadays.

I say something I do not remember now, maybe something like okay and sure and see you two next week, good-bye now.

When I step off the bus the air is dark—dark and cool as anything, maybe even cool like the way my momma kissed the inside of my wet knees after a bath when I was very little, like just a baby. Sometimes I remember things like this, just feelings from when I was too small to really remember the whole parts of my life. Outside everything is quiet like sleep. Quiet like I used to be when I was Wanda the rug woman busy getting my head beat all over the house and trying real hard to be real quiet, quiet as a mouse, so the neighbors would not get disturbed by my domestic problems.

My house is quiet with no lights at all but the blue flicker-flash from his tv which makes a blue flashing in the picture window like maybe a nuclear bomb keeps going off deep inside my own little house. He is surely in there watching tv. I know I am late for supper and he is very very hungry, so I creep just like an old dog in the back kitchen door cause I am glad he is asleep at the tv and I surely do not want to wake him up just in case his bad mood has not really passed like I have been hoping it would.

I feel around in the kitchen like a blind woman till my hands find the iron skillet which is his very favorite iron skillet and cooking piece. "Cook me everything in that skillet," he is always saying to me. "Cook me my eggs in that iron piece cause nothing ever tastes as good to me as iron cooked eggs."

And he is with his tv all right. He is sleeping all curled on his side in front of that tv so he looks like a big naked animal sleeping there in his puckered red undershorts. He has one long fat arm slung over his head and he has got tv light dribbling all over his entire body.

I am standing very nicely right on top of him almost and looking down at him and wondering who he is to me and thinking how awful heavy his skillet feels in my hand, heavy like I should lay it down and maybe go rest on our bed for just a while. Then something makes me take that skillet and raise it to my forehead with both hands, like maybe I will pray a bit before I put that skillet down and go to our bed to take a little rest. I squat on my knees with my legs bunched up under my ass and I lift that skillet till my breasts are all tight with muscles I do not even know how to use anymore.

I am standing like this wondering what in the hell am I going to do now, cause somehow it does not feel like prayer I am about. I am standing like this when he moves his arm and his one eye rolls up and he blinks to let me know yeah he surely does see me standing there. He is up like a light. "What are you doing up there?" he asks. "What is it?"

I think about his question but as I do not have an answer I just lower the skillet. "I am fixing your dinner," I say. "You want barbecue chicken or not?"

He looks at me like maybe he does not know about me or dinner or maybe anything at all, but then he shrugs and falls to the floor on his butt. He loops his arms around his knees. "You are very late," he says. "Where have you been all day old woman?"

"I have been out," I say. "I would have thought that was obvious to everyone, so you want chicken or not?"

"Fix it," he says as he flops backward and starts again to watch tv.

I go into the kitchen and plop his dinner chicken into the sink and start washing it real good, washing it real good till I feel my fingers getting all bloody. I am pulling back the pimply fat cause that is the only way to get all the old blood washed out when I see him right in front of me like in a movie and I see his lips working over that chicken sucking down that fat and then I feel like I have a good idea coming on in my head.

I go over to the stove and get on my knees and poke my hand behind the stove and feel everything that is back there including the stove cord which is gritty with dust and grease. Then I feel what I am poking after. It sticks in my hand like needles and it hurts cause it is glass, all broken, the glass of the beer bottle he threw at me right after breakfast when he was not feeling so well cause the neighbors got up earlier than usual and woke him up slamming doors when they were going out to get in their car and drive away to work.

When I felt that glass I wet my hand, licking it all over in the palm and at the fingertips too. My hand tasted like chicken blood which was not bad at all but kind of nice cause it was real salty. It was salty and it made my lips pucker. Then I stuck my hand in that glass and rolled it back and forth and all around till I had all the good pieces of glass sticking to me just like flour does to bloody chicken parts. When I had a shiny handful of glass I got up and went over to his chicken which I was going to barbecue and rubbed that glass deep inside them fat pieces. I did the whole chicken like that while he was either sleeping or watching tv, maybe both cause that is how he likes it after dark.

While I was fixing that chicken for him I was getting happy, very much so indeed. My mind was making a movie or something like that cause I was not thinking but I was seeing everything that would happen next like my head was not my own but a video machine. In my movie he was there all right and he was real hungry, so hungry like always that he started sucking down that chicken fat and he did not stop till he had sucked down almost that whole little chicken, then he called to the kitchen for me to come on in with his dessert, but he never gets his dessert cause all of a sudden he does not really feel so good.

He thinks maybe he has heartburn from all that barbecue and from eating so fast that he never did taste all his food, so he thinks maybe it is just like he has heartburn again. He calls for old rug woman Wanda to come on out and help him feel better, maybe bring the Rolaids, the big bottle I keep in the kitchen cause he is always getting a bad stomach cause he eats like a stray dog all the time no matter how much I have told him to please slow down and taste his food.

But I am not in my kitchen now cause I am at the downtown bus station and I am clearly wearing my one good blue-flowered dress, the same one I used to wear to church when I went with Momma from time to time. I am feeling very proud thank you to be wearing that good dress and I am so happy I am talking sweet, maybe even flirting a decent bit to the bus ticket man who has been flirting with me ever since I stepped up and said I needed a ticket, the kind which would cost me a lot of money. In my movie, which sure seems real enough to me, I have got a ticket which I know will take me someplace very nice thank you, someplace pretty where he will surely be too dead to find me even if he wanted to, even in his dreams.

In my movie I am happy at the bus station and even more happy on that bus. When the bus is whining up to roll out and the driver is letting off the brakes so there is that shoo-shoo sound like a space rocket shimmering all through the dark I think maybe I can hear him call me to come and help him be as decent as I had said I would try to make him once he was done with the prison. But then I think I cannot really hear him any more cause the bus is too loud and Wanda the old rug woman who I used to be has lost her ears for him. I am just Wanda the woman now and that means I am like no one special to him or anyone at all and I am in my one good dress which I put on so I could ride this bus and feel happy, oh so happy cause all I will ever see from now on is the world dancing like a crazy blue snake all around my eyes.

The Future Tense

Whoever said love conquers all was a fool.
Because almost everything conquers love —
or tries to.
— Edna Ferber —

Every arrival foretells a leavetaking.
Yet each departure comes as a surprise,
a sorrow never anticipated.
Life is a long series of farewells;
only the circumstances should surprise us.
— Jessamyn West —

Death Spell for a Departing Lover

Kate Braverman

We are good at opening dialogue.
It's our specialty.
That and the goodbye scene
we could recite in our sleep.
It's the middle that defies us,
the substance, the ordinary progressions
that weave events into patterns,
textures, the three-dimensional.

No. You cannot read my letters.
You cannot take your eyes off
your reflection in the mirror,
your extravagant rhetoric
and unshakable conviction
that you will always look thirty-four,
that your charm will be indelible
and bankable, like an occupation.

You sense I know your secret name.
You fear I will say it out loud
and I will. Whore.
You who live from interchangeable beds,
feeling passion a pressure
you can't deliver,
tangled in ambivalence,
trying to make love
while adjusting your silk tie,
shining your Italian shoes
spare sports jacket in the back
of your broken car.

Your secret name is whore.
You are in love with your mother.
No woman is perfect enough,
as pretty as you or her.
Know this, whore.
I am your greatest mistake.
I will hate you as the seasons turn
in August heat and sudden storms
as you drive from one woman to another,
one slice of city view after another.
You will sense this following,
this uniquely fashioned arrow,
this intangible wound that will not heal.

I am the shadow on the corner
and a certain way the neon will scratch
one window after another,
relentless and haunting.
You will come to know it,
taste it, dream it.

Me, lit from the inside,
whispering your whore name
mixing my burned mouth
with the Santana winds,
becoming part of you and the landscape.
In the smog, in the mist
in the moonlight and jasmine
digging in under your skin
in a way you will never forget.

Her Michelangelo

Enid Shomer

Riva Stern was going to save Paul Auerbach. She was going to save him for college and law school and a house in the suburbs and three or four children. She would save him for the world, like bolstering Albert Schweitzer at a crucial point early in his career.

Paul was the poorest person Riva knew. He was poorer than the maid who had taken care of the Sterns for more than fifteen years. He was poorer, even, than Tante and Uncle, her old Russian relatives who still had a party line and lived in a black neighborhood. They spoke hatchet English, and their dingy little apartment always smelled of candle wax and boiled beef with carrots. Riva had never seen Tante in anything but a housecoat. Because of their age and piety, no one in the family took note of their poverty in a critical way. No one pointed to it as a sign of failure. They did not drive a car. They couldn't afford to go anywhere but the synagogue, and they received the hand-me-downs and charity of at least 25 family members with utter dignity. And Paul Auerbach was poorer even than that, though his poverty had the same sort of grace, a kind of storybook quality.

Paul had been working for his uncle at the wholesale produce market in downtown Washington since he was nine years old. He hawked fruits and vegetables from 4 a.m. to noon on Saturdays and on Wednesday mornings until it was time to go to school. Once, right after she got her license, Riva had driven there and from her car had watched the customers surge along the narrow streets and alleys lined with pushcarts and trucks. Haggard men in knit caps and shabby coats weighed and bagged tomatoes, celery, endive, calling out their bargains to passersby. Torn vegetables slicked the pavements and the gutters ran with the juices of the discards, the overripe, the accidentally dropped. Paul, wearing big leather gloves and a dirty white apron over several layers of old clothes, was carrying bushels of something heavy, his body moving with the fierce rhythms of concentration, his face red with effort and the cold. He hadn't seen her.

You couldn't tell Paul was poor. Until she began to date him, Riva thought he was shy or antisocial. He had a beat-up car, which, she found out later, he owned with his older brother who had already left home. Paul, in fact, spent most of his energy trying to look and act as middle-class as anyone else, even though his home life was a nightmare. Riva didn't mind having to buck him up. He was worth it. Because poverty was abstract to Riva, she had a bottomless faith in his ability to overcome it, and her faith was contagious. Also, she was good at talking people into things.

Now she sat in her mother's Buick in a downpour in front of the public library waiting for Paul. She had told her parents she'd be out until ten, studying for a Latin exam. On the phone, Paul had said something was wrong. He needed to see her. Riva loved being needed. She thought she would make a wonderful wife for some brilliant, successful man, like a physicist or a writer.

Through the sheeting rain, she made out his finned, grass-green Oldsmobile. She pulled up the hood of her raincoat and when Paul drove up alongside, darted from her car to his. Then she slid across the seat and kissed him on the cheek. "I don't know why I came," he said, "talking about it isn't going to change a thing."

"Let's go someplace."

He headed in the direction of Tacoma Park, to a back road that dead-ended under a train trestle. They often went there to neck. They had discovered it one Sunday in the fall when they took a hamper lunch to the park.

It had taken Riva months to get Paul to confide in her. He was deeply ashamed of his family. But now he trusted her completely in a way that he would probably never trust anyone again in his life. His need was that great.

The sky was a dull red above the glistening street lights as he maneuvered through traffic along Georgia Avenue. The rain made liquid jewels of the neon signs for Little Tavern hamburgers and Midas mufflers and Ramco Auto Upholstery. Riva had become more aware of her surroundings lately. She would be leaving for college in the fall, and she would probably never live here again, except for the summers. She and Paul planned to write to each other and spend vacations together. She liked thinking about that arrangement—Paul tucked away in her life, like a lucky coin you could keep in your pocket and never spend. Riva was a "brain," and Paul was the only boy at Hoover High School she had ever dated. Unlike most boys, he wasn't afraid to date a girl who made better grades than he did. Or maybe he figured that his grades would have matched hers if he had more time to spend on schoolwork.

Paul parked under the trestle, and they cracked their windows. It was the end of March, and they could smell the change of seasons in the sharp, damp air. Outside the car, the first green shoots worked their way up through a thick brown carpet of dead grass.

"I won't be going to San Antonio," he said. He linked his hands together and cracked his knuckles. Paul had won the school debating contest. The prize was $300 and the honor of representing the school at the National Polemics Competition.

"Oh no," Riva said. The story would be terrible; it would make her cry for Paul. The story would be about his disreputable father and his pathetic mother. She put her arms around him and laid her head on his shoulder and waited.

"He heard about the money. He said he had to pay these bills. He showed me a bill for three months' rent for the apartment."

"How did he find out?"

"What difference does it make?"

"Maybe he heard your mother telling somebody about the prize." As soon as Riva said it, she could see Mrs. Auerbach herself telling her husband about the money—being proud of Paul, not realizing what would happen next. "You have to go. You could win the $2,500 grand prize."

"I know."

"You've still got three weeks. Maybe your brother can help you out. Maybe you'll let me help you out—"

"No!" His eyes flashed. He punched the dashboard with his fist.

"Don't do that to yourself." Riva stroked his hand.

He forced a smile and combed through his hair with his fingers. "Right. New topic. You've got your big test tomorrow. Come on, let's conjugate a couple of verbs." He whispered it into her ear. "You're so luscious."

"God, you're sweet." She kissed his hand. "You could take the money out of your college savings."

Paul had a savings account at the bank that only Riva—not even his mother or brother—knew about. In three years he had managed to save $1,500 toward tuition at George Washington University.

"I can't do that. I'm already short for the first semester unless I can get a loan. I'm counting on getting a loan."

She stroked his sand-colored, slightly greasy hair that felt like silk in her fingers, like silk embroidery floss. She comforted him, and together they tried to figure a way for him to accumulate the money before the end of April. Then they necked, just a little, just to cheer him up. She unzipped his pants and drew circles around his cock with her fingers until he was hard, and then they kissed a little more, and then he drove her back to the library.

The next morning was a Friday, and Riva lay in bed before the alarm clock rang pondering Paul's problems. Paul had a secret that no one at school except Riva knew: he supported himself. Sometimes he had to help support his mother and father. This had been going on since he was fourteen. In the past, in addition to working at the farmer's market, Paul had held various part-time jobs, most of them in sales. He had sold Kirby vacuum cleaners and the Encyclopedia Judaica and men's monogrammed golfing shirts. He had demonstrated the Kirby for Riva and her mother one Sunday evening. Mrs. Stern had taken quite an interest in it until she realized that she didn't care what kind of vacuum she owned since the maid was the only one who used it. But she admired its engineering, she told Paul. In two months' time, he sold only one Kirby.

Riva had tried to lend him money, but he refused it. The most she could offer was a gift now and then—a sweater for his birthday, a shirt at Hanukkah. Paul loved clothes. He took fastidious care of his few things, ironing the shirts himself, keeping them folded in Saran wrap in his drawer. He was the only boy she knew who polished his shoes. He couldn't achieve the flashy look of the wealthier boys, but he bought quality. He watched the papers for sales. He chose conservative colors and styles that blended together. Almost nobody noticed him one way or the other. When Riva first talked about dating him, her friends had difficulty calling up the matching face: "Paul Auerbach? Who does he hang out with?" And Riva would patiently explain where he sat in Chemistry or World Lit and that he didn't have time for a real social life like other kids.

She could remember the exact moment she had noticed him. It was the third week of school, in Civics. She was in her assigned seat in the first row and he was standing right in front of her giving an oral report and the edge of her desk cut into his thighs. He was nervous and stuttered a little. His intense hazel eyes stared fixedly at the back of the room where Dr. Voski sat, grading him on completeness, accuracy, and presentation. For a moment, it looked like he was getting a hard-on from his nerves. That happened to some boys, Riva knew, but then he shifted his weight and the bulge disappeared. He dropped a note card on her desk toward the end, and when she handed it back to him, he had looked startled, as if he hadn't noticed her before. That night she had dreamed about him. It was one of those dreams that makes you fall in love, whether you want to or not. This had happened to Riva before. When she was twelve, she had dreamed about Tab Hunter after she saw him in a movie. She had a terrible crush on him after that. And in 8th grade she'd had a love dream about Eliot Finkelstein that rendered her mute for weeks in his presence. After her dream about Paul, she had talked to him in school the next day. What had been the pretext? She had sold him a ticket for the Latin Club's raffle, and then he had walked her to the cafeteria and asked her for a date.

"Riva! Riva diva!" Barry called out. "I'm leaving here in exactly five minutes." Barry was her 21-year old brother. He dropped her off at school every morning on the way to work.

Riva lunged from between the covers and reached for the day's clothes draped across a chair, a cerise wool skirt and matching sweater. "Be right down," she called back.

Paul was absent that day from school. During lunch she called his house. She had to be careful about phoning there. His father did not like Paul to receive calls from girls. His mother was more understanding. His mother,

Riva thought with a start, would not know how to push a rat away that was gnawing on her face.

"Why aren't you here?" Riva asked.

"He's left again. She's very upset."

"He left even though you gave him the money?"

"Yeah. Look," Paul whispered, "I can't talk now. Call me tonight. I love you."

"Tonight."

That night, after she and Paul talked, Riva wrote in her diary. She made a list of ways she could help him raise the money for San Antonio. She wrote down everything she could think of, as fast as she could write:

1. *Get the money somehow and make him let me lend it to him.*
2. *Give the money to the school (after I get it) and have them give it to him, compliments of "anonymous."*
3. *Give the money to his mother to give him. Swear her to secrecy.*
4. *TALK TO POP GOLDRING!!!*

She had been keeping a diary for nearly three years. When she entered high school, her mother had bought her a "Chums" desk set—a matching blotter, pencil holder, scrapbook and five-year diary in pink leather. Carefree teenagers resembling the "Archie" cartoon characters strolled along each piece, their books slung casually across their hips. The diary had lasted a little more than a year. Then Riva spilled over into a serious-looking lined notebook with a black and white marbleized cardboard cover. She kept the diary and the notebook hidden in her closet at the bottom of a tall Kotex box, along with the novel she had written in eighth grade. "Once Only" was the story of a fifteen-year old girl who fell in love with an alien from another galaxy. It was based loosely on her crush for Eliot Finkelstein.

Riva had devised a code for her diaries. She stashed the code-key in the pages of an old Honey Bunch mystery. *The blood the first two days this month was the color of crushed rubies . . . . I like the sickening feeling I get before my period comes—like when you eat too much chocolate and the stomachache reminds you of all that pleasure. Only this reminds me that I can bring a new human being into the world any time I want!* She would have died if anybody else read these passages. Especially Barry. Even though he was grown up, she still remembered the days when he unscrewed the heads of her dolls, put raw oysters in her bed, and shot food at her across restaurant tables. Barry had grown into his lanky body and turned out to be handsome, much to Riva's surprise. Now he was engaged to Olivia Wykowski, a beautiful redhead two years older than he. Riva's family believed in early marriage. Her sister, Fran, had married at 18 and so had her cousin Melissa. Whenever Riva saw distant relatives, they talked about living to dance at her wedding.

Olivia had the look of an airline stewardess—a permanent smile and perfect makeup, her hair sprayed into a stiff beehive. Riva couldn't stand her. Her diary was full of invective for PV (Olivia's code name, short for Professional Virgin) who, five years Riva's senior, treated her like a little mouse. Now that they were officially engaged, Barry and Olivia were planning to go to Atlantic City the last weekend in April. They talked about it all the time in front of her parents as if to forestall suspicion that they would Do Anything. Riva was sure Olivia hadn't done it. You could tell by looking in her eyes, Riva believed. She got up from her desk and studied her reflection. Anybody could see she was still untouched, even though Paul had been pressing his case hard since January. Riva hadn't worked out a philosophy to justify why she hadn't done it yet. It was just safer to say "No." She felt the same urges Paul did. Sometimes she nearly went crazy when they were fingerfucking. She had to remind herself that it wasn't just a technicality, the difference between a finger and the real thing.

Riva had a 4 o'clock appointment with Pop Goldring on Tuesday. As soon as school let out at 3, she took the streetcar and bus to Dupont Circle, stopping for a cherry Coke at the drugstore on the ground floor of his building so that she wouldn't be early.

Pop Goldring was prosperous. He had a construction company with his son, Mel, and had built many office and apartment buildings around the city. Mrs. Stern kept a scrapbook of clippings about her father and brother, who were periodically honored for their philanthropy. Pop Goldring had planted a lot of trees in Israel. He probably had a whole forest by now. But he wasn't generous just for the publicity or the tax deductions. Once, many years before, he had supported an American artist in Italy. Alongside the plaques and certificates in his office hung a huge painting by the man, the portrait of a family of jesters. They wore velvety red clothing and stocking caps with bells. They were traveling to their next court performance, the artist had explained. The father jester walked along, playing the flute. The mother and one child perched astride an ox. A mysterious winged infant balanced on the ox's rump, his back to the viewer. Behind them, fields, sky, and mountains flattened into shapeless daubs of bright blue, yellow, and orange. No one in the family knew what had happened to the artist—whether he kept on painting or was butchering meat somewhere for a living. Pop called the painting "my Michelangelo," and he thought it just as artistic as the bust of Moses by the other Michelangelo that sat on his desk.

The receptionist buzzed his office, and he promptly appeared in the reception area. He was a squat, heavyset man with light blue eyes and wisps of white hair around a large bald spot. His face was wide and Slavic-looking, with high cheekbones and a broad forehead. "Sweetheart," he said, giving her a big hug. He had a heavy Russian-Yiddish accent. Years later, Riva would melt whenever she heard that accent, even from the mouths of second-rate stand-up comics.

His office was uncluttered, outfitted with modern furniture that was sleek and low-slung like cats relaxing all around the room. Even the desk top was clear except for a few letters and an ashtray with a half-smoked cigar in it. His home was the opposite—it glittered with gilt tables, Victorian whatnots, and crystal decanters. Grandma Bella was constantly rearranging it like a gigantic still life. Only the den was livable. As a child, it was the only room Riva had been allowed in.

"How's my Einstein?" he asked.

"Everything's great. I came to ask you a favor."

His gaze intensified. Riva had never asked him for anything before.

"I have a good friend who needs money, and I want you to give it to him. I want you to buy him an airline ticket to San Antonio, Texas."

"You're asking for a complete stranger?"

"Actually, you met him during Christmas when he picked me up at your apartment. His name is Paul Auerbach."

Pop Goldring narrowed his eyes, trying to recall the boy. He shook his head. "I don't remember any Paul. What does his father do? He's a Jewish boy?"

"Yes. His father drives a cab."

"A taxi driver?"

"They're very poor. His mother can't work. She's an invalid. She got polio right after Paul was born. She has an awful limp and a bad lung."

"A shame," Pop said. "He's smart?"

Riva told him about the debate contest and how hard Paul had worked all his life. He listened attentively. "You love him? You're going to marry him?"

"I'm too young to marry anybody," Riva said. It was the one area where she and her grandfather would never see eye to eye. While he celebrated her triumphs at school, he would never really be relaxed about her future until she married.

"All right. I'll do it. Call Nancy with the details."

Riva jumped up and kissed him. "Thank you, thank you, thank you."

"He'll take charity, your Paul?"

"He doesn't know about it yet. I hope I can make him accept it. He'll probably want to repay you someday. He has a lot of pride."

"I hope so, if only for your sake."

"Pop? Can we keep this a secret? I don't want anybody else in the family to know. It might be embarrassing later."

Riva's family had memories like elephants, especially for foibles and mistakes. The only way you could live something down with them was to be reincarnated. If she did end up marrying Paul, it would be bad enough when her family learned how disreputable the Auerbachs were. That would be soon enough for them to begin doubting Paul. Riva was certain that Paul's noble character had survived and maybe even been honed by his terrible family, but she knew how adults saw these things. They wouldn't praise him for overcoming so many handicaps; they would wait for the day when the offspring reverted to type, when the ugly head of the parent reared up in the child.

Paul lived in a small apartment building in a neighborhood tucked between a Trailways bus terminal and a complex of warehouses. Tonight, when she arrived, Riva was relieved that Mr. Auerbach's cab wasn't anywhere in sight. The parking lot was brightly lit, but the stairs to the entrance were dark, and the hallway smelled rank. The Auerbachs lived on the ground floor. Their living room was full of black vinyl furniture and cheap pole lamps. Everything in it was ugly except for the afghans that Mrs. Auerbach crocheted and draped over the furniture.

If she had called first tonight, Paul would have wanted to meet her someplace. She wanted him to know she didn't care where he lived or who his father was. She wanted to tell him about Pop Goldring. She would tell his mother, too, if she felt like it. There would be nothing any of them could do to ruin it. The airline ticket was in Paul's name. Nancy, Pop's secretary, had reserved a room at the Gunter Hotel, and when Paul tried to settle the bill, he would find that it was already paid.

Paul was embarrassed at first to hear her news. Then he was very grateful. Afterward, he followed her home in his car. They told Mrs. Stern they were going to the Hot Shoppe for a snack. She and Paul went to the park.

"How can I ever pay you back? It worries me, Riva. Money between friends can lead to problems." He was carefully unbuttoning her blouse.

"What kind of problems?"

"I don't know exactly. I know my father hasn't got a friend left in the world, and they've all helped him."

"You're not your father."

He buried his head between her breasts, then rolled from one to the other, kissing. He had the softest lips of any human being alive and a tongue like a sweet little animal. "Oh God," he moaned, "I love you so much. You'll never know how much it means to have your love."

Before he went to San Antonio, Paul spent every spare minute beefing up his debate skills on the assigned topic: Should the U.S. Recognize Castro's Cuba? Three-by-five index cards accumulated in drifts on his desk in study hall. Paul would be called upon to argue both sides. That was the thing about being a good debater—you had to be able to fake the passion of your argument, and you had to know what the opposition was going to say. Paul would make a fine lawyer. His poverty gave him an appetite for justice in the world.

Things at home improved. His father had returned after a spree in Florida and was driving his cab every day. A couple of mornings he had slipped Paul a five spot at breakfast.

Paul left for Texas on a Thursday evening at the end of April. He called Riva twice. On Saturday, he sounded ecstatic. He praised Tex-Mex foods she had never heard of—sauces concocted of chocolate and hot peppers, cactus fruit and *cabrito* and tequila. He had gone to a nightclub where a Mexican mariachi band with huge guitars played until dawn. He cursed the afternoon tour-bus driver, and called one of his debate opponents a "pubic hair" in Spanish. He had made dozens of friends, he said, despite the pressures of the competition. Everyone was so friendly. He loved the Lone Star State. It was southern and western at the same time—the best of both worlds. The weather was perfect. He'd even been swimming at the hotel pool. He didn't worry about the chlorine ruining his new madras shorts. He was having too good a time to worry about anything. His joy confirmed what Riva had long believed about Paul—that given half a chance in life he would be a raving success. He would know how to work hard and play hard. He would achieve what Pop Goldring had—the happiness of the self-made man.

"What about your debates?"

"I'm doing great. I'm here, I'm having fun. For the first time in my life, I'm really having fun. You know," he grew wistful, "now I see what I've missed all my life."

"You mean a vacation?"

"Some people's lives are vacations," Paul said. "I've got to go. I'm on early tomorrow morning again."

A huge storm front lashed the mid-Atlantic states that weekend. It rained in Washington and Virginia and Maryland and Delaware and even in Atlantic City, New Jersey, where Barry and Olivia huddled, no doubt, against the dampness in their hotel suite. Riva missed Paul. She watched her parents moving past each other all weekend and thought what a waste it was that they were in the same house yet kept their bodies completely separate. She walked from room to room, staring out at the rain. She imagined herself inside a paperweight, a raining paperweight. Beyond her windows, it wasn't raining. The sun was beating down everywhere else on shining streets, giving off that summery odor of heat and growth, especially in San Antonio, Texas.

Olivia and Barry brought back saltwater taffy twisted in waxed paper like party favors for everyone in the family. Paul brought Riva a silver pin from Mexico—the figure of a peasant in a serape drowsing under a huge sombrero, kind of like the Frito Bandito, he said, describing it over the phone to her late Sunday night when he returned from the airport. Paul finished seventh out of 200 in the competition—not in the money, but close enough for a special certificate of Honorable Mention. "Know Ye by These Presents," he read to her. "Well, you can imagine the rest." "I'm dying to see you. I really missed you. I love you so much."

"I know. I want to see you, too. Tomorrow," he promised.

Would she ever say these words to any other boy or man? She had nothing to go on but movies and the books she'd read. If her parents traded endearments, they did it when they were alone, never in front of the children.

She and Paul kissed outside of school the next morning, before the first bell rang, but he was busy after that. He was a celebrity, with tall tales to tell. She let him shine in his glory. This is what it would be like when they were older—Riva behind the scenes, modest, sure of his unswerving love. Maybe a couple of trusted servants to buffer them from the clamoring world. Deep, knowing looks—a raised eyebrow, the slightest inclination of the head. They would hardly need words at all. And Riva would take pride in believing in him when no one else did, like Van Gogh's brother, Theo. They would be completely devoted to each other. Forever. It would take that long for her to finish loving him.

This blood, Riva wrote that night. *This is the life blood. This blood belongs to Paul Auerbach. My wonderful, hardworking Paul who will never take me for granted.*

"I won't be going to college after all," Paul said. He gripped the steering wheel with one hand, turning it rapidly from left to right.

"What?"

He repeated himself. His voice was shaking.

"But it's all worked out, you'll get a loan, you might get a scholarship."

"Forget the scholarship. I never counted on the scholarship. That's just a fairy tale you believed in."

"I thought you had a chance."

"Maybe if I do well the first year. But they'd rather give it to an out-of-state student than to me."

"And the loan by itself isn't enough?"

"It might be if it were big enough."

"Well then, what's the problem?" Riva asked, her voice rising against her will.

"My savings are gone as of tonight."

"Oh my god. You gave him the money?"

"I had to." He started to cry. "I had to," he said again. "That bastard. I hate him. I wish he'd die."

"I'm so sorry."

"He doesn't care about my life. I'm his son, and he doesn't care shit for me."

"You have to go to college. You have to. Even if it's part-time at first. Even if you have to go at night."

"I'm so tired of fighting for every little thing."

Riva looked around. In the distance, past the train trestle, a few houselights glowed, smears of yellow and white beyond the windshield, blurred in the thick, low-hanging mist. The trees were fringed with little flaglets of leaves that shook in the evening air. They made a rustling sound, like something breathing out there. "You can't give up," she said.

"Yes I can. I can get that job at Hahn's. There's nothing wrong with selling shoes."

She took his head in her hands and kissed his forehead. "You deserve better. You're going to be a great lawyer. I believe in you." Riva's mind was already racing: how would he raise $1,500 in five months when it had taken him three years to save it up the first time? Maybe it was cruel to keep on encouraging him. After all, she had never been poor. Her closet was jammed full of clothes. She'd never ironed a shirt in her life. She didn't even pick up her dirty underpants off the floor if she didn't feel like it. "You'll get the money somehow."

"I don't care anymore," he said dully. He looked askance and nodded to himself. "I'm going to take you home now."

"No! I don't want to go home yet."

"I'm really tired," he said.

"This could be the most important night in your life."

"Just the worst," he said.

"This is the night you have to be very strong. I love you," she told him, pulling him toward her. She was going to make him believe in himself as much as she did. Couldn't he tell how much she loved him? "It would be like a betrayal if you gave up. What about our life together?"

"You should find somebody else."

"Come here," she said. She opened the door and got out of the car. "Let's take a walk." Within a few paces, she had disappeared into the ground fog.

"Riva?"

"I'm over here. Come on. Bring the blanket."

He got out of the car and walked toward her voice.

She kissed him all over after they lay down on the blanket. She traced his face with her fingertips and wrote "I adore you" on his brow. She could make him forget how bad he felt. She had that power over him.

"God, Riva," he said. "You're driving me crazy I love you so much."

"Do you have . . . protection?" she asked.

"I won't finish inside you."

Paul had met lots of subtle people in San Antonio. That was his word—"subtle." Cool, neat, hip. Sophisticated, though they were only kids. They came from New York City, Santa Barbara and Grosse Pointe, Lake Forest and New Canaan. They went to prep schools like Miss Porter's in Farmington and the Friends School in Shaker Heights and Groton and Andover. It wasn't just that they were rich. Money hadn't spoiled them, Paul said, it had refined them. They could afford to be nice to everybody, because jealousy was practically beyond them. They all had jolly nicknames—Puffer and Ships and Ironlegs for the boys, Beanstalk, Barnum, and Smash for the girls. Naturally, he'd also met kids from public schools; they were bright and well-off, too. The weekend had been a revelation to him. Riva tried her best to keep track of all the people in the anecdotes Paul told—a succession of minor pranks and triumphs over authority, at least half of which hadn't happened in San Antonio at all but had merely been retold there. "They made me feel like one of them," Paul kept saying. "They treated me like one of them."

"You *were* one of them, silly," Riva said. "You won the right to be there just like they did."

"I have to laugh now at the kids here at school, like Duke Weinstein acting so stuck-up because his father is the Pabst Blue Ribbon distributor. Ships Stewart's father owns a steel mill, and Donald, from Chicago, is the heir to the Quaker Oats fortune."

Now that Paul had had a taste of real money, his own poverty in relation to the wealth of the kids at Hoover High seemed less extreme. This despite the fact that his financial problems were never greater. He'd been accepted to GW, gotten a small loan, been turned down for the scholarship, and had no way of paying for the first semester. Somehow, though, when he talked about San Antonio, it soothed him. He had seen the effects of great wealth and they were so pleasant, so ordinary, that he was able to dismiss the present as a temporary state of affairs. He had, in short, learned that he was worthy, that poverty was indeed not a punishment but a caprice of fate. His pride softened and two weeks later, when Riva suggested that he meet Pop Goldring about borrowing the money for college, he agreed.

"What kind of lawyer? Corporate? Tax? Malpractice?"

Pop Goldring's voice was calm, like an animal grazing over a vast field. He spoke slowly, one question after another. The Spanish Inquisition, Riva thought. She had tried to prepare Paul for the interview. Now she had to sit quietly, without interfering or interrupting. She didn't want to make Paul look weak. He could answer any question himself, anyway. The worst would be about his family. His face would get red and blotchy and circles would spread under his armpits beneath his gray tweed sport coat. Inside the white collar of his shirt and the thin black suede tie she'd given him, his neck looked as delicate and vulnerable as an antelope's. The skin there was soft and smooth. His Adam's apple reminded her of his cock.

Riva studied the huge painting by her grandfather's Michelangelo. The watercolors were so soft and muted that the harlequins' bodies could have been clouds as easily as flesh. The jesters walked toward her as if borne in a wash of their own music and the sweet heavy breath of the ox.

"You plan to live at home?"

"I have to. If I could afford it, I'd join a fraternity and live at the frat house," Paul was saying.

"Your parents are a bad influence on you," Pop Goldring said. He flicked a gold Ronson lighter, and the end of his cigar glowed briefly while he sucked on it.

Paul said nothing.

"Your father drinks?"

"No, sir."

"Where does all the money go?"

"He gambles, sir."

"You're not a good risk." Pop turned away and pulled open a desk drawer.

Riva stopped breathing. Paul's face flushed with rage or shame or both. He looked down at the floor.

"I couldn't give you the money directly. I'll pay the school. Like I'm going to do for Riva. For the first year. Then, we'll talk again. You'll pay me back when you're established."

"I'll put it in writing, sir." Paul's voice cracked with emotion as he stood and offered her grandfather his hand. "I don't know how to thank you enough, sir."

"I don't need it in writing. I build apartments with 500 units on a handshake." He pumped Paul's hand, then inhaled on his cigar again. "You'll send me a letter, with the amount and the address."

"Yes, sir."

Riva kissed her grandfather and hugged him and kissed him again. As she turned to go, she eyed the harlequins, watching to see if their gaze followed her across the room. It didn't. She supposed that meant it wasn't a very good painting.

"You've saved my life!" Paul said in the elevator.

"I'm so happy for you. And proud. You made a very good impression."

"You've saved my fucking life." He slipped his hand under her yellow cashmere sweater and inside her bra in one swift move. "My life," he said again.

In Chemistry class, Riva stared out the window at the green curtain of mulberry trees that lined the athletic field and imagined the two of them lying on a soft blanket beneath them. Paul was on top, launching himself into her. Love was a presence, real and invisible as the elements that expanded and contracted that late spring according to the beautiful, orderly laws of gases. Exotic substances evaporated and then collected again, distilling in the beakers, dripping from the retorts. It looked like magic, and Riva could only fathom it a little at a time, like love or God. She and Paul sat miles apart in the old-fashioned classroom with the floor that sloped like a movie theater. She could see the back of his head, his shoulders attentive through an oxford-cloth shirt. She knew his body intimately now—how the knobs of his spine disappeared between his shoulder blades like an underground spring and rose up again where the neck connected to the torso; the lobes of his ears, delicate as the rolled edges of silk scarves; the tawny odor of his sweat and semen. They owned each other now. The radio was a boxful of love songs. The days grew warmer, and Paul already looked collegiate in his chino pants, V-neck pullover and plaid shirt. They never went anywhere on dates anymore. They lived in the car.

On the first Saturday in June, Paul called Riva. He had just returned from the farmers' market, showered and changed clothes. He sounded excited. His brother had a friend who had an apartment in downtown D.C. and Paul had arranged for them to use it that night.

"Use it?" Riva repeated.

"Yeah."

"Oh." Riva hesitated. Another technicality, wasn't it, whether they made love in the car or in some stranger's apartment? "Okay, great," she said.

"Do you want to go to the movies first?"

"Sure."

The movie flickered across the screen like the shifting patterns in a kaleidoscope. It felt like a long delay and only made Riva nervous. She remembered stories she'd heard of priests and rabbis being found in the arms of prostitutes after hotel fires. Whatever happened in the car, no one questioned their right to be in it. But an apartment was premeditated. It scared her.

"Here we are," Paul said. He turned the key in the second-story walk-up. They were somewhere on the unfashionable edge of Georgetown. The building was ugly red brick in a fake castle style with turrets and bulging bay windows. "This place gives me the creeps," Riva said.

"You'll feel better once we're inside."

"I hope so."

The furnishings were ordinary, but you could tell a single man lived there from the dark suit colors and the piles of sports magazines. Paul turned on a table lamp and held out his arms. She went obediently to his embrace. "Come on. I'm going to make you a famous Tequila Sunrise," he said. He walked her to the kitchen where a bottle of tequila was waiting on the counter. It was the first time they had ever had a drink together.

"You had this in Texas?"

"Right."

"Make mine real sweet," Riva said. "I hate the taste of liquor."

He added an extra measure of grenadine and she watched the fuchsia color swirl and dissipate into the orange juice. Her legs started to feel numb after a couple of swallows. "It's strong, isn't it?"

"Pretty strong. It's a shot and a half of liquor."

He took their glasses into the living room, turned off the lights and undressed down to his jockey shorts. "No steering wheel and no seat back," he said. "What luxury."

He came over and kissed her on the neck. But when she began to remove her skirt, he grabbed her wrist. "Leave it on," he said. "Please." He reached up under it and pulled her underpants down and unhooked her bra under her blouse. Then he dragged a bar stool into the middle of the room and sat down on it. "Come over here and sit on my lap," he said.

She sat on his lap sidesaddle, as if he were going to tell her a story. His soft lips nuzzled her ear and jawline. Everywhere his warm breath touched, she ached with longing. "Turn around and face me," he said, and then he was inside her, thrusting, his hands gripping her breasts under her blouse. A wave of nausea washed over her. "Wait," she protested.

"I'm really hot," he said.

"It hurts!" she lied.

He pulled out of her abruptly, still rocking back and forth slightly. She got up and sat on the sofa, her skirt wound tightly around her legs.

"I don't feel very good," she said.

"Maybe it's the booze."

"I don't know." But it wasn't the booze. "It makes me feel bad being here," she blurted.

"I thought you'd like it. It's like being married, in a way."

"It makes me feel cheap."

"I'm sorry."

"I want to go home."

"Come on," he argued. "We just got here. Come on." He sat down next to her and began kissing her neck again, and her eyelids. "Come on. It'll be all right."

But it wasn't all right. "Something's different," she said.

He sighed and sat back against the sofa cushions. "Yes," he said. "For the first time in my life I'm not worried about money. God, I'm so happy not to have to worry about money for five minutes."

He got up and went into the kitchen to fix another drink. When he came back, he stood at the window and stared out. "I just can't lie to you," he said. "You mean too much to me."

He was going to say something she didn't want to hear and she couldn't stop him.

"I met this person in Texas," he began. "Her name is Merle. She's from New York."

Riva pulled on her underpants and fastened her bra while he spoke. If she kept busy, if she could just keep busy, she could hear the words but they wouldn't penetrate, like knives clattering along the surface, not sinking in. Later, when she was alone, she could call up the words and turn them over slowly.

Merle this and that. Merle who looks like you, the same dark hair and friendly eyes. Merle whose father invented contact lenses. Something came over me. Merle who didn't know I was poor. She's written every day. We've been talking on the phone. I feel better now that I've told you. Oh Riva, I'm sorry. I didn't want to hurt you. Do you have to be hurt? I still love you, Riva. It's confusing. I didn't have to tell you.

"Yes you did," Riva said. "Oh yes you did. But you didn't. You made me make you confess. I don't want to hear your shitty confession."

He took her home, holding her hand as he drove, trying to comfort her, apologizing over and over. Making her swear she forgave him. By the time he dropped her off, he'd stopped talking about loving her and had made her promise they'd stay friends.

Mrs. Stern was insistent: she wanted the specific reason that Riva and Paul had broken up. Riva was too humiliated to say she'd been jilted and too loyal to use the loan from Pop Goldring as an excuse. She considered telling her mother the exquisite lie that they had broken up over whether to have sex or not, but a sense of dread and superstition stopped her. Finally, she said that she and Paul had incompatible values. When Mrs. Stern asked what that meant, Riva said he laughed at all the wrong parts in the movies and probably wouldn't make a good father.

So this is how the broken heart beats. The same way as the whole heart, only you feel every contraction like a refusal. That was very nice. It was really very nice. Someday, years from now, I will see Paul, maybe with this Merle, maybe with someone else. And we will greet each other and act very polite and civilized. But I will know the minute I see him, even if it's thirty years from now, I will know from looking in his eyes if he ever forgot me. And that, she wrote, is the only time, those are the only circumstances when I would ever consider making love with him again.

Someone Else

Ann Harleman

Mary Rose Klossner fell in love with my husband when she was eleven months old. We stood in my kitchen doorway, thirteen years ago this fall, the four of us: Mary Rose and her father and Loren and me. Early evening: the last of the sun, slanting in through the open door, cut right across us.

"We just, I don't know. We run out of just about everything again," Will Klossner said. He squinted against the light, and his dirty-blonde hair fell across his forehead in clumps. More and more, since Ella Klossner died, he looked like a caricature of a midwestern farmer. Standing there angled like a coathanger, too tall for the door frame, in worn jeans and a plaid flannel shirt missing a button.

Mary Rose was a long baby, held in Will Klossner's arms, long legs dangling down. Her feet were bare; that came of having no mother to dress her. But it was warm still, Indian summer.

"We've got plenty," I said. "Whatever you need."

He gave me a confused look. "Have you had dinner?" I asked. He shook his head. "Well, then. Let's see. We've already eaten, finished up a roast right down to the bone, no leftovers, even. How about eggs?"

Loren was paying no attention to any of this. He wasn't very good at practical matters because they didn't interest him much, or maybe it went the other way around. He left things like this—the what to do with what, how to get from here to there stuff—to me. He stood in the shaft of late sun, looking at the baby.

Not a beautiful child. You first felt rather than saw her; then, caught by that mysterious pull, you looked again. She had eyes that were luminous and almost without color. I saw them grow larger, saw her gaze catch in Loren's ruddy beard, which glittered in the light. He is tall and square-shouldered and reddish all over—he comes from good Swedish stock on both sides. The lines raying out around Loren's eyes deepened with his smile, which seemed to spread into the corners of the room. The child's eyes in that long moment gleamed like opals. Behind them you'd have sworn she was thinking, evaluating things, was—*amused*. And behind the amusement lay, even then, some kind of question. I had the strongest urge to move suddenly, to snap the thread that spun itself between my husband and this child.

Then she broke it with a deep, throaty chuckle—the baby. I watched her hands, surprisingly large, open and close, open and close.

"I'll get the eggs," I said. My words tumbled out fast. "Milk, butter," talking a list, "Rice Krispies for tomorrow morning." I got busy, finding a grocery bag and shaking it open, filling it with things they'd need. On top I put a banana to slice over the cereal.

Twelve—almost thirteen—years later, standing at the edge of Elbow Lake in the fizzy April air, I ask myself a question. Were we happy then? Across the lake, the densely wooded bluff is a rough weave of browns, threaded now with red-tinged new green and the bitter yellow of the willows. Sun strikes off the trunks of the birches, and here and there a house gleams through a chink in the trees. Happy. I thought we were, at the time. Isn't that as good as? Isn't it as close as you *come* in life?

Maybe *happy* is too wide a word. It's a little Minnesota town; life here isn't exciting. Content, then. We were content, at ease with each other and with the life we had. Oh, there were times—those lopped-off, midwinter, lightless fights—when Loren would go out ice-fishing and I would wish he'd fall into the hole and the water, black as oil, would close over his head, pull him far out under the ice and never let go. Once I threw all his things out into the driveway. I didn't bother with suitcases or boxes. They lay there on the gravel in the cold afternoon light: clothes and shoes and boots, a thunder of odd dark shapes; fishing rods snagging the air; his tools from the shed. I didn't stop to think how, if anyone came by and saw all that, it made me look more of a fool than him. In the morning, everything was gone. Loren had gone out in the middle of the night and brought it all in and put it away, stowing each thing where it belonged. He didn't say a word. Everything was the same as before. That was early on; I never lost control of myself like that again.

We got set in our ways somewhat, I guess, what with not having children. Not that we didn't try, at least the first six years. But when Dr. Sorensen told us for sure that we couldn't—*I* couldn't—the desire just gradually drained away. The act didn't seem natural anymore. Like fish, all that flopping and slapping, wet, cold. Something you only do in the deep of night, under the quilts, and your arms and legs so tangled up with someone else's that you can hardly tell them apart.

Loren was a thoughtful man, he saw how I felt. "Irene," he said one night, the two of us lying there afterwards, fish-pale arms and legs gleaming in the near-dark. "We don't have to do this, if you don't want to?" He made it a question, but his voice was steady.

I took back my legs and sat up, pulling down my white cotton nightgown. The lacquered cherry headboard that had belonged to Loren's parents was cool against my shoulder blades even in the humid August night. I bunched up my pillow and wedged it behind my back.

But Loren didn't say any more. In the dark I couldn't see his face. I thought, Maybe he doesn't like it all that much either, now. And I felt cold.

I swung my legs over the side of the bed and slid down off the high mattress. I felt my way out of the room and down the dark hall and went into the bathroom to take care of myself. When I snapped on the light, my reflection in the mirror ambushed me. I had to think for a minute who it was, this woman with her lips sewn tight across, eyes smoky-edged and blank, like the holes in the quilt from Loren smoking his pipe in bed.

About then I started collecting glass paperweights—antiques, some of them, greenish or purplish like old doorknobs—with things embedded in them, flowers or insects, a dinosaur, a silver horn. The sameness of their shapes despite their different contents was comforting. Loren would look over the half-glasses he wore for close work, his hair and beard glinting red in the lamplight. "Irene," he'd say, "you have more paperweights than Pinkham has pills," coming down hard on the p's. He'd turn back to his stamps, slotting them into place, squares of blue and green and dull red, in an album with a fat leather cover that I gave him for Christmas one year, to start him collecting.

So, for the most part, we were content. Isn't that the great thing about marriage? That the bad things even out under the steady lapping of days, that the long stretch of the whole is what matters? I was a good wife. Homemaker: I made a home. When I was growing up, my mother, a good Wisconsin German, more than once made me sleep under my bed with the dustballs; I learned. And Loren appreciated it; he liked neatness and order and certainty. I belonged to the Garden Club and the Lutheran Ladies' Auxiliary, which my best friend Jenny was vice-president of. Loren went back and forth to his job at the post office and cared for the few animals we had—cows and some chickens; usually a pig as well—and did carpentry, mending and building, in his workshop out by the barn. These things marked off the days, partitioned them and gave them shape, while the seasons slid by and the years ran together like the pattern in the rose-and-blue oilcloth on my kitchen table.

The ice has begun to break up on the lake. Huge slabs are piled bluish-white along the water's edge, pushed up onto land by the water's slow action. On the bank my feet in old rubber boots sink into softening mud and dead leaves.

She grew into a tall girl, Mary Rose, sapling-skinny like the young birches across the lake, leggy as the neighbors' colts pastured at the bottom of our land. She'd come over from down the road two or three times a week. She must have been lonely—no brothers or sisters, and her mother dying when she was born. Will Klossner had all he could do to keep the farm from going under, those years; though they said he spent a lot of time in town at the Ottertail Bar and Grill, and not only in the evenings, either. I knew how it was. Growing up, nobody in Whitewater had had much; my cradle was a box, an apple box. I didn't like to interfere. She wasn't mine. But the Klossner family and Loren's had been neighbors for forty years, and so sometimes I'd call Will and, just in passing, mention that Mary Rose looked like she needed new shoes or a warmer coat, didn't children grow out of things fast, though? And wasn't it hard to notice when you lived with them day in, day out?

Loren was twenty-seven when Mary Rose first saw him, and I was thirty. A man could want a child as deeply as a woman did; some men could. That was what I told myself. At first he used to make her things: tiny wooden puzzles, a dollhouse, a perpetual-motion machine out of cherry wood with silver balls that ran up and down, up and down. Then, when she was eight or so, he began to teach her. "You wouldn't believe how that child can use her hands, Irene," he said to me at the end of that first afternoon, stamping sawdust and wood-curls off his boots onto my clean kitchen floor. "She's a natural, is what she is." His face, ruddier than usual, gleamed with pleasure. Good, I thought then; it's good he has something to do that he likes, and someone to do it with. It made him look young again and light, and as if he believed in things.

I got so I counted on seeing her. I'd look out on fine days and see them together in the yard with their hacksaws and T-squares, fitting and joining and mitering. Laughter, like half-heard music. Loren's head of flaring hair close to her fair one, the two heads drawing even, as she grew taller. Once they made an oak and cherry birdfeeder with tiers like a wedding cake and carving as fancy as frosting. They were out there in front of the shed for hours a day, their two heads bent over the thing in perfect concentration.

Rapt—that was a word for her in those years. Gazing at the birds that came to the feeder; watching a new calf. Once I came on her with one of our neighbor's colts in the back pasture, had come right up to the fence where she stood under a tall Scotch pine. Their eyes were locked. The yearling trembled lightly all over as if caught in an invisible net.

She must have felt me behind her, because she turned. The tarry smell of pine was all around us and pine needles crunched under my feet.

"Hi, Mrs. Johansson," she said. She was always polite—well taught, for a motherless child. "Isn't he beautiful?" She hooked one arm around the colt's neck. He stood still, even when she laid her cheek against his shoulder. "Look at his coat, like silk. And his beautiful eyes." Her large hands opened and closed. "Isn't he *beautiful?*"

She sounded like any horse-crazy young girl; but her eyes held that question I could never make out.

"Yes," I said. "He is."

But they were both beautiful, standing there.So close together, her pale cheek against his shiny dark skin. A sudden breeze loosened a sharp little shower of pine needles, and the colt's head came up, white rimming his eyes. She turned to soothe him. Her shoulder blades strained her plaid flannel shirt, which was too small for her; her flat butterscotch hair, never really clean, fell in clumps against her neck. Looking at her made me feel dizzy and light, as if with the next puff of wind I could blow away. I wanted to put my arms around her to anchor myself, as she had put hers around the colt, to feel her shoulder blades sharp against my breasts. It was somehow hard to pull away, to turn and go back up the hill to the house.

That night, for the first time in years, I dreamed the dream I used to have, oh, two or three times a year. I am a nurse, a midwife. White light pooling around us, and the acrid smell of blood. I'm quivering all over but steady. I can't see the mother's face beyond the mound of her belly.

The whole stream of my attention has narrowed down to that one opening. Then it's there—the blue-veined head, wet hair plastered to it, round and hard as a baseball. My hands in thin plastic gloves guide it out, my two fingers make a track for the shoulders to ride out on, first one, then the other. The slippery backside thuds into my hands. Before I can even grasp the ankles to turn it over, I hear its narrow cry.

I woke up with sunlight striping the room like an Adirondack blanket and Loren humped up beside me, his back turned and his head almost covered by the worn blue summer quilt. At its edge, his dark-red hair curled. Closing my eyes again, I imagined the baby grown into a tall child standing in the ditches, in high grass threaded with wild onion and Queen Anne's lace. Rows of chigger welts embroidering the tanned skin of those long legs; head thrown back to the sun. Would it have Loren's smile, his ruddy brows that flared like wings? Beside me his quilt-covered shoulders moved slowly with his breathing.

A little wind sifts the fur trim on my parka against my cheek, light as baby fingers. As I walk the lake's edge, I remember how Jenny came to see me. I was busy with the canning, in August it's always a race between me and the tomatoes; but she stood on the mat and rang and rang until finally I had to let her in. She is small and fierce and birdlike. She darts. That day she made me feel even more like a scarecrow than usual, stiff and stolid.

She tried to talk to me. Missed you at the last couple of meetings, ought to get out more like you used to, and so on, and so on. Lighting on the edge of Loren's chair, she said earnestly, "A woman with no children." She has three, nearly grown. "Irene, you're not listening."

"I am," I said. "I'm listening." The house was filled with the wet-washrag smell of boiling fruit. Had I turned the gas off under the tomatoes?

". . . with no children. You should keep up your friends. Me, for instance." I thought I could hear a rough bubbling sound coming from the kitchen.

". . . or you could get a job, maybe. You need other *interests*. Where your treasure lies, there will your heart be also."

Jen likes to quote the Bible; she probably knows more of it by heart than any other Lutheran in Fillmore County.

"What?" I said.

She looked up at me. Greying bangs, escaping from the pink headband she wore, fell into her eyes; humidity from all the boiling turned them into corkscrews. Her voice slowed, as if she were explaining something to a child. "Your whole life is Loren and this house. If anything happened to him, you'd be all alone."

Alone. The word struck and echoed like a dinner gong. Breathy little words like *left* and *lost* flew out around it. I listened to Jen a while longer without hearing what she said, and then I gave her coffee and shooed her out the door. I had work to do.

I think now it must have been around that time that Loren began to get more and more *absent*. When he talked to me, I felt as if he didn't see me. Who was the person he looked at and moved his mouth to send words at?

He went to bed earlier, leaving me to eat supper alone. It got to be like those Identikit things that the police give to eyewitnesses so they can select this nose, that pair of eyes, this upper lip, flipping back and forth until they put together a face that matches the one in their mind. That's what I did with Loren. Only with the whole person, not just the face.

I'd select this movement, that smile, this touch. I'd sit the whole thing up at the dining room table and put words in its mouth so it would talk to me. So Loren would tell me about his day—who got a package from New York City, how far he'd gotten with curly maple chest. And I'd tell him about mine—church gossip I'd heard from Jenny, what seedlings were up in the garden. Over the vase of white and yellow daisies, his eyes, dark as the rubies in my wedding ring, trapped the light and held it, like water under ice.

Finally I asked him. He was at the sink washing up for supper. "Is there someone else?" I said. I sat at the kitchen table in one of Loren's mother's ladderback chairs, afraid to breathe, afraid to lift my elbows from the oilcloth. There was a sort of blank place in my mind, empty, with the wind washing through it. What I'd meant to say was, Do you love me? It would have been the first time I'd ever brought myself to ask. But what if he just said, No. Standing there in the kettle-grey light from the window over the sink.

He went still. "Of course not. You know that." The anise odor of Lava Soap pierced through the smell of corned beef and cabbage simmering on the stove.

"I'm—I don't—know that." I tried to reach across the space between us with my words. It felt as if they bounced off his broad blue-shirted back and came back at me. "Loren, I don't know that. You're different lately, you're—not there."

He turned and looked at me. He was all yellow-white lather up to the elbows. "Irene. Don't be crazy. Who could there be?"

I couldn't say it—couldn't *think* it. Behind him, framed in my red cotton curtains, the cows stood knee-deep in wet grass at the bottom of the yard. No one had brought them in.

"I don't know," I said, suddenly tired, my arms and legs heavy as wet firewood. "I don't know what got into me. I'm sorry."

He turned back to the sink. Methodically, he began to slough the lather from his arms.

Last night I saw them dancing. Loren likes to play the radio while he works on his projects. It was early evening, but Mary Rose hadn't gone home for supper. They were finishing something—a bench, I think it was. "Don't dish up till late tonight," Loren had asked me earlier in the afternoon.

The sound of the radio drew me; maybe it was louder than usual. There was something about the music, too. It wasn't the smooth, honey-sounding music that Loren likes, the kind you hear in elevators, but some bouncy, brassy stuff. I checked the roast, which crackled pinkly, still far from done. I pulled off my apron and smoothed my hair back into its knot and went outside.

It was warm for early April, but the darkening air held a chill underneath and there were small, shrunken piles of snow in the corners of the yard. The lighted shed window flung a rectangle of light onto the hard-packed dirt beneath. In it two shadows twisted, rhythmic, elongated, stretching and disappearing and filling it again. Why did I feel like an intruder in my own yard? When I got close, I stood to the side of the open window, up against the splintery boards of the shed, and looked in.

It was as if I'd been pushing hard against a door that opened suddenly from the other side. I had to grab the rough wooden sill to keep from falling. They dipped and swayed and twirled without touching. Mary Rose was lanky and awkward in her jeans. Her breasts, small and pointed under her T-shirt, were hardly more than a boy's. In the back corner of the shed, Loren's father's old radio was turned up full volume. It was a standing radio, tall as a child, with a large hole in its belly for the speaker. The music sounded ridiculous coming out of its squat, old-fashioned bulk: fast, thudding and wailing. *Jump, jump! For my love. Jump in!* Shavings and wood-curls flew up around them. When they whirled to face each other, their eyes met. Mary Rose pushed her damp, flat hair back from her forehead and laughed out loud.

She made me think of the imprisonment of life in the world. She made me feel it. She made me see everything that moved—the birds at the feeder, the colt, her and Loren and me—as if it were sealed in time and place like a butterfly in a paperweight. And still she could dance. The smell of sawdust filled my nostrils like fur.

When I got back inside, I sat down at the kitchen table with my head on my arms. I felt like someone had taken off my skin and every nerve was hanging out. Through the glass of the storm door, I watched the slanting oblong of light on the ground as it emptied and filled, emptied and filled. The gritty oilcloth under my arms smelled like old rubber boots. Feelings I'd never had before, feelings I couldn't even name, swarmed over me. *Jump. Jump in.*

I stop beside a large white birch that the piled-up ice has knocked over, lying on its side half in and half out of the water, its roots obscenely exposed. Small frozen clods cling to them. I touch a smooth spot on the trunk. It is cold as silver against my palm, where the splinters from the shed windowsill last night still sting. In the tree's upper branches a few of last year's leaves, still clinging, flicker in the little wind coming off the lake. The wind carries the damp-earth smell of things opening. At my feet, the ice hisses, shrinking, settling deeper into the water.

How will it happen? She'll come the day she turns sixteen. I'll know, because Loren will have spent the whole week making a jewelry box to give her for her birthday, tailoring and smoothing and polishing until it's like a jewel itself.

She won't come to the kitchen door the way she always has. She'll come to the front. I'll open the door and she'll stand on the threshold wrapped in a man's sheepskin coat, stained and dull at the edges. Her hair, freshly washed, flying around her head in wisps; her breath coming in little frosty puffs. Frost behind her prickling on the grass, throwing off darts of light straight into my heart.

Behind me Loren will be sitting in his leather rocker by the window with the newspaper in his lap, as he's begun to do so often, gazing out at the shed. He'll have shaved off his beard. I'll have forgotten about the cleft in his chin—I haven't seen his face naked since the first year of our marriage. How beautiful he was then, rosy as a silk-shaded lamp; now only the bones will be the same, the shelf of his brow and the square jaw sweeping forward. For an instant, his eyes will meet mine, and I'll see her question in them.

Mary Rose will stand still in the doorway. Her eyes, those strange colorless eyes, will hold mine; I'll have to look up to see into them. They'll shine on me like moonlight. She won't say a word; but I'll know what she wants as clear as if she'd spoken. It will be as if a sound I can't decipher, indistinct and sweet, were threading through the room, weaving itself around the three of us. I'll feel it in my body like a shiver all over my skin.

"Mary Rose," I'll say, as if this were an ordinary day, an ordinary visit, but moving lightly, throwing the door wide.

She'll shake her head faintly and she'll smile.

I'll start toward the closet then, to get my coat. Moving light as air.

But she'll hold out her hand to him, those long fingers. He'll pull himself out of his chair, the seat squeaking as he leaves it, and go and stand beside her in the doorway. They'll stand there together, the two of them. The distance between us will stretch larger and larger. I'll try to say something that would throw out a line to them; but there won't be any words. The empty rocker will titter ghostlike back and forth, back and forth on the wooden floor, slower and slower until it stops.

Golden Chances

Alice K. Boatwright

The day Elmo left to join the Weasels' National Tour, Emily tore the wallpaper off the bedroom walls. The loose parts came down easily in large satisfying strips, like pieces of sunburned skin. As she flung them to the floor, she remembered how once, after a long day at the beach, she and Elmo lay naked on the bed, peeling each other. Emily was surprised at the way he worked—the slow surgical attention he paid to getting the biggest possible piece. She preferred a quick pull, the thrill of seeing how long it would last, the soft crackle of skin ripping away from skin. They had tried to graft each other's skin onto their own, caught up in a vision of mingled flesh and spirit, but it didn't work. The skin was already dead.

A thick fog rolled in while Emily worked, muting the lights across the river. The persistent crying of the fog horn reminded her that she had another ending on her hands. Contemplating the debris surrounding her, Emily wished the wallpaper would fly back onto the walls, that Elmo would come back through the door, that dead skin could stick.

If she squinted at the ceiling over the bed, she could see a white space like an afterimage where Elmo's American flag had been. Emily had laughed at him when he stapled it up there. Maybe if she had offered to help instead, he would be here now.

All day long she had stayed holed up in her sound booth at the radio station watching records spin and replaying their last scene:

Elmo, his long curly hair unruly from sleep, shyly stroked her back while she put on her shoes. Emily knew he was trying to be nice, but she was not in the mood for "nice." She was thinking of the time, a few hours away, when she would return home and all that would be left of Elmo would be the fingerpicks in her bobby pin box. When she wouldn't face him, he hugged her around the waist from behind.

"This has been really great, Em," he said.

Emily stiffened, shoe in hand.

"Spare me your company manners, Elmo," she said. She stood up, pulling out of his grasp, hiked up her pantyhose and went to the mirror to comb her hair. In the glass she could see the reflection of Elmo's hurt expression.

What if, instead of pulling away, she had turned to him and said calmly, "It's been good for me too, Elmo. Come back any old time."

What would he have done if she'd said: "Let's not blow it then, OK? Promise me you'll come back and I'll wait for you."

Or better yet: "Don't leave. Please don't."

Emily stared at the bare spot on the ceiling and remembered when she was young she thought love meant, "I'd let my golden chances pass me by."

She didn't want Elmo to let his golden chances pass by. She genuinely didn't. She was happy for him. He'd gotten what he wanted; the only thing he'd ever worked hard for in his life. He was off to join the Big Time. He had two Weasel t-shirts and a contract 20 pages long to prove it. It was the dream come true of every boy who ever looked down at his feet and saw blue suede shoes.

How could Emily begrudge him that?

How could you love someone and not want him to have what he wanted?

When Emily first met Elmo he was playing the club circuit in New England as a solo. He sang city and country blues—old stuff from the 20s and 30s—peppered with original songs about being on the road, lost love, and corruption. He had a good voice and an easy-going stage presence that made him very popular. Now and then he recorded a single, and when one of them became a local hit, Emily invited him to the radio station where she did a blues show for an interview.

Elmo smoked throughout the interview, filling the tiny recording room with clouds of smoke.

"You spend all day in here?" he asked her. "You like living like this?"

"I can't think of any place I'd rather be," said Emily, adjusting her volume controls. "This is a test. Do you like being on the road?"

"Oh sure, I spend half my life humping my way over icy mountains to get to some bar where sixteen drunks are watching the basketball game. I play for them and most of the time they don't even remember I was there."

"Oh come on. Why do you do it then?"

"I guess I can't think of anything I'd rather do either."

"Everybody loves you here. Don't you think they're listening?"

"Yeah, I guess some do. Once I was even recognized in a grocery store. That's when I knew I was getting famous."

"OK, we're going live now."

The day after the interview, Elmo was waiting for Emily outside the station, slumped down behind the wheel of his baby blue '60 Pontiac. He was eating potato chips.

"Hey!" he called, waving the bag at her. "Can I give you a lift?"

Emily looked at him skeptically, her head cocked to one side. The back of the car was weighted down with amplifiers; loose laundry; boxes of records, CDs, and tapes; and empty beer bottles.

"Come on, I'll buy you some fried clams."

At home an empty refrigerator and her own full laundry bag awaited her. "I'll bite," she said. Elmo smiled and leaned across the seat to open the door.

"I just wanted to tell you," he said, as he made a rapid U-turn and headed down toward the river, "that I'm not really a drunk. In fact, I hardly ever drink anymore when I play. It's too depressing and I break too many strings."

Emily sat sideways, her back against the door, looking at him. The way he drove, one-handed, slouched down like the star of a teen movie, made her smile. She was glad he had come.

"So—you were worried about that? What I'd think?" she said, then faltered.

He glanced at her. "I wanted to set the record straight."

Emily laughed. "Just to coin a phrase."

"Right. Get it spinning."

After that, Elmo dropped in whenever he was in the area. He would meet Emily at the station and they'd go to the Clam Hut. There they'd sit with a quart of beer on the front seat between them, eating clams and talking music. On sunny days, they toured the flea markets looking for old records, and stopped in dank country roadhouses to play the juke box and drink.

Emily was cautious at first. On her bad days, she considered herself, at 28, a three-time loser. She had only recently broken off a long-standing relationship with a photographer, a married man who had courted her with this sensitivity and intelligence and then pinned her with jealousy and indecision. Before that she had lived with a potter who was consumed with guilt over not joining his father's law firm; and in college, she had been married briefly to a writer, whose one and only novel collected dust in mountains of battered file folders under the bed. In between, there had been what she referred to only as "the unmentionables and the regrettables."

She had promised herself not to get into any more hopeless relationships without knowing exactly what she was hoping for. She did not believe she was naive. She had seen the big love of her life, the one authenticated by family photographs, a white dress handed down from her great-aunt, and four juicers, turn into a three-year conspiracy of silence. She knew that marriage wasn't the answer to anything and that relationships didn't necessarily turn out to mean what you thought they should. It was just the idea that they might not mean anything at all that unnerved her.

And yet she found Elmo charming. Sometimes—such as the day she borrowed his denim jacket and discovered the silver birds sewn inside—she even loved him. So she had no particular misgivings when, on a rainy afternoon, they became lovers, even though she knew he was living with another woman.

Emily did not know the woman but she knew where she lived. It was a large Victorian house with fancy gingerbread trim on a shady side street of town. It had a tall tower with windows all around it, and at Halloween there was a jack o' lantern in each window. Emily had always thought a family lived there, but Elmo said it was just her—the woman living alone.

"Does she know that you come over here?" Emily asked him one evening. Elmo shrugged.

"The subject has never really come up."

"I don't believe that, Elmo."

Emily got up from the couch and began flipping through a stack of records. The records slapped against each other as they piled up on the floor.

"Well, it hasn't. We aren't in love or anything. I met her at a club one night and started seeing her. We started sleeping together. She has a big house so she invited me to stay there when I wanted to. That's all there is to it. It's not like us."

"Is that supposed to be some kind of compliment?"

"Come on, Em."

"All right—how is it not like us?"

Elmo leaned his head back against the wall, feigning deep thought.

"Well, you're different. For one thing, we both like the same kind of music. For another, you've got brown hair."

Emily picked a record off the stack in front of her and hurled it at Elmo. He ducked as it hit the wall, shattering.

"Emily, for Christ' sake, that was Buddy Holly!"

"Tough shit," she said, bolting out the door.

Elmo caught her halfway down the stairs to the street and pinned her by the shoulders to the wall.

"Emily, I was only teasing you. I thought you knew how I felt about you. I haven't slept with Jane in months. She has a boyfriend in the city. We're just friends, really."

"You expect me to believe that now?" Emily struggled to get out of his grasp. "Let me go," she said.

"Emily, are you in love with me?"

"Let me go, Elmo!"

"All right," he said, sitting down on the steps. "Now answer me."

"I think the ability to love has been bred out of us."

"Well, that's a shame," said Elmo lightly, leaning back on his elbows. "This feeling I have about you must be caused by low blood sugar then."

Emily frowned.

Elmo moved over and patted the space on the step beside him.

"Will you sit down, please, Em? I'm sorry I teased you."

Emily hesitated, thinking how easily he dismissed the problem of the woman with the jack o' lanterns.

"Come on, Em. I'll talk to her this weekend. OK?"

"Elmo, if you're lying to me, I'll kill you."

"I believe it. Now come here, please?" Emily sat down next to him. Elmo put his arm around her shoulders and hugged her.

"I didn't know you cared so much about me, Em."

"Ha."

"That was your Buddy Holly, you know."

Of course once Jane knew about Emily—other boyfriend or no—Elmo was not as welcome there, so he began staying at Emily's. Emily watched doubtfully as his possessions appeared and began to drift from one room to another in her apartment. Her neat kitchen table was now littered with overflowing ashtrays, capos, finger picks, and scraps of paper covered with song lyrics. Elmo's razor was always on the bathroom sink and, in the closet, his dirty jeans nuzzled up to hers.

It was a pretty good arrangement, though, she had to admit. Elmo paid half the rent, but he'd formed a band and was on the road a good part of the week. Emily was free to concentrate on her programs which she now imagined as going out to Elmo, wherever he was. She could see her friends and enjoy the pleasures of being alone, knowing that Elmo would soon be back.

She was just beginning to think she had it made when Elmo's band split up.

"I've had it," he announced. "I never want to see the inside of another bar as long as I live." Emily nodded sympathetically, trying to hide her dismay.

"What do you think you'll do then?" she asked.

Elmo looked at her disconsolately over the edge of the joint he was sealing. He lit the joint and took a long drag before answering, "I don't know."

What he did was hang around the house, depressed and stoned. Emily tried to be supportive. She didn't want to become a nag, even though from the day he stopped working, Elmo also stopped functioning in almost every other respect. She tried to continue her own life, but it was hard to think of Elmo as her audience anymore when he would say things like: "Everything you hear on the radio these days is shit. The music business is dead."

When she brought home records and asked him to preview them, he advised her not to play any of them. "Elmo, that's Eric Clapton's new album. I have to play that."

Elmo shrugged and went to the refrigerator for a beer.

"You have to take a stand somewhere, Emily. Either you stand for good honest music or you stand for shit."

"I stand for making my own goddamn living at least," Emily said. "I'd like to know what you stand for. If you're not going to be a musician, why don't you go back to school and learn how to do something?"

"I've thought of that, believe me. But it's not easy to shuck off your entire life's dreams." Elmo looked at her in a way that made Emily feel chastened.

"You're right," she admitted. "I'm sorry." Emily took a beer out of the frig and sat at the kitchen table opposite him.

"You know, I've been thinking a lot lately," said Elmo, touching her knee tentatively.

"Uh-huh," said Emily. She wanted to know what he'd been thinking, but she didn't want to say what she had been thinking—that lately he had been a real drag.

"When my father was my age, he had a job, a wife, two kids, a house, a car, three dogs, and a washing machine bought on time."

"So?"

"I think he felt as if he were paying for us on the installment plan. So much for shots, dentist bills, clothes, toys, food, education, and in the end you make the last payment and it's yours."

"He must have been awfully disappointed."

"Yeah," said Elmo. "I think he was."

"So what does that have to do with us?"

"I don't know. I was just thinking about it. I mean, I think my father's way was fucked up, but we don't seem to be doing any better. I mean, look, here we are, we love each other, but are we going to do anything about it?"

"What do you mean? We're living together. Isn't that doing something?"

"Yeah, but I mean the serious stuff. Like getting married."

Elmo glanced anxiously at her face. He put his hands on her knees.

"Did you ever think about that, Emily? We could get married and have kids. Get a little house. I could push the lawnmower on Saturdays, and you could work in the garden."

"Elmo, you must be drunk. What would you do if I said yes?"

"I would sweep you into my arms," he said, pulling her up from her chair by both hands, "waltz you around the kitchen, hang out the flag, and buy a bottle of champagne."

Emily pulled away from him, surprised by the panic she felt. She looked at his face, a face she loved, would always love, and then put her own cheek against his shoulder.

Elmo put his arm around her, resting his chin on her head.

"So what'll it be, Em?" he asked. "Laundry for two?"

"Elmo," she said slowly, "I don't really know if I want that or not. But I do believe you'd never forgive me if I said yes." Emily felt the excitement drain out of him. They stood for a long time just holding each other.

At last Elmo said: "You're probably right."

Three days later Elmo heard that the Weasels were looking for a rhythm guitarist. He went down to Boston to audition and, when he got the job, he was jubilant. "This is it, Em," he said. "This is the break I've been waiting for. It's been a long time, but I knew it would come." Emily found his smug acceptance of success as hard to take as his gloom. She watched silently as he tossed his belongings into boxes and talked about the future. Of course, he was right. It was a good break. The Weasels were a long way from the backroads of New Hampshire. After two weeks of rehearsal, the band was going on tour for four months. In the winter they would be cutting an album in L.A. There was even talk of a European tour.

The night before he left, Elmo and Emily smoked a joint together, sitting on their bed. The room was shadowy, lit only by the street lamp outside the window. From the river they could hear the fog horns and an occasional boat whistle.

The obvious question weighed heavily in the silence between them for so long that finally Emily asked it.

"Will you come back here after the tour?"

Elmo inhaled deeply. The burning tip of the joint flamed up, illuminating his face. Emily remembered the first time she'd seen him.

"I don't know," he said. "I don't know what will happen."

In the middle of the night, he roused her from sleep.

"Shall I go? Is it silly? To want to play rock and roll? It's no good for me here any more, is it?"

Emily looked at him, lying beside her with his arms folded under his head, staring up at the American flag on the ceiling. "I don't know what you want me to say, Elmo."

"Say you love me."

"Does my loving you make any difference?" Emily asked. She hoped he wouldn't answer that and he didn't. He just sighed and turned his face to the wall.

August Sunday

Patrice Vecchione

Pressing your hand to my ass
you hold it like a guardrail
and follow me to the bedroom,
up to the lace curtains, push
me against the plate glass
where the rose petals
separate in our rising heat.
I grab at your thinning hair,
as you stroke my breasts, press
my lips to your coin-flat
nipples, hold my head there.
Spreading my legs into the air
you glide inside me like an iceskater
whose quick blades melt the pond
floating you closer to the center
of earth. I feed you
my cries, the salt from my fingers,
and we suck at our shared past,
all day we linger in it:
the early morning ocean walks,
the food I prepared for you,
all our arrivals and departures,
past the moment when the plane
leaves the ground.
Between the sheets of my bed
we eat our lost days together.
My kittens lick at your toes,
and your cock throbbing in the air
is the signal I bend to,
rub with my cheek, hold in my mouth.
We eat tomorrow this way too;
my skin disappearing beneath your touch,
as our future together
dissolves slowly like bitter fruit
under my weeping tongue.

In Cold Blood

Karen X. Tulchinsky

When Amy and I first met, sparks flew between us with an intensity that threatened to start three-alarm fires everywhere we went. We couldn't keep our hands off each other for the first six months. We spent every night together, sometimes staying in my room at the lesbian co-op house I lived in, but mostly we went to Amy's one-bedroom apartment in the west end.

"How can you sleep on this?" I asked her, half laughing when I first saw the small single bed against the wall in one corner of her spacious bedroom.

She shrugged, "Works for me."

"Honey . . ." I'd beg her later, when we were crammed together on the child-sized mattress, "you're a grown-up now. You make good money. Why don't you buy a proper bed—a queen-size would be nice. There's plenty of room in here."

"We'll see," was all she'd say.

Other than the bed, I was happy with Amy. We had fun together. We had great sex and good conversations. She was a terrible dancer, but she was charming, beautiful and sweet. I fell in love with her right from the start. I was sure she was the woman for me. In September, on our second anniversary, we had a big party and invited all our friends. They bought us a triple-layer cake with two brides standing together and the words "Happy Anniversary Amy and Toby" written on the top. Everyone made speeches about our relationship and we drank and danced all evening.

That night, I decided it was time I came out to my parents. They live 3,000 miles away in Montreal and so most of the time I ignored their existence. Somehow, marking two years with Amy changed it for me. I wanted my parents to know her. I knew that Amy and I were going to be together for a long time and I wanted to claim her to my family. I wanted to bring her home and introduce her, just like my older sister had done every time she was with a guy longer than two weeks. I decided to go for a visit in the spring, after the snow melted.

The day I left, Amy drove me to the airport. I looked over at her and felt a wave of love sweep through me, warming me inside. We had been having such a wonderful time together that day that I almost didn't want to go. As my plane took off I watched the city from my window seat. We flew out over the Pacific ocean and I felt happy. My life was going the way I wanted it to go. I lived in a beautiful city, I had a great lover and a good job in a gay-owned vegetarian restaurant. I lived in a co-op house with three other dykes and we all got along great. Even so, maybe it was time for Amy and me to try living together. I decided to talk to her about the idea when I got back from my trip. I dozed off as a fresh batch of April rain clouds settled in over Vancouver.

A week later I waited by the airport conveyor-belt for Amy. She was going to pick me up and we had agreed to meet in the baggage area. I checked my watch. She was only ten minutes late. She might have got stuck in traffic, so I waited. A half hour later, I called her house.

"Hello?" It was Amy. She sounded funny, out of breath.

"Did you forget about me or something?" I tried to keep the anger out of my voice.

"Oh shit." I thought I heard vague sounds of someone in the background and strained to hear more.

"You did forget, didn't you?"

"I'm sorry, Toby," she said. "I thought you were coming home tomorrow."

"Tomorrow? Honey, don't you remember? We decided I would come home on Saturday so we could still have half a weekend together."

"Oh. Right." She didn't sound convincing. "Well, hang on, I'll be right there."

"Don't bother. I might as well take a cab now. I'll meet you at your place."

"Here? Uh . . . . Why don't we meet at your place?"

There was dead silence for a moment.

"Amy, what's going on? You're being all funny."

She paused before speaking. "Look—here's fine. Come on over. We'll talk then."

"You're scaring me, Amy. Your voice sounds different."

"I'll see you when you get here, Toby." She hung up and left me standing alone at an airport pay phone. On the way to her house I didn't know whether to be terrified or furious. Something big was going on. I needed to find out what it was, but at the same time, I didn't want to know. I wanted Amy to be sweet and loving and playful like she usually was with me. I paid the driver and slowly made my way up the three flights of stairs to Amy's apartment.

"This is going to be hard," was the first thing Amy said to me after she hugged me stiffly, not—"How was your trip?" or, "Honey, welcome back, I missed you." Not, "Drop your bag and let's go to bed," but "This is going to be hard."

I looked her cold in the eye. "Come on, Amy, whatever it is—just tell me. Don't torture me like this." I hugged myself with my arms and stood in the middle of her room, glaring at her stupid single bed.

She looked up at me sheepishly and said, "I've met someone new."

"You what?"

"I didn't mean for it to happen, Toby, but I think I'm falling in love."

"I was only away for a week!" I screamed, standing in the middle of the floor shaking my head. "What are you talking about?"

She sighed deeply.

"Who is it?" I demanded.

She didn't answer. She just looked at me with a guilty expression on her face, shuffling her feet on the floor.

I turned my back to her. "Come on, Amy. You've told me this much. Tell me who it is."

A minute later she said something I couldn't hear. I turned to face her. "Speak up!" I ordered.

"Melissa," she whispered.

"Melissa! Melissa!! For fucks sake, I can't believe it! You've known Melissa forever." I balled my hands up into fists by my side and began pacing back and forth in front of Amy. "I wondered about you and Melissa when we first met. You said you would never sleep with her. What changed, Amy? How did this happen?" She opened her mouth to speak, but I wasn't ready to hear the answer. "No! Don't tell me. I don't want to know. Oh god." I sat down on her cot and leaned forward, my head in my hands. My eyes were filling with tears, which were pouring down my face. Amy kneeled down on the floor in front of me and tried to take my hands.

"No!" I pulled them out of her reach. "You don't get to be nice to me. That's too easy."

"Okay." She held out her hands in front of her as if I was a maniac who needed soothing.

"Just tell me one thing." I wiped my eyes with the back of my hand. "How long has this been going on? And don't lie to me."

She sighed deeply, and, looking down at her feet, said, "A few months."

"What? I didn't quite get that."

She looked up at me, wincing. "A few months."

I folded my arms across my chest. "How many months?"

"Toby . . . . please."

"How many? I have the right to know. You at least owe me that."

She looked down at her feet again. "Six."

The only word that could describe how I felt about her in that moment was hate. The woman I loved, the woman I was ready to commit to for the rest of my life had been lying to me for six months. I counted out the months backwards on my fingers. October. Right after our anniversary. I shook my head at her. Six months. For half a year our entire relationship had been a lie.

"Toby . . ." She looked up at me. "I don't know what to say. It just happened. I didn't know how to tell you."

"Nothing 'just happens.' " I said, standing up. I gave her a look of disgust, turned and left the apartment, quietly shutting the door behind me.

By the time I got home I was more humiliated than angry. I wanted to talk to my friends, my housemates about Amy, but at first I was too embarrassed. I went up to my room and closed the door behind me. I put a tape in my cassette player and threw myself down on the bed. Every time I thought about Amy and what she said, I felt so angry I wanted to kill her. I jumped up and began to pace back and forth in the small room. It was one of those times when I wished I still smoked. If I did, I'd smoke one cigarette after the other, flailing the burning butts around in the air like Bette Davis used to do and when I was finished, I'd crush each one on the floor with my foot.

Instead, I reached for the bright green tennis ball that sat on my desk and began to bounce it against the wall, catching it and throwing it again and again. My mind was working a million miles an hour. All I could think about was revenge. Hundreds of scenarios rolled around in my head, as I stomped back and forth in my room.

I saw Amy and Melissa in front of a firing squad. They were dressed in prisoner's clothes and their hands were tied behind their backs, as big macho dyke-soldiers pushed them mercilessly against a red brick wall. Melissa's long blonde hair was tangled and in her face. Amy's pants were torn at the knee and her feet were bare. I sat perched on a majestic black horse and gave the order to ready, aim, fire! As the shots rang out, they clutched at their bellies and then fell in separate directions onto the dusty ground.

In another fantasy, I saw them squished against each other in Amy's stupid single bed, as I burst into the bedroom, dressed as a gangster, Al Capone style. I held a massive machine gun in my arms. They sat up in bed and tried to hide behind Amy's midget-sized quilt, as I plugged them with round upon round of machine gun fire.

My favorite image was of the two of them having an after-sex shower while I crept into the bathroom. Like Norman Bates in Psycho I threw back the shower curtain, screamed and stabbed them over and over mechanically, with a huge butcher knife. I heard scary violin music playing in the background, as Amy and Melissa slumped into a heap in the bottom of the bathtub.

I surprised myself at my level of violence, but then I remembered what a creep Amy had been about the whole thing and I felt completely justified in my horrible revenge fantasies. After devising six or seven horrific scenarios, in which both Amy and Melissa died terrible, cruel deaths at my hand I felt better. I went downstairs to the kitchen to have something to eat.

Later that evening I told my housemate Rona everything. She poured red wine while I sat beside her on the couch, crying, yelling, venting about Amy, and crying some more.

"I never trusted her," Rona declared at one point. "What?" I was shocked. "How come you never said so?"

Rona shrugged. "Would you have believed me?"

I thought about it for a minute. Until today, I thought Amy was perfect. "No," I said. "You're right. Oh god, Rona, I feel like such a fool. That's the hard part. And I hate her. I hate them both. If I have to lose Amy I don't want her walking around town. I want her out of my life completely. I want her to vanish into thin air. Maybe someone will give her a one-way ticket to Brazil, or maybe at this very second she's being hit by a truck. Bang!" I slapped my hands together. "Dead on impact." I got off the couch to go and get more kleenex. This was going to be a long night.

On Monday morning I called in sick to work. I was too upset to cook for other people all day. If I was going to get dumped for another woman, I at least wanted a day off. I had breakfast, put on a pair of jeans, a tee-shirt, my black leather jacket and went for a walk by the ocean. It was a beautiful spring day. Daffodils and tulips were blooming. Seagulls squawked noisily above me. All the trees had bright green buds starting. All in all it was a lovely day, one of those days that make you feel good just to be alive, except that underneath it all I was seething. Part of me wanted to fight for Amy and part of me just wanted to let her go and get over her.

Fighting for her would have done no good, and I think deep inside I knew it. I spent most of the next two weeks venting, whining, crying and complaining to anyone who would listen. One evening during my two-week vigil, Rona took me by the hand and sat me down on the living room couch.

"Toby," she said, "why don't we go out tonight to the club for a drink or something? I know you're not in the mood, but I think it will do you good to just get out and have some fun, get a little bit drunk even or have a few dances. I really think it's a good idea."

I said no, but Rona kept trying, until finally she convinced me.

The club was more crowded than I expected for a Monday night.

"Where did they all come from?" I asked Rona as we stood at the back of the bar, letting our eyes adjust to the dark room.

She laughed. "They've been here all along—you just haven't been looking."

I was actually having a good time, standing against the wall with Rona, watching women and moving my hips to the music when it happened. The world went into slow motion. I clutched at Rona's arm and held tightly, unconsciously digging my nails into her. Straight ahead of us, on the dance floor, bumping and grinding slowly, and looking deep into each other's eyes were Amy and Melissa. They actually looked good together. I thought I might vomit.

"Steady, girl," Rona pried my fingers from her. "Let's go." She put her arm around my shoulders protectively, and steered me toward the door. "No point in torturing yourself."

Two days later I decided it was time to get Amy's clothes and things out of my house and to pick up the last of my stuff from her place. I still had a key to her apartment, and wanted to go when she wouldn't be there, so I left work early.

It was a dark and rainy Wednesday afternoon. It had been raining all week and everything was soggy. Inside the lobby of Amy's building I shook out my umbrella and walked the three flights of stairs to her floor. Outside her door I stopped and reached in my pocket.

I pulled out my key, slipped it in the keyhole and turned. I heard the deadbolt click back and I entered the dark apartment, locking the door again behind me. I switched on the hall light and headed for the bedroom. I reached for the floor lamp to turn it on and knocked my knee against something hard. I yelled and grabbed at my leg. "She must have rearranged the furniture," I thought to myself. I stood still, looking around as my eyes adjusted to the darkness and slowly it came into focus. There it was, sitting proudly in the room like a huge piece of salt to rub in my wounds. A gigantic, enormous, extra-large bed. A massively overgrown, king-size, natural-fibre futon on a dark wood frame. It was so large and so new it sparkled before me. Rage bubbled inside my stomach. It tasted sour. For two years I slept with her on a single bed, made for a small child, not two adult women. For two years I lay beside her, night after aching night, smashing my knees into the wall, banging my elbows, and sometimes my head. How many times did I wake to find my leg asleep because she was crushing me? How many times did I beg her to treat herself to a real bed, an adult-sized double or even a queen-size? This was an outrage. If she was going to buy a brand new olympic-pool-size futon, why did she wait until she broke up with me? The timing could not be explained away as coincidental. This shameless act was the ultimate in cruelty.

All of my revenge fantasies flooded back into my head. I stared at her bed and I knew what I wanted to do. I clenched and unclenched my fists over and over as I let the idea settle in my brain. I knew if I gave in to my desire my name would be mud in our small, local lesbian community, but I knew I didn't care. I looked around the room. What I needed was not there. I stumbled out to the hall and into the kitchen. I knew exactly which drawer to open. Reaching in, I pulled out Amy's freshly sharpened, twelve-inch butcher knife. The handle slid into my grip. The weight of the knife was just right. Calmly I went back to the bedroom, where the new bed sat in all its giant glory.

I was so angry I was teetering on the edge of reason. As if the bed itself was laughing at me I glared at it, clutching the knife tightly in my right hand. The brand new sheets and down comforter were pulled back and crumpled up in one corner. I was sure that Amy and Melissa had made love on the bed that very morning and in their haste left it unmade. I imagined them tumbling around together luxuriously on all that space and the bile rose in my throat.

I tightened my grip on the wooden handle and slowly raised it in the air above my head. Coldly, I lunged forward, plunging the blade in deep, and then dragging it toward me. Adrenalin pumped through my blood. A fiendish laugh poured from my mouth as I pulled the knife out and stabbed again. I smiled to myself, knowing I would plead "temporary insanity," as I hacked and chopped, over and over and over until I was dripping in sweat and the muscles in my arm ached.

I was breathing heavy as I stood back up to my full height. I let the knife slip from my hand and watched it bounce on the floor by my feet.

I stood there for a long time smiling and gloating. When I'd had my fill I reached in my pocket for her key and threw it onto the tattered bed. Then I turned and let myself out of her apartment for the last time.

As I walked down the street I pictured Amy walking into her bedroom later that day. Maybe Melissa would be with her and together they would discover the hacked-up bed. Of course she would know it had been me. I wondered if she would have the guts to confront me directly or if in her guilt and shame she would just let it go. Either way it didn't matter. My heart still ached for what I had lost. There was nothing else that Amy could do that would make me hurt any more than I already did. Usually, I was not a violent person, and if I heard about someone else doing what I had just done, I would have been shocked, but somehow it felt right. Amy had it coming to her, and even if nobody else saw it that way, I had no regrets.

I looked up at the late afternoon sky. The rain had stopped and the clouds were breaking up. All over the place spring flowers were poking up through the earth. Everything in my life had changed in a short time. It was overwhelming and I didn't know what would happen next. One minute I was in the middle of a happy relationship, the next minute I was killing my cheating, lying ex-lover's new bed. One day I was heading into the future with some idea of what it would look like. The next day everything was up for grabs. I thought about what I had just done and I knew I was a whole new person. The old me would never have inflicted my rage on Amy's bed. I would have gone home and cried about it for the next three months instead. I looked at the hand that had moments ago held a butcher knife. There was a faint red mark where the handle had rubbed against my skin. It hurt a bit, but it was a pain that I liked. There was satisfaction in it. And something you barely hear about these days—justice. I was sure I'd be condemned for giving in to violence, but I didn't care. I'd had what every scorned lover wants. I'd had my revenge and if it wasn't exactly sweet, it was, at least, all mine.

Getting Out

Thea Caplan

They are going to the hospital; her husband has finally agreed to take her. He knocks snow off his boots, then looks up to the sky, frowning.

The child stands by the pickup truck making faces, sticking out his tongue. His brown snowsuit is open. His nose is dripping. The woman says to her husband, "I can't lift him." She stuffs her hands in her pockets. She has forgotten gloves.

"Can you put him in the truck?" she asks.

The child holds snowsuited arms up to his father.

The man looks over his shoulder at his frame house, darkened by the mountain's shadow.

"Pat cake, pat cake," says the child, thumping the door of the pickup.

The man grimaces at the child. He wraps his arms around the boy's bottom, lifting the little navy boots an inch off the ground. The woman sees her husband's strong legs bent at the knees, his sneer. He puts the child down.

The woman knows he resents her for being too ill to lift the child. He's deliberately taking his time getting her to the hospital.

She sees Daniel and her husband have moved away from the truck, and are standing beside a struggling pine, staring at each other. The child's breath flutters in the cold. With the heel of his boot Daniel taps the snow, like a horse in a stall. Clouds hover against the sharp sky.

Aviv says to her, "I've got to get something. Get in the truck." He starts leading the boy toward the house but when Daniel throws himself onto the ground, flinging his legs and screaming, "Play in the snow," Aviv turns abruptly leaving the child lying on his back, speechless.

"Make a snow ball," the woman says gently to her son, who sits up and grabs some snow, eyes big and blue and bright. She opens the door, slowly lowers herself in.

In a fantasy she roars off in the truck. Zooms down the mountain she has travelled only three times in ten years, past the old dirt road, past the house that probably still sells cheese and brown eggs, coolly steering the truck through an icy patch as if negotiating hairpin turns is just another thing you do on Tuesdays.

She could slide into the driver's seat, start the ignition. She's got the extra key hidden in her purse, and she knows—at least she thinks she can remember—how to drive.

She'd flick on the radio —a radio!—and a voice would announce the escalation of conflict in the Middle East, the winners of a trip to Acapulco. Music! She'd open the window, music whipping through the truck, bouncing off the grey rocks, her face warm and sweaty like the time she'd raced from her final nursing exam, gunned her startled Beetle, squealed down Rue St. Catherine to pick up her wedding gown. Johnny Cash blasting on the radio. Even country music had sounded encouraging. At their wedding, Aviv, cool and dark. She'd heard a bridesmaid remark that he'd stole the show.

She flicks her son's blue eyes out of her mind.

Her fantasy ends, as it must, at the stop sign in the valley, where one has the choice to take either the Interstate 5 north or south, for she cannot imagine the truck with her in it driving beyond that point. Although . . . once she got away. Three years ago, when Aviv was in town selling a van he'd rebuilt, she and Daniel—he was an infant then—and four-year-old Emily, and several suitcases she'd been told to pack, were bundled into a rented station wagon. Daniel was given a baby bottle of milk and she and Emily were each handed a cupful of orange juice. She was told to lie low in the back seat. "Just like we planned," her father kept saying. "You can never be too sure." A tarp was thrown over their heads. Eight hours later she woke up, groggy, in Canada. They dropped off the rental car at the airport in Vancouver and flew to Montreal. Daniel screamed throughout the flight and Emily pooped in her pants. Her father was upset he'd run out of valium since it had worked so well during the long drive from Oregon, keeping the three of them quiet as mice.

Once they reached her childhood home in Montreal her father forbade her to mention Aviv's name. She and the kids were supposed to start a new life; she took French refresher classes, got a perm. With her hair frizzed out she looked electrocuted. Daniel shrieked when he saw her, refused to suckle her left breast, leaving her lopsided and dripping. "Be positive. Look to the future," her parents kept saying. "You're in a rebuilding phase," said her father, a plumbing contractor. "Rome wasn't built in a day," said her mother. "Have some porridge." Emily was enrolled in French kindergarten and got proficient at saying, "Donnez-moi les haricots, s'il vous plaît."

She liked the telephones with the little square finger pads. "Dialing," her father said, "has been out for years." Everything had become so complicated. To make hot cereal you had to use a microwave bowl, cover it with plastic wrap—vented or unvented? she couldn't remember, and "enter" the proper time on the fingertip control chart. She kept setting off the burglar alarm system. A functional idiot with wet spots on her blouse. She left a sour milky trail that embarrassed and nauseated her mother. Her smell was oddly victorious against her mother's perfumes, sprays, and disinfectants.

Aviv loved her best when she didn't wash. He'd sniff her neck, thighs, drawing in deep breaths, smiling. "I love your earthy smell," he'd say. "It's sweet, and musky." Sometimes when peering into an engine, he claimed he could smell her essence on him. He said it made him dizzy. He was positive others could smell it too and that made him wild, and often clinched the deal. Her mother baked every morning and wouldn't look her in the eye. In the afternoon her mother talked on the telephone, switching to an inane chatter whenever she entered the room. It was years since she'd used a phone. Standing on her father's overshoes in the hall closet, a heavy black receiver pressed against her ear, giggling to Ruthie about a cute football player in their home room class.

Getting a phone was the one thing she had fought with Aviv about. "What if one of the children gets sick?"

"We aren't getting a phone, and that's it," he said. She could still hear the door slamming.

There were six telephones in her parents' house. They gave her a cordless phone she could use in the bathroom. At night, in her old pink bedroom (the kids down the hall in separate rooms), the telephone sat gleaming on the wicker night table, mocking her. She had no one to call in Montreal. No one she could bear to speak to. She had trouble sleeping. The sirens howled, even at three in the morning. Montreal had only cranky birds, most of them perched on her window ledge. It was impossible to see a sunset and the mountains were a joke.

Every night she cursed Aviv. She took to pounding her pillow, though it seemed juvenile, then spitting into it. She imagined Aviv tied to the headboard, his hairy arms and legs splayed. Straddling him, she'd slap his face, rake her fingernails down his chest. Blood would bubble in neat lines. He'd try to bite her hand as it whipped across his cheeks but she'd be too fast for him. When his face was red and puffed up like a cabbage, he'd say, "Sit on my face." And she'd raise her hips to him.

In the mornings the ivory phone gleamed in her eye. Once she flung it across the room, and it ended up in her sneaker, beeping rudely. She should have asked Aviv for a phone when he held his wrists together, eyes shining as she tightened the knots. She should have insisted on a phone then. If she had, she could call him, hear his voice now.

The last time she rode in the truck was in July, the day Emily died. The doctor at the hospital in Eugene asked to meet with both parents; he had some questions, strictly routine, he said. She had been in shock and was relieved to hear Aviv explain the accident. How Emily had climbed the tree, how he warned her to stop at the second branch. How he had found her, a little later, lying face down under the tree, moaning. She remembered serving tea to the county social worker after Mrs. Grant had sat down but before the questions started. Aviv had said, "Right." She had been too ashamed to admit to Mrs. Grant that she couldn't remember what her daughter had been wearing that morning. Couldn't remember giving her breakfast, tying her running shoes. All she could remember was Daniel screaming, and Aviv standing in the sunshine holding Emily over his arm, drool bubbling from her mouth. At the hospital, Daniel, in new pants and a clean white T-shirt Aviv had bought him, kept howling, "Em! Em! Where's Emie!" To shut him up, Aviv stopped in town and let Daniel eat a chocolate ice cream cone in the back seat. The stains are still there; a cloudy mess of brown, looking like a small child's accident.

Right after the funeral Aviv went into Emily's bedroom and came out twenty minutes later dragging green garbage bags. A pink plastic sandal tumbled out. Daniel scooped it up and ran into his room. After Aviv dumped the garbage bags into the pickup truck, he went into Daniel's room and emerged holding the pink sandal.

"Let him have it," she said.

Aviv made a final trip to the truck, reached deep into a garbage bag, stuffed the sandal in. He double tied the bags.

Later when she tucked Daniel in, he curled his thin body away from her, and when she changed sides and crouched on her knees, she saw his eyes, dull and milky like a fish's.

"I'll find you wherever you go," her husband had said. One morning Aviv appeared on her parents' patio while she and the children were having breakfast. She can taste the fresh bite of the grapefruit juice and Aviv's kiss cool on her forehead. She never said goodbye to her mother and father who were still sleeping. She hadn't been able to decide if she was unhappy Aviv had come for her. A part of her felt rescued and discovered. Daniel hardly ever speaks to her.

Aviv still isn't back. She unzips a small compartment in her purse and opens a flat metal pill box. She unwraps a piece of tissue. The key is warm as a breath in her hand. Leaning over, she inserts the key into the ignition. The truck is still mute but with a flick of her fingers she could . . . She yanks the key out. It falls beside the gas pedal. "Stupid," she says out loud, staring at the key.

She is startled by the boy lying on the ground beside the truck. His skin is the color of old snow. His eyes jerk in their sockets. They do not seek her out. They ask nothing of her. Her son turns his head slightly. She follows his gaze. Aviv is approaching the rear of the truck, three strides from the child. The next instant Daniel is flipped, draped over Aviv's arm like a dish towel, eyes lost to the sky, a film of helplessness stuck over them.

Emily's head, hanging over Aviv's arm, her eyes still as a pond. It comes back to her. The blue shorts, the giraffe T-shirt, the glint of sun off the pink plastic sandal dangling from Emily's foot. The pink sandal. She re-examines her memory, turning it over like an artifact. She is looking at her daughter lying on a steel table. It is very quiet in the large white room. Emily looks like any little girl napping in her shorts, T-shirt and running shoes. *Blue running shoes*, perfectly and tightly laced. Running shoes, to climb a tree, always running shoes. Now her mind is pushing beyond itself, pushing. She is crawling under that tree, madly parting the long grass. She finds nothing. No running shoes. What she sees, what she saw, what was dangling from Emily's pale foot when Aviv held her that day was a pink plastic *sandal*.

She rolls down her window. "Put him in the truck," she orders. She can feel Aviv glaring, a block of ice against her neck. His breath smokes the blue air. The clouds drift.

Eye fixed on the key, she takes a deep breath, tightens the muscles in her stomach, and bends over. The pain becomes unbearable. She's hemorrhaging again. This will be her second miscarriage. Not long after Emily died she miscarried in her fourth month. She had wanted to take the pulpy mass to the doctor but Aviv said no. Her hand is trembling. She can feel the curved edges of the key on her thumb and forefinger. Her stomach is ripping apart. Blood pools between her legs, and for a moment it is warm and sensuous.

When she opens her eyes, it is snowing large lazy flakes and the windshield is fogged up. The key is gone. It's not on her lap, not on the floor, nowhere. She can't see it, but she knows it's wedged between the seat and the back rest, hidden. The truck door clicks open, wind hits her teeth. Daniel is placed beside her, on his back, staring up. His breathing is steady. While Aviv settles behind the wheel she plans it. Sneaking out of the house one night carrying Daniel in a blanket, and retrieving the key. Adjusting the driver's seat. Snapping on the headlights. Zooming through the stop sign in the valley.

"Why are you smiling?" It's Aviv asking her something.

"Am I smiling?" she answers, watching his breath hang in the air then disappear.

Cleft

Martha Collins

Cut in half, the breast bone broken, opened,
flattened, flight, if it ever flew,
preserved in the angle of the skinny wings,

and the cleaver raised, *whack*
to the board—A woman wanted to kill
herself, she drew a noose where her name

had been, but last night his fist
came down, across the table she watched
it rise, she watched it fall, as if

for the first time. Then the thud, the glasses
spun, it took her back, an arm rose behind
the frightened child who stood at the window.

Now she remembers the hangman game,
gallows, noose, the man filled in, head,
body, arms, legs, *whack* to the wings, *whack*

to the legs, she could throw the carcass against
the wall, could break the window, climb
on the ledge, letter by letter could spell

her name, the clouds that day, the sharp
bones of the child's small back, wings,
she could fly, she could walk out the kitchen door.

Norway

Wendy White-Ring

Jimmy is laughing. He has this high-pitched cackle that sounds like a parrot's caw, which either makes others laugh along with him, as I used to do, or annoys people. A man pushing a woman in a wheelchair turns around and stares at Jimmy as they pass us outside of Sears.

I'm not laughing, either. I stop at the pay phone near the entrance of the store and check for change in the return slot. I find a dime on the ground, which I put in my wallet, where I also keep a list of all the things about Jimmy. Shopping for a dishwasher will be the next entry.

"Just look at this card," Jimmy keeps saying to himself. "His name is Bobby 'BIG BO' Bouton. Who would put a nickname like that on a business card?"

"How would you like to sell dishwashers for the rest of your life?" I finally tell him. "Let him have a nickname." I step up into Jimmy's truck that always smells like peppermint chewing tobacco and wet dogs. We don't even own a dog.

I say this loudly: "You said you'd buy a dishwasher," although it is not the broken promise of buying a dishwasher nor his making fun of the salesman that makes me nag on him. I want to argue because, these days, when presented with an opportunity for a fight, I am like that scientist's dog who drooled whenever he heard a bell, anticipating the expected outcome.

"I know what I said," he says, shutting his door.

"You said you'd buy a dishwasher," I tell him again, which sounds like I'm disappointed that he didn't follow through with the purchase, although that is far from what I mean.

"You know how most people get ready to buy something, and do all this research, and they price everything, and then they buy it, and then it goes on sale the next day . . . you know?" he asks.

"You know, what?" I say.

"You know how that is?"

"I know how you are," I tell him. Although I really don't. Everything about Jimmy is different now and I have nearly given up waiting for the Jimmy I know to return to me. There is so little time left.

Today is Saturday, January 14, the day Jimmy promised he'd buy a dishwasher, something he never would have worried about before. But this dishwasher is for his father's house, where we live too, and have for the past two years. Tomorrow, Sunday, is the beginning of the third year we've lived with Hugh: 730 days, 104 weeks. I keep track of these things—numbers, days, dates, and years. I write it all down. I have been washing dishes by hand for six days.

Jimmy sighs. As he exhales I think I hear him say "Louise," which was his mother's name, a name he'll use to damn me with one minute, a name he'll fiercely protect the next.

"What did you say?" I ask, my voice sparking, automatically trying to set the fire of another argument.

"Please, just one more week," is all he says.

"What's the big deal, Jim? Hugh said he'd buy it himself," I answer, hoping that maybe, just maybe, Jimmy will lose all interest in this dishwasher business.

"Hey, I don't want to get ripped off. I'm priming Big Bo. He wants me to come back. I'm breaking him down. He'll be giving me a Maytag at the Frigidaire price by next weekend. I don't want to screw this up," he says as he starts the truck.

The money I keep in my jewelry box at Hugh's house would pay for the Frigidaire twice over. But I cannot talk to him about this money, which he thinks is for something else, so all I tell him is, "Then you can wash the dishes."

I don't say another word to Jimmy on the way home and sit over on my side of the truck. We were never this way before. When we used to have fights—about him drinking too much at The Raven, or staying out too late with his carpet and tile buddies, or blowing his paycheck at the dog track—we'd yell at each other loud and long until our voices went hoarse. Sometimes, if I'd been alone all night and he made me mad enough, I'd make a comment about Louise, which usually sent Jimmy beyond words.

Once he grabbed my upper arms and shook me so hard—telling me never to mention his mother again—that my hands went numb. Another time he threw a phone book that hit me in the thigh so hard that I thought my leg had been broken in half. I had a bruise like the shape of Indiana, which turned from red to purple to blue to green to yellow over the next two months.

But right away, Jimmy would put his big arms, like Jose Canseco's, around me and kiss wherever it hurt, whispering, over and over, how sorry he was. Then, pretty soon, we'd start pulling at each other's clothes and he'd push inside me and I could feel again, every part of me, which made me shake. Like how I've seen those time-elapsed science films on TV that show a tiny tundra flower blooming, the petals uncurling, the stem twisting everything toward the heat of the sun. At the end, when the plant is fully extended, watch how the leaves tremble.

Sometimes we had fights while Jimmy was driving the truck and he'd pull off the road, the tires skidding on gravel, the doors rattling as he braked. We'd have it out and, afterward, he'd pull me close, driving with one hand on the steering wheel, the other fiddling with my hair or rubbing up and down my thigh until we got home. Sometimes we'd do it in the truck, on the shoulder of the road.

But today he only looks like the "do" example from a driver's ed class, hands at the 10 and 2 o'clock position, hands that haven't touched me hardly at all in a year, hands that don't seem to miss me. He doesn't even turn on the radio like he used to, which means that he won't be singing off-key to Merle Haggard or Johnny Cash or Randy Travis. Jimmy used to love Randy Travis and tried to make his voice crack that way.

I stare out the window at the roads that Jimmy and I used to drive as teenagers, the roads that were lined with farms, farms that are now golf courses, strip shopping centers, housing developments. I see the new subdivisions that have been built even since Jimmy and I moved out here two years ago. I watch kids playing in what used to be cotton and alfalfa fields. Most of Jimmy's father's friends sold their farmland to developers and moved to Litchfield Park, to expensive condos on the golf course.

Hugh's one of the last to hang onto his farm, even though he hasn't worked it since he got sick. He leases the land to another farmer. Even when he was so ill a year and a half ago that the priest gave him last rites, he was still strong enough to whisper to Jimmy, "Don't you the hell sell this out to no one." Then he got better. He's been in remission for a year. If I was so inclined, I'd say it was a miracle. But I just think it's because he was so angry. I've come to understand how he feels.

When we arrive back at the house, Jimmy's dad is sitting on the front porch swing, waiting for us. He's reading one of the *National Geographics* the nun with red hair brought him when he was sick. She dropped off the magazines by the sackful, and I used to read them to Hugh: stories about crop duster pilots who fly five feet off the ground; kingfisher birds that dive into lakes or rivers to catch fish; and a town in Norway called Tromsø, within the Arctic Circle. The houses there are painted in bright oranges and reds because the sun doesn't shine for 58 days between late November and January. It's called *Mørketiden*, the murky time.

"What time is it?" Jimmy finally says when we reach the farm. He brakes the truck to a quick stop, the dirt from the driveway blowing around us.

I look at my watch. "Twelve-fifteen," I tell him.

"Game's on in fifteen minutes."

"You're washing the dishes first," I say, watching him shut the driver's side door. He doesn't bother to disagree. He doesn't even bother to look at me.

I climb down from the truck. "Hey, Hugh," I tell Jimmy's dad, kissing him on the tuft of gray hair on top of his head as I walk to the front door.

"Twine time," Jimmy says to Hugh.

"Swisheroo for two," Hugh says, making like he's shooting a basketball. They high-five each other as Jimmy climbs the porch steps.

"Slam bam shazam," Jimmy says, mimicking Al McCoy, the play-by-play announcer for the Phoenix Suns. Then Jimmy laughs and Hugh joins him.

I want to laugh with Jimmy, like I used to, but I can't. I remind myself that Jimmy was shopping for a dishwasher today and today is his last chance. I can't stand to listen to them so I walk inside. And what do I do? The dishes.

I run the hot water and squeeze in a few dabs of soap, filling the sink with cereal bowls, plastic Phoenix Suns cups, a variety of silverware, pots, pans, plates, and the skillet, greasy from last night's hamburgers. I start humming a song I make up as I wash. I like composing this way. I do it for the three kids I take care of during the week, thinking up tunes and naming the songs for Carrie, Michael, and Matt—the last two are twins. It makes them feel like they're celebrities, me telling them that I'm singing a song no one has ever heard before, that it's just for them. They dance around.

You don't have to have a day-care license in Arizona with only three kids, so I've kept my operation small. I take a little money for myself, and tuck it into the false drawer of the jewelry box my father made me for Christmas when I was ten.

I give the rest of the money to Jimmy to put in our bank account. But I keep the dollar bills I find in Hugh's and Jimmy's pants pockets when I do the wash every three days; I check behind the cushions of the couch and chairs for more money; and I look in every change return slot on pay phones and vending machines. This year, I've saved $673. I don't tell anyone this.

Jimmy walks into the kitchen and opens a cabinet, pulling out a box of Cheezits. "You sure have been acting Louisey lately," he says softly so that Hugh, sitting in the next room, won't hear but I will. I know that this is my opportunity to pull Jimmy back.

I hold on tight to the sink, bracing myself for the way my skin will sting and I whisper to him, "Louise was the smart one," although she was one of those people you read about in the newspaper and shake your head and say, "What a shame." She drank too much and smoked in bed. One night she blacked out with a lit cigarette in her hand, which started a fire that burned her to death. Hugh and Jimmy were out setting a head of water in an alfalfa field when it happened. Jimmy says all he remembers is the yellow lights flashing on the fire truck. He was eleven.

"She was lucky to cut out early," I say, closing my eyes when I see him raise his hand. And then there's a slap. But it's not my skin he hits. He's slammed the cabinet door shut. He turns to the refrigerator and pulls out two bottles of Coors, then opens the freezer and takes two frosted beer mugs from the shelf.

"Turn on the pregame show, Dad," is all Jimmy says.

I am left alone in the kitchen. Just beyond the pass-through, Jimmy and Hugh sit in their matching easy chairs. From the back, now that Hugh's gained much of the fifty pounds he lost, you can hardly tell Jimmy and his father apart, except that Hugh doesn't have any hair. They're both tall, about 6'4", and remind me of the glass buildings in downtown Phoenix, reflecting each other, so much alike.

And as I wash and rinse the dishes I think about how, before we moved here two years ago from Tucson, Hugh and Jimmy were never close. When Jimmy and I married out of high school eight years before, and didn't take over running the farm, I honestly thought we'd never see Hugh again. But when Jimmy found out how sick his dad was, he wanted to be near Hugh. Jimmy told me it was temporary, that it looked like his dad wouldn't be hanging on long, that we'd leave for California where he'd contract to build custom homes for movie stars. I thought we'd stay in Phoenix a month or two.

At first I didn't mind moving back. I had been working in Tucson at a bank as a teller and Jimmy worked for a home builder laying carpet—two jobs you can find just about anyplace.

We took those jobs after we married because Jimmy said Tucson was a stopping point on the way to Texas, specifically to Dallas, where Jimmy said he could cash in on the boom down there, contracting to build custom homes for oil millionaires. And he said he'd build us a house, too, with room for four kids. He wanted two boys and two girls. But he said we couldn't start a family until we'd worked steady, reliable jobs and saved up money to start his contracting company. He didn't want to struggle financially with a business and kids the way his parents had. He remembered eating too many pinto bean dinners.

So we saved, never taking vacations, or buying hardly anything until we had $7,312 in the bank. Those eight years just blend into one long one, working toward a life that never happened, that probably was never meant to happen. It was like we were waiting for bread to rise, not knowing we forgot to mix in the yeast. We're people missing an ingredient.

The oil boom went bust and we stayed in Tucson trying to figure out where to go next when we got the word on Hugh. We rented a small apartment in west Phoenix. Jimmy hooked up with a carpet store, and I was just starting to interview with banks when Hugh's condition worsened. He was too sick to take care of himself and he refused to be admitted to the hospital. So we moved in with him.

I was the one who looked after Hugh. And I didn't mind because I found some comfort in being with him, in keeping him clean, dressing him in pressed pajamas, and making him eat, even when he didn't want to. I felt like I was helping him fight, even though I thought the fight was temporary.

Hugh was a 52-year-old man in a 90-year-old body, his skin pinched around his sick bones. But I discovered a youthfulness that surrounded him when he came so close to dying. That one night he lay in the fetal position and told me he saw geese walking across his bed and waterfalls cascading down from the closet. He laughed. It was a peacefulness he hadn't felt for a long time.

When Jimmy came home and saw Hugh in that state, he called the priest and the doctor. That's when Hugh started moaning, a low rumble that seemed to paint every wall in the house with the hurt he felt inside, about Jimmy and the farm, about Louise, about his body that had withered away. And I knew then he wasn't going to die. Nobody who can moan like that is going to die. It was the anger inside him that kept him living.

I know it scared Jimmy to watch his sole surviving parent go to the edge that way, to hear that moan. And I think Jimmy got it in his mind that the whole situation was his fault for not taking over the farm in the first place, but that by living with Hugh the way they did before he ever met me, Jimmy could, in some way, hold off the inevitable. So that on the night Hugh lived, Jimmy and I died.

Hugh's recovery wasn't an instant process and our marriage didn't disintegrate overnight. No, both took many, many months. In the meantime, Jimmy and I spent our savings—$7,312—on 24-hour-a-day nursing at the house. Jimmy said Hugh was too much for me to take care of, and maybe he was, but Hugh's insurance policy didn't cover the nurse's services. We didn't tell Hugh this. Our savings account was empty by the end of four months. That's when I started the day care.

"What counts is that he's still alive," Jimmy still says.

And we're still on the farm. Those things haven't changed. But what's different is that Jimmy doesn't make plans like he did when we first met our junior year in high school on Friday, September 10, 1975, at the filling station where he worked, which was next to the resort where I waitressed in the coffee shop. I asked him for $5 of regular for my mother's station wagon. He asked me out on a date, saying we'd go to a Neil Young concert, have dinner at a restaurant on the top floor of the Hyatt Hotel in downtown Phoenix, and drive to Camelback Mountain in his sports car. I believed him. He drove a truck and we went out to the desert and drank beer, me in my high heels and best pants suit. He passed out. This is the first item on my list.

I didn't mind the big schemes then—going to Alaska to work on the pipeline, or building homes in Texas and California. At least we were planning together for the future, even though I knew it wouldn't work out exactly as we expected. If we had moved, Jimmy would probably still be laying carpet, I'd be counting money at a bank, and we'd have two kids instead of four. It's strange how you can live for years counting on fulfilling plans you made a long time ago, when you were a different person. Jimmy doesn't dream any more, not even about small things.

When I finish the dishes, I walk into the living room and sit on the couch while Hugh and Jimmy watch the game. I read a couple of the magazines the nun gave Hugh: an article about Las Vegas showgirls, a story about women astronauts, and a piece about the hunting behavior of baboons. Hugh and Jimmy yell at the television, about bad calls and lousy passes and missed shots, but I hardly hear them until the game ends and I realize that they're talking about the farm. Hugh isn't renewing the farmer's lease to work Hugh's fields. He wants to farm it himself this year with Jimmy's help. Hugh tells Jimmy that they'd be partners.

Jimmy says, "Put it there, partner," and they high-five each other again.

They talk as if I'm not there. I look out the living room's picture window and watch the sun tuck itself behind the White Tank Mountains, streaking the sky with orange and pink bands. I hum to myself again, not thinking, not seeing anything until I hear Jimmy telling me, "Come on." He's pulling at the sleeve of my shirt. "We'll be back soon, Dad."

"What's going on?" I ask Jimmy as he walks to the front door and I follow. He holds the door open for me and, as I pass through, I want to feel Jimmy's hand skirt the small of my back and ease me into the crook of his arm, my arm sliding around his waist and us walking together, our feet matching step for step, a balance between us that we've never found. Instead, he turns and locks the door.

"We're going to buy ourselves a dishwasher," Jimmy says as we walk down the porch steps.

"What about waiting until next week?" I ask as I climb into the truck.

He opens the driver's side door and sits down. "Unless you want to wash those dishes for another seven days." He says this smiling, his arm reaching back. For a moment I think he's going to put his arm around my shoulder, lean over, and kiss me, making my scalp tingle. Instead, I watch as he reaches into his jeans pocket for his can of chewing tobacco, putting a plug into his mouth.

When we get to the store, Jimmy asks a salesman at the counter where we can find Bobby "BIG BO" Bouton.

"He's left for the day. Can I help you?"

"No," Jimmy says, and starts walking toward the exit. I smile at the salesman, whose nametag says DOUG. I actually think that Jimmy doesn't want to buy the dishwasher after all. For a span of five, maybe ten, seconds, I actually believe that the old Jimmy has returned. And I half-run after him, to where he's standing by the front door.

"Hey, I'm thinking why don't I sport the hundred bucks extra and get this Maytag?" he asks me, and I realize that, while we're standing by the door, we're also at the edge of the dishwasher display section.

"What?" I ask. I'm thinking why doesn't Jimmy save the hundred bucks and build up our savings account again so we can go on, together. By this time, Doug the salesman is standing beside Jimmy and rubbing the front of the dishwasher as if it were a show horse.

"It's five hundred bucks but it's a nicer model that'll last a long time," Jimmy says.

"Last a long time?" I say this loud but, for a change, not in order to start a fight. I'm just making sure I heard him correctly, just making sure that this will be the last item on my list.

"Then we don't have to worry about another dishwasher breaking," Jimmy says. "You know, on those Maytag commercials the repairman's always lonely."

Jimmy and Doug are staring at me, waiting for me to say something, anything.

"Yes?" Jimmy asks. "No?"

"I don't care," I say, which to Jimmy is as good as a yes.

I watch Jimmy and Doug walk to the counter to fill out the paperwork and I know, right then, that it's too late for me. Jimmy is smiling and joking with Doug, happy that in a year, two years, or five years from now, he'll still be out there on the farm with Hugh and the dishwasher. I walk outside and sit in the truck, ready to go.

After dinner, after I've stacked the dishes in the new Maytag that Jimmy installed when we got home, Jimmy and Hugh sit down in the living room, in their easy chairs, with their matching beer glasses placed on the low table between them. Hugh turns on the television with the remote control. Then he flips through the forty-five cable channels in a span of five minutes, lingering on each station long enough to catch a key point of dialogue or a clip of an action sequence. I sit on the couch and watch the numbers on the cable box change for a full round. Then I stand up and tell Hugh and Jimmy good night. Jimmy lifts his hand as he stares at the TV, watching a replay of Wayne Gretzky scoring a goal.

"Feeling OK?" Hugh asks me.

"Fine," I say, walking from the room.

I shut the door to the bedroom, the one where Louise died, the one that was rebuilt after the fire, the only bedroom big enough for a double bed. Hugh stays in Jimmy's childhood room next door, but most nights he and Jimmy fall asleep in their chairs while watching TV.

I take the list out of my wallet and write, "January 14—shopped for and bought Maytag dishwasher." I have a total of 27 reasons.

Then I open my jewelry box and pull out the false drawer. Inside there's the $673 from the day care money I've earned, mostly in ten and twenty denominations, as well as the coins from Hugh's and Jimmy's pockets, pay phones, and vending machines that I've wrapped in rolls; my passport; newspaper ads for SAS Airlines with fares to Stockholm and train information to Norway; and listings of employment agencies and day care services. I put all of this in my purse, along with the $20 bill that Carrie's mom gave me. I didn't tell the mothers why I was quitting the day care, but I think Carrie's mom must have known that I'd need extra money whatever I was doing.

I'll make it to Tromsø by Sol Dag , January 21, when the light reappears and is greeted by the town's children, who make paper cutouts of the sun, hanging them everywhere. I have enough money for a one-way ticket, train fare, and a cheap room. All I have to do is show up at the airport an hour before the flight tomorrow.

A year ago, after I came up with my plan, Jimmy walked into the bedroom as I was counting my money. "What are you doing?" he asked.

"Nothing." I couldn't think of anything else to say. But I wanted to tell him of my idea after all the years of listening to his.

"What's all this? Where'd you get the money?"

I still couldn't answer. I was surprised by his expression, the way his mouth looked, so soft, after all our hard years.

"The baby fund, Jimmy," I finally said, gathering the rolls of change and the dollar bills into my hands. "I'm saving money for our babies."

He believed me, trusted me, because he had no reason not to. And I knew I could go on with my plan because he'd never suspect what I was doing. The only obstacle was me. The more I disappeared from Jimmy's life, the more I seemed to vanish from myself, my memory like a tape erasing. That's when I started writing down the reasons why I needed to leave, with dates—the spent savings, unachieved plans, the lack of attention. I don't know when the last time was that Jimmy called me by my name.

I turn off the light and look at the digital clock by the bed. It hums as it flips over its numbers—8:56. I try to warm up the sheets by kicking my legs, like I'm swimming. I hug my pillow and fall asleep the way I do each night: I think of waking up at four o' clock, automatically, like I've been practicing for months; getting my packed suitcase from the garage, hidden near where Jimmy put the old dishwasher after he installed the Maytag tonight; walking the three miles to the resort where I used to waitress, next to the filling station where Jimmy worked; riding in the resort's shuttle to the airport; watching my suitcase glide down the conveyer belt as I get my seat assignment; sitting in the terminal and having an older woman ask me where I'm going.

"Norway," I see my mouth forming.

A cold cricket is trying to squeeze out a sound from a corner of the room when I wake up four hours into my third year on the farm. I ease myself off the bed and dress in the dark. As I walk out of the bedroom, I can hear the television, still on from the night before, the fuzz of a station that hasn't yet started programming for the day. I tiptoe into the living room. Hugh and Jimmy are sleeping. In the light from the TV screen, I unfold the two blankets that are stacked on the couch and drape one over Jimmy, his big arms crossed in front of his chest, and tuck the other blanket around Hugh. I softly kiss the tuft of gray hair on top of his head, then turn off the TV, and leave.

Grace

Robbie Clipper Sethi

She should have known that her marriage of convenience would be anything but. She had seduced him easily enough. Their love affair was all a big cliché: they'd met at a party near the University of Pennsylvania campus; he was one of the few people there who cared anything about design, perspective, the re-creation of life in two dimensions; she had asked him if he'd care to see her paintings.

He liked her geometric heads, their crossed eyes and twisted lips. "I wanted to study photography," he said, "but we were middle class."

"*We're* middle class." Worse: her father worked the line at Campbell's Soup.

"In India only the rich can take a chance on not making money." He had come to Wharton for an M.B.A.

"I can't support myself with this," Grace said. She was looking for an assistant professorship; meanwhile, she was waiting tables, which paid more than part-time teaching.

In some ways marrying a well-paid man seemed easier than supporting herself, as long as he was willing to spend his salary on paint and canvases, and save Grace the time she would otherwise have had to waste taking orders, wiping tables, and picking up tips.

Living together might have been enough if she had known what to call him: "boyfriend" seemed too immature, and when she referred to her "lover," everyone assumed that she was living with a woman, so thoroughly had homosexuals expropriated the term.

Her parents didn't like the obvious cohabitation without papers, but they had spent all their lives avoiding conflict; they went out of their way not to mention marriage. "What is he," her mother asked, "a Hindu?"

Her father said, "At least he's not a Catholic."

When Inder finished his degree, his parents and his sister wrote him letters asking him to come back and "settle down" with "a good girl of your own choice."

"That means they're finding me a wife," he said.

"Don't they know about me?"

"Are you kidding? They don't even know I've given up the turban, or shaved my beard! They'd be over here in a minute, trying to persuade me that I'd been seduced, that you were only interested in my money."

"You have been seduced," she said, "and your money is keeping me out of the bars six nights a week."

"I can't go anyway," he said. "Immigration would never let me back."

They were married in city hall, the statue of tolerant, immigrant William Penn standing over them. They didn't dare tell Grace's parents. Only after Inder was sure that he could get back into the country did he write a letter to his mother and father:

I am planning a trip to India in January. I have met someone I very much respect. I would like to bring her with me to meet the family, according to your wishes.

With highest respect, your loving son,

Inder Singh

The first call came in three weeks: Inder's mother was ill, he had to come right away; his father was weak, only God could say whether he would live to see his son again; his sister shouted so loud that Grace could hear her voice across the room.

In the end they got on a plane together, watched four movies, ate five meals, and leafed through every magazine in the racks.

At the airport Inder's mother clung to his neck and wailed while big tears disappeared into his father's beard. Until they could pry his mother off him and lead her to the taxi—hordes of people were watching this display—Inder's sister crushed Grace in her fleshy arms. Grace was glad her parents had not had the money to come and be on hand to witness this display of excessive emotion.

Days passed on the string cots and jute mats in the courtyard of Inder's parents' house. His mother shouted in Punjabi while Inder sat, hardly reacting, on one of the steel-and-linoleum chairs of their dinette set.

"My brother was so handsome with the turban and the beard," his sister said. "Bibiji and Darji cannot accept."

Inder's uncles came, their wives, their grown-up sons. Everybody had something to say, mostly in Punjabi.

Grace finally saw Inder alone, on his way out of the bathroom, which was separated from the house by the open courtyard. "What's going on?" she asked.

"We're getting married."

"Here you are!" his sister said, walking across the courtyard. "I've been looking all over for you."

Grace wore one of Inder's sister's saris, rose silk embroidered with silver marigolds, wrapped around her own black leotard. She stood before a crowd of people in their temple and heard a bearded priest say something like her name—Ga-race Mad-i-son. Then she and Inder walked four times around the holy book and stood under a shower of flowers, the like of which were used to decorate their marriage bed, the only double in the house.

"This is the first time I've been alone with you the whole trip," Grace said.

"We've got our whole lives to be alone," he said.

She didn't see much of India, either. She got up to the smell of dung smoke every morning, the sound of vegetable hawkers and prayers. She sat in the courtyard and sketched the sunlight coloring the cement walls of the house. "What are you drawing?" people asked, and they looked from her sketchpad to the walls and back again.

"We would have had the whole house painted," her father-in-law said, "but you gave so little notice."

She dressed in brilliant skirts, saris, or baggy pants, rode taxis through streets teeming with oranges, golds, yellows, and reds, and then slept for an hour or two. Inder's sister would wake them up, saying that it was time to visit some relative.

She couldn't wait to get home.

Back in the bigger and sunnier bedroom of their new two-bedroom apartment, she painted the evil eyes of peacock feathers, the stripes of the Bengal tiger. She framed the batiks and Rajasthani paintings she had bought, and painted Philadelphia girls, their breasts bulging out of midriff tops.

Inder let her paint. He was the only man who had ever let her paint. Other men had interfered, tried to finish the paintings for her, tried to outpaint her. Inder told her what he thought only when she asked for it.

"This is the most productive summer I have ever had," she said.

In the fall his mother came. She cleaned the apartment every day, from time to time bursting in on Grace with a handful of comer dust for her inspection. In the afternoons she sat behind Grace, coughing every time Grace opened a tube of paint. Toward evening she banged pots loudly. The smell of cooking oil seeped into Grace's oil paints.

Grace watched, speechless. Unlike Inder's sister and father, his mother spoke no English, and Grace was far too busy painting to learn Punjabi. The closest language to it that she could have studied was Hindi-Urdu, and the University of Pennsylvania was so expensive that she couldn't afford to take the course anyway.

"Why doesn't your mother go home?" she asked. "Two months is long enough to visit anyone."

"She has a four-month visa," Inder said.

"I can't take another two months!"

"I can't tell her to leave. In India a parent is always welcome."

"But this is not India!"

"She doesn't care about that. I'm her only son. She wants to make sure I'm well settled."

"Well, tell her. You're very well settled. She can go home and get on with her own life."

"She will. She's worried, anyway, about my father and sister"

And she did go home, but not until six months later, after her visa had been extended for four more months.

Another summer, and Grace painted folds of fabric, cascading hair, the sun on russet skin. She and Inder bought a house and made love on the screened porch, waking to the songs of birds. "This is even better than last summer," Grace said, and she wished it could go on forever, but just as the nights were turning cold, Bibiji came back, with Inder's father.

"I cannot live alone," he said. "I am infirm."

"What is he talking about?" Grace asked. "They live with your sister."

"He's retired," Inder said. "His pension won't even pay the taxes, let alone the bills, and in India you don't take money from your daughter. People say you're stealing from her dowry."

"Your sister's forty-four years old!"

"They tried for fifteen years to have me," Inder said. "When mv father lost the business. Behanji had to go to work. Her dowry went to pay for my school."

"You already stole from her dowry! Are you saying this is it? They're here to stay?"

"Of course not. They're happy in India."

In the mornings, after Inder went to work, Grace would go downstairs for her coffee. Her father-in-law always joined her at the table. Her mother-in-law went right on cleaning. One morning her mother-in-law shouted from the family room, where she was on her hands and knees, dusting the floor.

"Bibiji wants a baby," her father-in-law said, almost blushing.

"Isn't she a little old?" Grace asked.

He laughed. "Not hers," he said. "She is impatient for a grandson to carry on the name."

"It's your name," Grace said.

She told Inder, in the bathroom, the only place she could get to him alone when he came home from work, "If I thought you wanted babies, I wouldn't have tied you down with me."

"What are you talking about?" he said. "I don't want babies."

"Well, your mother does."

"Of course she does. She has no other chance for grandchildren, and in India children are everything. Don't you remember all the jokes my aunts made about American grandchildren?"

"I couldn't understand your aunts. Do you want babies?"

"I don't know," he said. "I've never thought about it."

"Because if you do, you never should have married me. If I had a baby, I'd never get any work done. Even now I can't concentrate on a simple sketch with them shouting at each other—"

"What do you want me to do? I can't tell my parents what to do."

"But you can tell your wife she can't live the way she wants to in her own house."

"You can do anything you want," he said. "I've never told you what to do. Have I? Have I?"

She had to admit that he never had.

"It's only temporary, Grace. A few more months." She tried to turn away. "Grace? Please let me handle this. I just don't want to hurt them."

She stuffed her ears with wax, couldn't even hear when Darji knocked on the door. He would come upstairs to the third bedroom and stand behind her, for how long she never knew. She'd turn, jump, sometimes let out a little scream, which he would return, and Bibiji would shout from the kitchen. He would tell Grace, every day, "We have no milk, no eggs. What are you cooking for dinner?"

When Inder came home, she would corner him in the bathroom. "They're mature adults. Why can't they get their own groceries?"

"They can't drive."

"Teach them."

"Me teach my father how to drive? He never even drove in India."

"This is not India."

"They'll only be here for a few more months," Inder said. "If they need groceries, I can buy them on the way home."

She could never get them to complain to him directly. Darji would wait until Inder had gone off to work. "Your mother-in-law is not feeling well," he'd say. "She must see a doctor."

"What's wrong?" she asked—once. After that she learned.

"Some pains in the neck," her father-in-law said.

"Have you mentioned this to Inder?"

"She does not want to worry her son."

She took them to a doctor she had confided in when she was still supporting herself serving double scotches to medical students. Darji translated Bibiji's complaints; then he told the doctor about his own muscle pains, fatigue, indigestion, confusion with the fast talk on the television.

"Get a little exercise," Joel said. "Your wife, too. Walk an hour every day."

"We cannot walk," Darji said. "Our legs are weak."

Joel sent them out into the waiting room. "I could order tests," he told Grace, "but my suspicion is it's arthritis, lack of exercise, old age. And tests can be expensive. Do they have insurance?"

"I don't know." She felt like crying—if only Joel had specialized in psychiatry.

"Yo," he said. "Where's the Grace who used to get me drunk? Professionally speaking, that is." She had to leave, she knew it. He had other patients. Besides, she scared herself with a sudden urge to rub her face against the auburn stubble on his pasty cheek.

On the way home Darji asked if they could do a little shopping. With whose money, Grace wondered. She had just dropped sixty bucks for their medical hallucinations. Their very presence in her Japanese subcompact depressed her—Darji on the seat beside her with his turban pressed against the roof, Bibiji in the back in her polyester pantaloons and 1940s dress. Even the Philadelphia boys in their tight black pants and tank tops made her want to stop the car, get out, and hang out on the corner. She was, she realized with a touch of alarm, beginning to prefer her own kind.

Grace had never been able to approach a conflict with anything more flammable than paint, but arguing with Inder had given her practice. "Darji," she said, "why don't I enroll you in a driving school, so you don't have to keep asking me to take Bibiji shopping?"

"I cannot drive," he said. "My legs are too short!" The old man's eves filled with tears, and he shouted, his voice breaking, "It is for the children to care for the old. What is time to them? We have little time left. How much trouble can it be to take your Bibiji and Darji to the shopping center so we will have some time outside our stinking, paint-smelling house?"

Grace tore home, left them in the driveway, and backed out again to scream at the highway. "The bastard! It's bad enough I was stupid enough to marry one man. Now I have to deal with two. Who is he to expect me to walk him around the local mall? How does he know how much time I have? I wouldn't put it past him to outlive me!"

When she came home in the evening, they were sitting in front of the television, watching a situation comedy with a laugh track so loud that Grace could hear it even before she touched the doorknob. Darji turned around, a smile stretched across his face. "Hello, daughter!" he shouted. "Did you buy the milk? Potatoes? Cooking oil?"

She found Inder in the bathroom. "Send a letter to your sister," she said. "Tell her that we just can't take it anymore. She has to take them back."

"I can't say that!"

"Well, you'll have to say something. I drive around for hours not wanting to come home and face the noise, the demands, the expectations. When does their visa run out?"

"It doesn't matter. They've applied for permanent residency."

"What? They can't stay here! Are you crazy?"

"It's not to stay here. It's just so they can come back any time without being hassled by Immigration."

"I'm not sure I want them to come back any time." "They won't," Inder said. "They're bored. That's why they have so many aches and pains. Do you think they like being dependent on us?"

"I don't know what they like," Grace said. "Except for afternoon TV, shopping, and—oh, yes—babies."

"It's hard for them," Inder said. "Everyone they know is dying."

"It's hard for me," Grace said. "I'm dying."

"Don't say that!"

"I'm dying, you're dying, we're all dying!—"

He put his arms around her. "Don't even say it. If I ever lose you, I'll lose everything."

She wanted to believe it. She even thought she wanted to have his baby—someday, when she'd done enough work, had enough success. His arms still felt good. Even with his parents downstairs, he was sexy, dark like the Philadelphia boys, but different—educated, on his way to wealth, exotic.

"I need a place to work," Grace said. "I'm going to have to rent a studio."

"How much will that cost? They'll be here for only a few more months."

After another month he finally sent the letter. His sister answered it by telephone, collect. "What? You have the whole house to yourself," Inder said.

And his sister said all the rest: she was bankrupt; the house was a mess; she had nothing to repair it with, so she had rented it to Uncleji, who had moved in with a woman of a different caste and questionable morals; Bibiji had told her that Inder had three bedrooms, air-conditioning; she had no place to go; she had no husband, no children of her own. She threatened to commit suicide if she could not see her mother and father again, her brother and his wife.

They put her in the third bedroom. Grace moved her canvases into the basement. While she carried a still life down the stairs, Inder's sister stood in the doorway, apologizing. "Do not worry. When you start your family, I will sleep in the room with the baby. When he cries, I will get up and bring him to you in the bed."

"I can't stand this," Grace told Inder. "We've got to get them an apartment."

"Behanji will go back," he said. "She'll never be able to live without doing business, and this country operates so differently from India, she'll never get a job."

But she stayed for weeks, months. She sat up all hours with her mother, sobbing. "When are they going to take her back?" Grace asked. "I thought Bibiji wanted to go back and kick her brother out of the house."

"It's difficult to get rid of a tenant in India," Inder said, "especially if the tenant is a relative. Besides, none of them have an income."

"Well, send them cashier's checks," she said. "I'm looking for a job. At a college or a school—where I can use the studio. I can't work in this house anymore."

"Anyone will hire you," Inder said. "Your stuff is ten times better than it's ever been."

"I haven't painted in weeks."

"It hasn't been that bad, has it? You can paint in the basement."

Inder put track lights in the basement, his father supervising. The effort was wasted. Her colors came out wrong. The dampness warped the canvases. She bought a dehumidifier. The noise helped to drown out the TV, the floorboards groaning under Behanji's weight, Bibiji's shouting from the kitchen. The smell of onions, spices, and simmering meat drifted down the steps every day.

Still she tried to paint. She'd trace a perfect jawline, dead set on re-creating that face in her mind.

Behanji would knock on the door. "Am I disturbing you?"

Grace would hold the image just behind her eyes. Unlocking the door, she'd tell Behanji, "Yes. Later. I can't."

"One second," she'd say. "Mummy is afraid you will ruin your eyes, so I have ground up almonds with milk. You must drink it. I will bring it to you. I will not disturb you. One second only."

"Okay, put it there." She would go back to her canvas. "I will, only you must drink it. Mummy told me, 'Make sure she drinks her milk,' and I must. She worries. Even I worry."

It would be hours before Grace could even think of that face again, and by then the jaw was ruined.

She spent the night, whenever she ran out of tolerance, with her parents. They were no help. "Those Indians," her father said, "they're just like the Italians. One of them gets over here, they bring the whole family."

Grace's ancestors, a hundred years ago, had each come over from Europe alone, forgetting even the countries they came from.

"Why don't you get them an apartment?" her mother said. "How old is Inder's sister? They're hiring at the K-mart."

"In India," Grace said, "it's just not done."

She sent resumés to every college and private school within a hundred-mile radius. Sometimes she wondered why she didn't look for schools a thousand miles away.

"When you're working full time," Inder said, "it won't be all that bad. You won't have to come home until the evening, and they're all in bed by nine."

"I've got a better idea: why don't we blow my first three months' pay on three one-way tickets?"

"It's not the money. If it was the money, they would leave. Grace, you've got to get used to them living with us."

"Can you get used to them living with us?"

"They're my family! Behanji gave up her life to send me to school,"

"To study something you didn't particularly want," she reminded him. "In America you give up your family to take a wife. I thought you could do that."

"I did do that."

"No," Grace said. "No."

With a full-time salary at last, she had enough to rent a studio across the river, in the city they had moved away from when they needed the room that Inder's family had filled. She set her easel in front of a long, bare window overlooking the street, and furnished the room with chairs and tables she found by the curbs on her way to work. She bought a mattress for one corner; then she went out and bought sheets, a comforter, and two feather pillows. Her own bed, filling up one corner of the room, scared her, but she lay on it and almost fell asleep. Then she made a cup of coffee and stared at her half-done portrait, pretty bad, in the waning light of the afternoon.

Through the window she watched the men and women in their winter coats. How lonely she had felt in the house in the suburbs, but with no peace to justify the loneliness! She would have preferred the trees, even the lawn mowers, to the traffic, but the city was the place where she had started with Inder, so it was the only place she could return to. Besides, the campus was a block away. From a phone booth across the street she called Inder at work.

"I've got a studio," she said.

"That's great!"

"Move out with me."

"Are you crazy? We can't."

"It's the perfect solution. Let them have the house. We can go back to being lovers. I married you, not a whole damned household."

"Don't say that. I'd like to be irresponsible too, but we can't."

"We can be anything we want. You told me that."

"I meant it. I'll be getting six figures by the time I'm forty, and you'll have so many shows you'll have to hire someone—"

"I don't want to hire anyone," she said, sobbing.

She unwrapped her palette and stroked a little paint onto the canvas. Then she walked to the bank where Inder worked and waited for him. "Let's go home," he said. "They'll stay up all night if we don't come home."

"Don't you ever make a move unless they make it first?"

"What do you want me to do? Give up my family?"

"You don't have to give them up," she said. "Just put them up. Somewhere else."

"They wouldn't go," he said, "even if I asked them to move out. They made a pilgrimage to every temple in India just to have me. They sacrificed themselves to send me to the best schools."

"So now you must sacrifice yourself," Grace said. "But you can't sacrifice me."

"I'm not asking you to sacrifice."

He looked as gray as the paints she'd been pushing around that afternoon. "Come home with me," she said.

"You come home."

"Couldn't you take them out some night, so I can come and pack my clothes?"

"I don't have to take them away," he said. "They forgive everything."

He could have called her any time, but she could understand. She might even have welcomed the silence if it hadn't left her staring at the phone, lunging for it on the first ring, dialing him at work and then hanging up before his secretary could answer. She didn't dare call him at home, even at night.

She threw her energy into teaching, spent too much time with her students, though she couldn't wait to get home and work on her painting: long, lugubrious faces, their complexions gray, their eyes mere holes.

After three weeks he called. "I wish I'd never supported you in the first place," he said. "You might not have left as soon as you got some money of your own."

"It's not the money," she said. "I thought you understood."

"I do. They don't. You've got to come over."

"Are you alone?"

"I thought you'd rather see them here. They're talking about looking for you at the college."

"They wouldn't?"

"They need to feel like they tried to reconcile us. That's how things are done in India."

"This is *not* India," Grace said. "Don't they know that their 'little India' split us apart?"

"You won't say that, will you?"

"Neither one of us says anything," she said. "That's the problem!"

When she walked through the door, Darji took off his turban and laid it at her feet. Bibiji, kicking it out of the way, threw her arms around her and made kissing noises in the air. Behanji wept: "I will give you my gold, all my diamonds, if you will return."

Inder stood in front of the door, his face blank, as if he had never had anything to do with any one of them. Grace stared at him and remembered her painting. She wanted to slap him; then she wanted to comfort him—anything to shock him into loving her again, but not in this place. She pushed Bibiji away. "I haven't come to take your gold or your turban—"

"You must come back," Behanji said. "This is ridiculous. You and my brother have no differences that cannot be reconciled. If you wish, you can sleep in the room with me. Look at you, you are young, you are healthy. You will have many children. It is true what I say, no?"

"No," Grace said. She stared at Inder, unable to find words. "Tell them," she said. "Tell them, damn it."

"Grace needs some time alone for a while," he said.

"No!" she said. "No. What Grace needs is a house of her own. If you want to stay with them—"

"I can't!" he said.

"I can't either." She pushed him aside and opened the door.

"Wait!" Darji said. "I am elder of this family. I forbid you to divorce my son."

Grace laughed. His mouth fell open. Inder said, "No one said anything about divorce."

"Do not go," Behanji cried. "You will stay tonight, have some food. Leave that place in Philadelphia. I will give you new clothes."

"I left my clothes here," Grace said. "All I have in Philadelphia are my paints." She turned and walked out the door.

"Grace!" Inder said.

Darji stood up and fell on his face on the threshold. "I have humbled myself!" he cried. "Witness: I have touched my daughter-in-law's feet!"

Grace drove away before he could throw himself in front of the car. The silence of the road felt almost warm, like the comforting silence of her mother when as a child she was too sick to go to school, and lay on the sofa all day, sipping ginger ale. Her studio was even quieter. She lay on the mattress sipping wine until the voices stopped ringing in her ears.

Inder had seemed not to be there at all. Turning himself off was the only way he'd managed to accept the situation. Grace understood that. But she could never have learned to ignore what was going on right in front of her face. For one thing, it would have killed her work.

Living without him wasn't easy. She taught. She painted. Sometimes she spent a weekend with her parents, but after a night outside the studio she began to miss the smell of paint, the incomplete portrait, the hours spent looking into space while lines and figures flashed before her eyes. Within a few more weeks she had almost grown to like missing Inder.

For months she heard about him. Behanji sent accusatory letters to her at the college. At first Darji was dying, Bibiji had lost ten years off her life. Inder lost weight daily and snapped at his family all the time. Then Darji was better, but would never smile again; Bibiji was eating, but only small-small bites. Inder was developing a horrible temper and would listen to no one.

The last letter shunted all the blame:

> I have been blind, my sister. Now I see. He is cold. He is my own brother, but I call him cold. I do not see how you could have made a love marriage. When he was born, the only son, he was spoiled by too

> much love. I tell you, they are my mother and father, but they are wrong. He grew up expecting everything and getting everything he wanted. And because of him—this boy—because he went to the best schools, wore the best clothing, and had more toys than I got in my lifetime, because of this I have had no dowry. I did not marry and have sons of my own because my brother got everything. It is a fact. That is why I am forced to live on his charity, to share his home. If I had any other choice, I would not.

So, Grace thought, a six-year-old child is supposed to prevent his family from killing itself for him. That would make a good mythic triptych. No: a twenty-one-year-old woman is supposed to know she can't give up her future for a six-year-old brother, who will one day leave the family and find a woman of his own. No doubt in India people had different ideas. She wrote a letter:

> Look here, Behanji, maybe he is cold, though for a time I thought he gave me all the warmth I need. Maybe you should blame your parents. But blaming anybody after twenty-five years is no way, to get on with your life. Get a job, for God's sake. Learn to drive. You're only forty-five. Lose a little weight and you might meet some lonely divorcé a damn sight warmer than your little brother.

Her letter may have been a bit harsh, but absence had made Grace's heart a good deal harder, and though the same absence told her that she'd never again live with Inder, she thought the least she could do was leave him with a better life than they had lived when they had tried to live together.

She avoided other men. Men had always gotten her into trouble. Why had she expected Inder to be any different? She went to the campus. She came home. She painted. She was happy with her latest. It portrayed a gray-faced man, abstractly outlined with a skeletal jaw, a hanging, startled mouth, and big, uncomprehending eyes. A little derivative, but it worked. Her current canvas was so far nothing but a blur of the same grayish white.

As the months went by, she put off the decision to file for divorce. She knew Inder was putting it off too. That had always been his way. She loved him. She always would. But she had loved other men, still loved some of them, and had gotten over them, except in memory. Such memories were often sweet.

In the corner that she had turned into a rudimentary kitchen, she watched half a pot of coffee materialize, feeling as if with this little space that no one else trod, no one else dirtied, no one else cleaned, she owned the world. Pouring a cup, she unwrapped her paints and began to put the finishing touches on a piece she liked even better than her last—two gray-white faces this time, with just a touch of yellow. Elongated, the figures stretched from crown to abdomen as if they were hanging from the skyline behind them. They wore the same wide-eyed stare as their frightened brother, but she'd managed to work a touch of comprehension into their eyes, like the reconciliation to fate she envisioned in the heart of Christ, hanging on the cross, right after he had cried out to his Father, "Why have You forsaken me?" and understood the silence of God's reply.

Someone knocked on the door. She hesitated. This was her day to paint, and she'd been saving the whole day to finish this portrait, *Grace*. She'd begrudged every minute spent showering, brewing coffee, getting dressed.

She opened the door. Behanji stood there, lugging two big bags. She dropped the suitcases and threw her fat arms around Grace.

"Sister! We will not be alone."

"Are you crazy? What is this?"

"All that I own in the world."

"I told you," Grace said, "I don't want it. Inder and I are no longer together. There's no changing our minds."

"I know, sister. Oi! So many steps! I must sit."

Her big haunches spread out on the mattress. "We need furniture, sister." From the mattress she could see *Grace*. Its dual stare turned her face as gray as the paint. "You made that?" she said.

"I haven't made it yet. I was about to make it when you came in. How did you find my studio?"

"Telephone, sister."

"I never got your call."

"The address book."

"Inder told you? I'll kill him."

"No, no, you can't do that," she said. "Listen, I will tell you. I know that you and Inder are divorced."

"We're not divorced."

"Do not worry, I am reconciled. Even Mummy and Daddy are reconciled. Perhaps it is too soon to say, but when he is ready, they will find him another wife."

"Another wife?"

"He will be happy. Don't worry, sister. I will lose weight, I promise. As for marriage, what is a woman when she is too old to have children? We will find for you, my sister. I have wasted my life for my brother, but I will not waste it with my sister!"

"I'm not—" Grace started, but what Behanji wanted to call her was not entirely the point. "You're forty-five years old! When are you going to live your own life?"

"I will find a job," Behanji said. "You will paint."

"I can't paint! I can't even breathe when you're around. I need privacy. I need to be alone."

"Paint. I won't disturb you. I'll unpack quietly. Like a little mouse."

"No! No, no. I want my own home, my own space, not just to work, to live in."

"But we feel it is the same house," she said. "My brother's house is my house. Just as it is your house. You see, it is the same house, brothers, sisters, mothers, husbands, and wives. Just because you are divorcing my brother does not mean you are not still my sister. I think of you that way. And my sister's home is my home. See?"

"No," Grace said. Behanji would never understand. Grace wished she had learned Punjabi; maybe it would have been easier to communicate with them, even Inder. "Would you like a cup of tea?" She remembered that they always took tea in the afternoon. Behanji shook her head.

"Well, I'm going to tell you, even if you don't understand. My problem was never with Inder. It was with you."

"Me? What have I done?"

"I can't work with you around. I can't work with anyone around, and I need to work, all the time, even if it's only in my head. Even if it looks like I'm not working."

"Everyone works too hard in America." Behanji sat, staring at the painting.

Grace stared too and found herself longing, more than ever, to get back to it. "Shall I call you a cab?"

"I can manage," Behanji said. "There are many taxis on the corner."

Grace kept staring at her painting after Behanji had left. She didn't like it nearly as much. She dialed Inder's office. "Your sister was here."

"Oh?"

It was the first she'd heard his voice in months. She almost forgot what she wanted, hearing that voice. "She wanted to move in with me."

"I take it you didn't let her."

"I'm sorry it took me so long to call," Grace said. "I didn't want to bother you."

"That's news."

"I made a big mistake. I'm sorry.."

"Is there anything else? Because if that's all you wanted to tell me, you could have told me months ago."

"I haven't exactly been out of touch," she said. "Your sister has been writing me letters."

"That's not all she's been doing."

"I think you ought to pay her back that dowry."

"What?"

"It wouldn't take much: her own apartment, driving lessons, and if you're feeling generous, a car, some employment counseling."

"Are you coming home?"

"I am home. And even here I can't get away from your family. They should hate me. Why don't they hate me?"

"In India a marriage is for life."

"Is that why we haven't filed for divorce?"

"Do you want a divorce?"

"It's not why I called."

"Come home," he said.

"You come here."

"I have a meeting in two minutes."

"I've got work to do myself."

But neither one of them hung up.

"If your sister can stop by," she said, "I don't see why you can't."

"If I stop by," he said, "I'll be caught in the middle again."

"You are in the middle."

"I've got to go."

"Good-bye."

She cursed her stupid luck. The lines of her portrait blurred in front of her. She tried a wash. By nightfall she had managed to blend the foreheads of the figures into the cityscape behind them. The painting needed something. She opened a tube of primary red, put a dab of paint on the tip of her finger, and touched a dot above each figure's eyes.

Elephant Rope

Trudy Riley

"We can't let what happened yesterday happen again."

"Of course not," I answer, feeling the fur of deception growing in my mouth.

I hear him drumming his nails on his desk. He is waiting for me to take an oath. No, he wants me to say, never again. Instead I think of those nails. They are tended by a manicurist but not polished. He is not the kind of man who would ever have shiny nails.

"Are you there?"

I don't want to say yes to anything so I let out a long sigh.

I thought, "The Chez Kristo."

"That restaurant reminds me of the quiet room in a mental hospital, all that maroon padding and Muzak." He doesn't answer.

"Oh, I get it. You want to have lunch some place where I'll have to behave." "Oh, Audrey," he says as though he is helpless. "All I want is a civilized discussion."

I want to tell him I am no longer civilized.

"You must admit running out of the restaurant was hardly called for."

"Really," I say, remembering that I'd run, not only out of the restaurant, but in several mad circles in the parking lot. He continues, "It shouldn't be that difficult."

Through lips that feel like they are blistering, I say, "Later, I'll talk to you later," and hang up the phone.

Within minutes it starts to ring. I unplug it and saunter into the bedroom. I slide into my queen-size bed trying not to displace the fritos, paperback murder mysteries, remote control, video and regular, and a collection of erotica. There is a book of poetry buried somewhere. I find it and open it. The poem I read is about "memories burned into the soul."

The memories, powerful as physical blows, struck me mute when my former husband called yesterday. "We must meet for lunch," he said. "Today, if possible." A pause. "Audrey, are you there?"

"Today!"

"Yes, there are some things I want to go over with you."

"But it's been twenty years!"

I hear him take an impatient breath. "Well, OK," I say in a whiny, little-girl voice I haven't used in ages. He is in a hurry, he tells me, and rushes through time, place and directions.

The moment I hang up my knees go watery. I sit down on the floor next to the telephone table and curse myself for letting the sound of his voice transform me into the scared, skinny kid I was the night I met him.

It was the Freshman dance and I'd worn a red dotted- swiss dress that my mother had bought before I left for college. The color was bold but the flouncy skirt and high neck announced, "Look at me, I'm a virgin."

He found me toward the middle of the evening in the darkest corner of the room. He was so serious when he asked me to dance and I was so grateful to get out of the corner that I became giddy. I tried to stifle it but that only made it worse. Finally I was composed enough to follow his slightly hesitant step. I remember feeling pleased by that hesitation. It was just enough to suggest that even though he said he was twenty-six and a Teaching Assistant at the University, he was not all that sophisticated.

"You're so vivacious," he kept telling me. It was heady stuff for a girl just out of twelve years of parochial school, where clear-complexioned nuns had insisted I face the world with lowered eyes and terminal humility.

"Am I?" I remember asking so I could hear him say it one more time.

"Oh yes," he said and I knew this was a man who could truly appreciate me. And indeed he did, particularly at the end of the evening. When he bent to give me a tentative kiss I responded with the kind of lush passion I had been taught by the high school boys in the back row of the Mission Theater. My effort was not wasted because right after that kiss he looked at me with such longing that I knew he was mine.

That night I lay awake in my narrow dormitory bed and dreamed of marrying him. It would be perfect. He was a scientist, reliable, solid—a Taurus. He would ground me so I would never again feel like I was going to spin off the planet. And he thought I was beautiful! I knew my looks fell between plain and somewhat pretty but that no longer mattered. I liked that he didn't care what people thought. When a friend of his danced by and accused him of robbing the cradle, he'd answered, "You should be so lucky," and twirled me to the other side of the room. It was an arrogant gesture and I loved it.

"Oh God," I moan and caress the telephone table. It offers no comfort, so I force myself to get up, and find my favorite full skirt. It is a cotton print, the kind I always think should be worn with bare feet in some dusty Mexican town. I put on sandals and a white cotton shirt. With the tan I've gotten from walking along the beach and my best silver earrings I manage a sexy-peasant look. It is just right.

I know he will be wearing a suit.

I am on the way to Malibu before I begin to question what I am doing driving twenty miles to a restaurant I don't have the wardrobe for, to meet a man whose capacity to hurt has haunted my life. I begin to feel claustrophobic in the car and my palms are sweating. I want to pull into a gas station, call the restaurant and leave a message that an emergency has come up. I savor the transparency of that excuse. It will anger him and when he telephones me later he will say, "I want to make this clear, I have no time for games." I know how he'll look when he says this. His head will rest higher on his neck: his nose will point toward the ceiling. It's the way he looked twenty years ago when he told me he was leaving. "It has to be this way, I cannot spend the rest of my life married to a frigid woman."

I was twenty-five when he said this; he was thirty-two.

I remember going numb and wanting him to leave our bedroom but he stayed and continued. "All the psychiatrist's bills, years' worth and *nothing* has changed."

After he left I curled up on the bed. A numbness was starting at the base of my spine and spreading outward. I knew if I moved its progress would stop so I lay still waiting for it to reach my brain. Sometime in the middle of the night I realized that not everything he said was true. It hadn't been years of psychiatric care, just a few sessions. If I'd reminded him of that would it have slowed his exit? Probably not. A few sessions or years, he'd have said, you'd have screwed it up anyway.

The first therapist had been a psychiatric social worker recommended by one of Marks colleagues. That was eighteen months ago. Her name was Laurel and she had straight, perfectly cut blonde hair and an eastern seaboard accent. After each question she asked, her brow would furrow and she'd ponder my answer. As the session progressed I became increasingly confident that this woman seriously wanted to help me.

About midway in the hour she said, "You call yourself frigid. Tell me about that."

"It's so hard to talk about and it's getting worse. I used to at least enjoy the kissing and cuddling part but now I can't stand for him to touch me."

The way she looks tells me she expects more. "And it's really not fair to him. He's such a good husband—very attentive—in fact if I'm ill or anything he hovers over me."

"You sound like you feel more indebted to him than in love with him."

"Oh, that's not true. It's just that he's been so patient about this and so caring. Even when he's out of town he calls every night.

She begins to ask about the other men in my life—father, brother. I answer automatically because I am preoccupied about whether I should tell her about Mark's business trips. He takes them more frequently now and when he returns there is a buoyancy about him that makes me believe he has been with another woman. Part of me is grateful because it takes the pressure off. But another part spends hours in the bathroom crying.

When, at the end of the session, she tells me she would like to see us together next time, I'm grateful that I did not tell her about the trips.

I watch Mark settle in the chair across from Laurel.

I feel ragged. They seem composed and professional. Laurel begins to ask him questions but after the second one Mark says, "What you must understand is that I love Audrey and I want us to have a very special marriage." I listen and realize I've heard it all before. The first time he spoke his romantic dreams to *me*, everything else in the room disappeared.

I look at my therapist. Her angles, bone structure and blunt haircut seem to be softening. Mark is talking as though he wants to share a special gift with her. When she speaks he leans forward and gives her his full attention. I have seen him behave this way at parties. He will encourage a woman to talk and when she does he acts as though she is saying the most important things. When, after much urging, he begins to speak I watch her bend toward him without even knowing she is doing it. It makes me jealous even though I know that if I ask him to recall one of these conversations a few hours later he will say. "Talking with who? Oh her. I don't really remember."

As the session progresses I feel more and more invisible and I'm relieved when a distracted Laurel says her goodbyes.

Mark is shaving when I tell him I don't want to continue with Laurel. Our eyes meet in the mirror. I look for signs of lost opportunity. There are none. "I wondered about you seeing a social worker but thought it was worth a try. Next time we'll go for the best," he says.

I leave the bathroom knowing I have betrayed a woman who might have had only a momentary lapse in her desire to help me. It doesn't matter, I tell myself, remembering the spellbound look on Laurel's face.

Three weeks later we are sitting in Dr. Sherman Senfeld's Beverly Hills waiting room. "Better neighborhood than the last one." Mark whispers as the doctor opens his office door.

He is a buddha-shaped man with frog-like eyes. He shakes my hand. I am embarrassed by my sweaty palms. He settles himself in his leather recliner, leans back and waits.

Mark begins to talk. "Her problem is . . ." I hear Mark say. I am struck by the fact that he would describe it differently if Doctor Senfeld were a woman. *Our marriage or our life challenges*, he'd say. I look around the softly lit windowless office and try to recall when I changed from a vivacious young woman to a child that needed fixing.

"What prevents your wife from being fully responsive may be buried deep in her past," Doctor Senfeld says, "In my judgement hypnosis would be the treatment of choice."

I do not hear myself gasp but I must have because they both look at me.

Yes? Dr. Senfeld asks.

"Nothing." I look at Mark. *See how much I love you. I am willing to be forced further into passivity by this man, who terrifies me, rather than continue to see someone who might be attracted to you.*

"It's the way he breathes," I tell Mark three weeks later.

"What do you mean?"

"He always wants me to talk about something sexual. Even stuff as innocent as what I did when I was little and played doctor with my cousins."

"Of course he asks you about those things. That's what we're paying him for."

"But it's the way he does it. He wants me to be so specific and when I am, his breathing changes." Mark walks over and holds me by the shoulders, an arm's length away from him. "Your imagination," he says, shaking his head. "I'm serious. I can't see him because he sits behind the couch but I swear every time I talk about sex he sounds like it's hard for him to breathe." "Oh, c'mon, Audrey. He's a man of enormous reputation." Mark pulls me to him and puts his arms around me. "Just give it a few more sessions."

I nod into his neck. The following week I drive to Beverly Hills but cannot make myself go to Doctor Senfeld's office. The Church on Roxbury is open so I go inside and sit for an hour. The next week I go to the library. In the evenings I wait for the phone to ring. When the call finally comes I am relieved.

Mark does not speak to me that night. He sleeps in the den and the following morning comes into the bedroom. There are tears in his eyes. "Why the hell did you quit?" Unable to speak I roll over and face the wall. A month later, he's gone and I am in the bed waiting for the dead feeling in my body to reach my heart. At dawn I realize it's not going to so I drag myself down to the kitchen for a cup of tea. While I wait for the water to boil I force myself to nibble an English muffin. It tastes as dry as cardboard but that doesn't matter because I have now decided that I will do everything possible to stay alive. *Someday he will want me back.*

When I arrive at the restaurant I sit in the parking lot, remembering. Even now, when I am no longer the skinny, vulnerable kid he left, there are longings

I can't explain. I wonder if he's changed. When he sees me will he regret not being with me through the years of my transformation? No, probably not. That stuff only happens on Oprah.

I see Mark the moment I walk through the door. He comes toward me, arms outstretched, and we give each other one of those California ex-spouse hugs, casual and fleeting. I want to hang on a moment longer but he backs away and smiles, his blue-grey eyes soft and welcoming. I remember how easily that warmth could drain away.

"You've changed," he says, looking me over. His eyes linger on my breasts.

I look down. There must be a trickster loose in my brain. I have left three buttons open rather than the usual two.

"So have you." I find the courage to take a good look at him. He is still slender; his face is hyper-alert, intelligent. I hear my mother's voice, "Good-looking man," she said when she met him, "And what a catch!" Five years later, the accusation, "You could have hung on to him if you'd learned how to act in the bedroom."

I hate remembering. It must show in my face because he says, "Are you all right?"

I nod.

He backs away, another survey. "You look as though life has treated you well." There is a heartiness in the way he says this. He makes it sound as though my well-being has something to do with him.

No thanks to you, Buster, I imagine saying. He puts his arm around me to lead me to the table and I cannot find my voice.

When we are seated he opens the wine list. "A Chardonnay would be nice to start." He reads off a couple of names. It amazes me that he gives the wine selection such careful attention but then I remember he did that with everything. I never felt I could provide a worthy distraction.

"Either of those will be fine," I say and he raises an eyebrow.

When the waiter has taken his request he settles back.

"I'm working in design now—robotics."

I make jerky movements as I pass him the bread, but stop suddenly, ashamed that I am still trying to be cute for him.

His smile is indulgent. "I've started to play racquet ball too," he continues. "Great way to stay in shape."

I look down at my generous body, "Is that so?" My heart is going double time. "You know, Mark, you're talking like we see each other every week."

"I'm sorry. I'm beating around the bush. I've never been good at talking about personal things."

But you were great at accusations, I want to say.

"You know my second wife left me a while back. She walked out and won't talk about the reasons." He looks baffled. His old arrogance seems gone. I feel the crusty armour I donned in the parking lot beginning to break away. Not yet, I warn myself.

"To tell the truth I feel pretty much a failure in every area except my work."

I am about to offer sympathy but something stops me. "You say that, Mark, but you look so, God, I hate this word, together."

He smiles and leans back in the booth. "I didn't mean to imply it's been all tragedy since she left. It's made me think about the future. That's why I asked you here."

"What do you mean?" I try to ignore the voice in my head that whispers, *leaving you was the biggest mistake of his life*.

He doesn't say anything but smiles in a way that is so charming it takes my breath away. Finally, he says, "I told you this is awkward for me, but with the money I'm paying Doctor Green I'd better look under every rock he suggests."

"Doctor Green."

"My analyst."

"You're in treatment!"

"Yes. It's actually at his suggestion that I'm here. He's taking a great interest in my past. Most of the time it's my childhood but he keeps going back to my marriage with you."

I proceed cautiously in this unfamiliar territory. "What is he saying about it?"

"That I should look at it more closely—that there are probably connections between the problems that arose with you and the things that are coming up in my present relationships."

"Your present relationships?"

"Yes, I've joined a video dating service. He smiles awkwardly, "It's called Great Expectations."

The sip of wine I have just taken catches in my throat. I spray the tablecloth and collapse into a fit of rapid-fire hiccoughs.

"Are you all right?"

No, I want to say. *I have just turned homicidal*, but I can't let him know that. "Yes, I'm all right. It's just the name. It's so . . . so optimistic."

The smile again. He puts his hand over mine. "You really can help me with this. Our marriage was so long ago and . . . you know . . ." He shrugs. "Details fade." I pull my hand away. "Are you telling me you don't remember very much of our marriage?"

"Well, the high points, of course."

"After the first month there were no high points."

"See, that's what I mean. Your memory is . . ." He gives me a look like it's the eighth wonder of the world. I am having trouble breathing so my words come in short spurts, "You want me . . . to tell you about our marriage . . . so you can go over it with your analyst and the two of you can plan how you're going to form idyllic relationships with one or more women from your dating service? Is that what you're asking of me?"

He looks pleased that I have gotten it.

I grab my wine glass. There must be madness in my eye because he starts to reach for it. "No, don't!" I say, louder than I planned. Diners and waiters stop. The only motion in the room is me, dumping my half full glass of wine in his crotch and heading for the door.

I drive south on Pacific Coast Highway hoping to put as much distance between Mark and myself as possible. When I run the light at Topanga Canyon I realize I am in no shape to drive so I pull into the first beach parking lot and turn off the engine. The ocean is weekday quiet with a few surfers astride their boards and some never-say-die joggers braving the late fall heat.

I feel too vulnerable to leave the car so I open the window and rest arms and head on the steering wheel. I picture Mark. He will smile apologetically to the other diners and go to the men's room to dry off. When he returns he will select the rest of his lunch with great care. He will finish it without a shred of indigestion. Not fair, I think, and try to remember how, before his phone call, I had been congratulating myself on how well I had arranged my life. There's my writing, which demands much, my job, which demands little, and a lover who provides a delightful distraction from both. I try to find solace in these thoughts but they are crowded out by a past that is far more vivid than what I did yesterday.

The body numbness that started the day Mark left grew to such an extent that I would look at my hand and wonder if it belonged to me. Then came the desire to isolate myself. A couple of friends tried to intervene. "He's not worth it, Audrey. Sure, he's bright and charming, but underneath he's a cold, mean guy." I changed my phone number so they couldn't call and tell me things like that.

It was amazingly easy for me to ward off male attention. All it took was a studied attempt at looking plain and tensile-strength reserve. But then Sal came to work at the bookstore and was so persistent and seemed like such a harmless, good-natured man that I agreed to go out with him. We went to a movie and for a long walk. He said a lot of funny things and I finally relaxed enough to laugh. I began to like him but when he bent to give me a pristine goodnight kiss I drew away.

"You look terrified," he said. I started to cry. "I'm not leaving until you tell me about it." He sat down on my front stairs and invited me to join him.

I was afraid to ask him into my apartment so we sat there shivering in the January chill and I told him about my first marriage. I ended by saying, "There's something very wrong with me."

Instead of the sympathy I expected he had thrown back his head, laughed and said, "I got a feeling you just found yourself a man who didn't know how to make love to a woman."

It was a strange and gradual reawakening beginning with massages that avoided all private parts followed by a period of time when Sal insisted I simply relax and not pay attention to what he was doing. He would hum some tuneless song, like I'd seen my father do when he'd repair a broken toy. He began to touch the traitorous parts of my body with great tenderness and then with increasing intensity.

It was on a Sunday afternoon that, aroused beyond imagining, I turned to him and breathed, "Now, please."

We made love into the evening. At first, because I was unsure there was an urgency but as I learned to trust my body our lovemaking turned languid and sensual. It was a day that could be described as perfect except for one alarming occurrence. At the height of my passion, when I was calling out to deities that I no longer had a relationship with, an image of Mark appeared. He was naked making wondrous, experimental, acrobatic, worshipful love to me. I did not know then that this image would be with me for years, sometimes reaching such intensity I would call his name. Occasionally, this unwelcome fantasy spilled over into what should have been post-passion bliss. "Damn you," I said, more than once, only to have a lover whisper into my hair, "What's wrong, love?"

Ten years ago I became so concerned, I went to a therapist, "I haven't seen Mark in years but I still feel attached in some way," I told the grey-haired woman sitting across from me. "Some of it is sex." "Well, he is not here, so we must deal with your part of that bond." She leaned back in her chair. "I am reminded of a story I once heard, a parable, really. It has to do with the way they train elephants."

I felt my cheeks redden with anger. This is my third session and each time she has told me some obscure story from which she expects me to draw marvelous insights. Fix me, I want to say, and be direct about it. But she was already into it. "When an elephant is quite small the trainer tethers it to a post with a rope that is about the width of clothesline. It struggles some but soon learns that to resist is fruitless and after a short period of time, stands quite still whenever the rope is around its neck and fastened to the pole. Now the interesting thing about this . . . Are you listening?" "Yes, of course," I say, promising myself that I will never make another appointment with this Mad Jungian.

"Good. As I was saying, the interesting thing about this is that the elephant, now immense, can still be made to stand still by tethering it with the same slender rope, which, relative to its size, is as fragile as a strand of hair. Fascinating, wouldn't you say?"

I keep my promise and cancel all future appointments.

Sitting in this deserted beach parking lot I feel my own rope. It attaches to my lower belly and makes me feel like I cannot move. I start the car with effort and drive home slowly.

I lie in bed, darkening my mood with depressing poetry and wonder why I have lost my courage. I get up and reconnect the phone. "I'm ready for you," I say and it begins to ring. As I listen to its persistence I wonder if Mark is also bound to me. Of course he is, I tell myself, but what does it matter? He will never recognize it.

I reach for the receiver and interrupt his greeting. "No, Mark, I can't see you—not ever." He seems not to have heard so I repeat, "not ever." I feel no lighter after saying it. I am only aware of a dull ache at the base of my belly.

He is going on and on. From his tone I can tell he is irritated. I hang up the phone gently, hoping he does not realize he has been disconnected. I want him to call my name: Audrey, Audrey, into the dead instrument.

Post and Beam Construction

Gene Zeiger

These familiar hills, bare in winter,
seem the hides of extinct animals—
brown rounded. I am back thinking
how much cannot be seen:
the past when we met, met again.
made love, a house between two hills, a garden.

At night I'd sit alone at the oak table
watching the moon throw away its level light
on dwarf apple trees that never produced.
There was neglect.
Our love began to live on something
thin and bird-like.
Behind the doors you made, we hid remorse
until what was left was the space,
rigid and neat between us.

I tried to believe that posts and beams
were ordained, akin to other final unions.
But each year I saw the space
between the joints increase.
The wood kept drying,
losing what had kept it full.
And our bodies in the bed
beside the double-paned window,
how quietly they left each other.
In the loud spring mornings,
in the silent winter nights,
I hardly heard them leave.

Taking Charge

June Hudson

Essie Lee says, "The best revenge is a happy life." She even printed up those very words in silver ink on pink paper using fancy writing—like the Declaration of Independence—and put it in a mother-of-pearl frame for me to set on my dresser to help uplift myself first thing every morning when I wake up.

Even though she's been my best friend since grade school which is longer ago than I like to remember—and I wouldn't say anything out loud to hurt her feelings I thought to myself, Essie Lee, your uplifting saying is bullshit.

Having a happy life isn't even on my top ten list of best revenges for getting even with that yoyo of an ex-husband for sneaking around, then divorcing me for that red-headed nympho, who I knew was trouble the minute she sang solo in church last Easter Sunday. She never took her eyes off Clyde and me. Clyde had insisted on sitting in the front pew even though I didn't want to because I'd slept on my hair funny and it was all flat in the back. I knew she wasn't thinking of me when she belted out "How Great Thou Art," like she was the Queen of Sheba in that tacky purple choir robe that clashed with her hennaed hair.

It's not that I even miss Clyde all that much. I just miss the life I had. I'd gotten used to him being in charge of everything. He decided what style furniture to buy for the house, what bushes to plant in the yard, if and when to go on vacation, and whether to and how many kids to have. I worked hard all those years biting my tongue and doing what he wanted. And what did it get me? A new budget so tight it makes my old one look like I was royalty, a house half the size of the one I used to live in, four sets of stretch marks, a head embalmed with so many years of hair spray, perms and fake color it hardly knows how to think for itself anymore, and a sharp tongue that Essie Lee says is going to keep me from going to heaven if I'm not careful. Well, to this tongue, revenge in the here-and-now tastes sweeter than anything I can imagine in the hereafter.

That Clyde is such a smooth talker he thought for sure he was going to finagle a divorce settlement where his lifestyle barely had a crimp in it, while I squeaked by clipping discount coupons for A&P and shopping in Wal-Mart's bargain bin. He told me he worked hard all those years for his money and now he deserved to enjoy it. He was planning to take up water skiing, motorcycle riding and two-step dancing—hobbies his new wife-to-be liked doing. He said it would do me some good to try new things myself. Now that the kids were all grown up, I should learn to take charge and expand my horizons by going out and getting a job and learning some independence He suggested I help out old man Hedley again at the feed store where I worked before we got married. I surprised both of us by telling him in a loud voice that didn't even sound like my own, that that was twenty-five years ago! The only way I could help Mr. Hedley now was by putting some flowers on his grave since he'd been dead for at least ten years. His thick-necked son—who was always trying to get his hand up my skirt when we were in high school—ran the store now, and I was sure he wasn't interested in anything hidden up there at this late date.

I was going to say more but had to stop a second to catch my breath when Clyde started shouting back at me, asking hadn't I heard of women's lib? He kept repeating how I needed to take charge of this, be in charge of that because from now on I was on my own. The blood vessels on his forehead were popping out like night crawlers and I was relieved when he slammed the door and left. If he was going to have a stroke, I didn't want him to have it here and have my first act of being in charge to figure out how to load all 280 pounds of him into his truck and drive him to the hospital.

Next time I saw Clyde we were sitting in divorce court with our lawyers. I watched the judge with her thin lips shut tight listening to our lawyers argue. I was feeling pretty sorry for myself, deciding I didn't have any luck left when she began asking me some questions. I don't remember how I answered, though I wish I could because the next thing I knew my luck changed. She told Clyde he better get down off his high horse, then nipped his plans for new hobbies right in the bud. I almost wet my pants when I heard her say alimony for life or until I remarry. He did wet his pants or something worse because he went running from the court room.

Now that I don't have to get a job, I spend part of every day thinking up new ways to get even with Clyde. Essie Lee says I never used to be this un-Christian and I say I guess being dumped for a woman half my age has brought out my true nature. Since Clyde's dick is what got him into trouble in the first place, I plan to tell all the ladies at the brown bag lunch get-together after Wednesday morning Bible Study, that the real reason he left was because his nozzle was so small he couldn't satisfy me. I'll make them promise not to breathe a word of this to anyone, then say I learned from the Donahue show how dick size is related to self-esteem, and how it must be true because during all those years we were married I had to tell him over and over that it didn't matter to me that his member never got any bigger than a gherkin on a pickle tray. But since he never trusted much of anything I said, he set out to prove himself with that pimple-faced floozie. It's not that I really expect everyone to believe me but enough of the story will get around to Clyde's friends that no matter how hard they try not to, their eyes will just automatically sneak a glance down to his trousers to see if there's any bulge there at all. He is so shy about being naked in front of anyone, I'm sure he won't whip it out to prove me wrong.

The other thing in Clyde's trousers I'm working on is his wallet. Essie Lee's cousin who keeps books for Wiley's Pharmacy and fills out tax returns on the side, can give me the address of the IRS. I'll send an anonymous letter hinting strongly that a certain cement contractor in this town might have a second set of books, an idea I got from an old Perry Mason rerun. There's only one cement contractor in this town big enough to keep even one set of books, so if they want to, it won't be hard to go after Mr. You-know-who. I don't know if the IRS would even read my letter, but I figure it's just like fishing. You bait the hook with a worm, drop it over the side and if you wait long enough something's going to bite.

When Essie Lee and I were leaving church last Sunday, she lingered at the tract-rack then handed me the schedule for the summer revival corning up and asked if I'd go with her. By the look I gave her she could tell I wasn't much in the mood for repentance just yet. And from her look I knew she was getting ready to offer me one of her sweet sayings about forgiveness being good for the soul, so I say real quick, "Essie Lee, I hope you don't mind that I've cut up the pretty sign you gave me and rearranged the words to better fit my present disposition. It truly gives me strength every morning to wake up and read, *A Happy Revenge Is The Best Life.*

after repeated attempts

Pamela Gray

after repeated attempts
to get over you

i've decided to just
give up

accept the fact that
fifty years from now

i'll be sitting in a wheelchair
in the Home for Aged Dykes
muttering your name

some cute volunteer
in a dungaree jacket
will pat me on my wrinkled arm
saying "there, there,
maybe she'll come tomorrow"

my weak heart will flutter
each time a phone rings
or a visitor's announced

oh and i'll get visitors:
all the women I wouldn't
sleep with over the years
because i was waiting
for you

they'll show me pictures
of their collective land
in the country
their alternatively
reproduced grandchildren

occasionally they may ask,
"have you heard from . . ."
and i'll lower my gray head
"well," they'll say,
"she must be very busy"

at night, rereading
my tattered antique copies
of *Twenty-One Love Poems*
and *Beginning with O,*
looking through the yellowed
photographs of our vacation
in P-Town, fifty years back,

i'll ask myself
what it was about you

and i won't remember

Up Date

Candida Lawrence

I want to tell you about my ice-cream date with my high-school sweetheart, thirty-nine years ago. I mean the date was last week and the high school was back then. He had been calling me and asking when I would be visiting my parents. They're housebound and ill and they appreciate his funny visits and my mother loves him. He planned to visit them on Friday evening and I thought I would be there too, but then I began stalling. I wasn't sure I wanted to see a man I hadn't seen since we were kids. I called him to say I'd be quite late and not to wait for me. I parked down the street until I saw him leave in his car and then as soon as I walked into my parents' house, the telephone rang. He's no fool and he must have figured I'd been lurking, as was my habit in high school. We arranged to meet at the ice-cream parlor six blocks away.

By this time it's 10:30 and we go first to 31 Flavors but they are closing, so we walk to Vivoli's in Walnut Square. He says, "Let's not go in" and I say, "You don't want anyone to see you with me, right?" He says, "You're smart." So we sit on a bench around the corner, under a rubber tree. He says, "You're going to laugh at me," and I say, "No, I won't laugh at you." But of course he's a comical man and once upon a time, he made all of us laugh. He looks the same, only more so, as some wag once put it. He's lean, fit. He says that after he got married, to his "best friend," and after his children were born, he began going into Berkeley to see a woman or hang out with the guys playing basketball at Live Oak Park, or to visit my parents. He asks: "Do you ever think about high school?" "Sure I think about high school," I answer.

"Do you ever think about sex in high school?"

"Sure. Of course. I have to think about it, because that's when it all began."

"Do you know why I stopped taking you out?" he wants to know. I don't want to know. Inside, I'm cringing with not wanting to know. "Beats me," I say.

He's mucking around with his ice cream, the tiny spoon scraping the sides of the cup, his powder-blue sweater glowing in the street light. I haven't thought "powder-blue" since high school.

"I was embarrassed and scared by the intensity of the two of us together."

For a few moments I let silence sit with us. What does he know of intensity? At sixteen, I loved him so much I devised a plan to kill him—"push him off a granite cliff with a 1,000-foot drop—and then I wouldn't have to share him with Bev and I'd be the heroine who hiked down to find his body, and would vow to other mourners that I would love him forever and be true to his memory. I don't reveal this drama to him. I reply sweetly: "But you took out many girls and I assumed that you preferred Bev."

"No," he insists, "she was my best friend. I married my best friend."

I don't know where this is going so I say: "But what about all the other girls in college, before you married? What did you do with them, while Bev waited patiently for you?"

"I screwed them," he grins.

"Why didn't you marry one of them?"

"Because I needed a best friend. We have a good marriage."

I am not one to talk about good marriages, never having known one, so I zag into something that interests me more. "I don't remember too well, but I don't think we ever really did it, did we?" Remember, we're sitting on this bench, around the corner from the ice-cream parlor, thirty-nine years later.

"I've been visiting your parents for years, hoping they'd tell me where I could find you. They wouldn't give me your address."

"When did you start doing that? As if I would believe you. I remember you were an artful liar."

"You might as well believe me. I begin visiting for that reason but I became very fond of your mother and father."

He is my storehouse of high school memory. I'm not going to let him schmalz. I say: "Remember Jack Pine and his girlfriend Helen, and you said that when they made love she would lose consciousness? Jack told you that and then you told me. Remember?"

"You are the same as ever."

"Do you remember that I went out with Jack once?"

"I guess so."

"Here's what I want to ask you. He kissed me and I kissed back. The next week I heard from my little black friend Cora, who knew all about what the white folk were up to, that Jack did not like me because I kissed back and I should have waited. She thought that was most curious."

"Is this the sort of junk you write about?"

"I'm interested," I plead. "The shameless hussy arched her back. If you responded too quickly, you lost the first round."

"You weren't supposed to *like* it." He chucks his cup into the green garbage can at the end of the bench. "I was incapable of realizing, at that time, that someone who liked it would be really good to have around."

"If you're telling me something about your marriage I don't want to hear it. Why didn't you ever introduce me to your parents?"

"I was ashamed of them. Compared to yours, they were dull and stupid. They were poor. That's another reason I married Bev. I married her family."

We inspect each other's vehicles, preparing to say goodbye. In the back of his station wagon are boxes of ball weights for salmon fishing. Bev teaches aerobics. You put the weights in your hands to help prevent or cure upper-arm flab. I have one more question: "Why weren't Erie and I invited into the girls' social clubs, the high school sororities? Not even an initial screening? Did she *like* it too?"

"I thought you *were* invited. I assumed you were. I know why Erie wasn't. No bra. Hula dancing. Open talk about sex. It's no wonder she later married Henry Miller. But no one knew anything about you. Except me, and I didn't tell."

He's standing on the sidewalk, leaning in my window as I put the key into the ignition. "You're wrong. We did it. I used a rubber and it kept slipping off." He sighs and straightens up. "I don't know any goofy people except you."

"I'm sorry. Sorry. What a funny word. Sorry."

The Future Tense

Kathryn Chetkovich

Tom and I lived together for two years, a relatively long time in the graduate-student world, where lives are shuffled and redealt every fifteen weeks and where a temptingly fresh set of new face cards is introduced to the deck every fall. But we finally broke up about a year ago, when it began to seem as though everything that was going to happen between us had happened.

Driving home one night, we quarrelled about a movie we had just seen. I don't now remember even what movie it was or why our disagreement seemed so important, so telling, but I do remember the feeling that our relationship, like one of those collapsible plastic drinking glasses, had reduced itself to this one argument.

Tom was driving, and in the green glow from the dashboard I could see his hands resting in his lap, his fingers hooked loosely around the bottom of the steering wheel. He seemed more weary than anything else. "How come our normal conversations keep turning into fights?" he said finally, and the question, which was a good one, made me so mad I was swept by the sudden, ruthless wish for an accident. I wanted him to lose control of the car and run it off the road; I wanted to stand around in the damp air with my arms crossed, waiting for the police to show up. I wanted that much to blame him for something.

Our breakup was punctuated, like our courtship, by a series of phone calls and dinners out. And there was some of that same awkwardness that marks new relationships: every phone call had an ostensible purpose—"I've been looking for that old Sarah Vaughn tape and I was wondering if you had it" or, stretching it, "I thought you might know the cheapest place to rent a car around here"—and each one always began with the gingerly phrased gambit, "Am I calling at a bad time?"

One night when my new apartment was feeling particularly cramped and poorly lit, I decided to go out to the café at the back of the bookstore, a place where you can get a drink in an atmosphere that doesn't make you feel as though, on top of your other problems, you are probably becoming an alcoholic. As I was circling the new-book table, trailing my finger across the glossy covers and generally trying to look more interested in the life of the mind than in fact I was, I glanced toward the café and spotted Betsy McIntyre, the woman who runs the women's center on campus, sitting at a table with Tom.

I think of Betsy as a serious woman in low-heeled shoes who uses the word *intercourse* when other people would say *have sex,* but she has an ungainly beauty that can sneak up on you. Her hair, for one thing, is one of those startling shades of red that remind you what a deep disappointment being a brunette really is. And her seriousness is tempered by an unexpectedly rich laugh, a sound that can make you feel clever and loved. I heard that sound now, sailing over the hiss of the coffee machine and the clatter of cups and saucers; and when I looked over I saw Betsy leaning back with her face tipped toward the ceiling, laughing, her feet resting comfortably on the rung of Tom's chair.

"Jenny!" Tom smiled and waved me over in that friendly, unconscious way of his that I had at first loved and later tried to change. "Are you here by yourself? Join us!"

"No, oh no," I said. "I should get going. In fact, someone's waiting for me in the car." I waved, though we were close enough to touch, and began awkwardly backing away. We were several feet apart by the time we called out our final goodbyes and I turned and headed for the door. All the way home, I smarted from the obviousness of the lie, the idea of leaving the motor running and a handsome man riding shotgun while I ran in to buy a book.

After Betsy moved in with Tom, the three of us went out to dinner a few times, she and I demonstrating that unearthly zeal women have to please and make nice. The conversation at these meals usually felt like something scripted for a public-radio newshour, but Betsy and I managed to work in a number of conspiratorial jokes at Tom's expense, which he seemed to enjoy and which gave us a jocular version of intimacy. I was always tired by the time I got home, but these seemed to be what my mother would have called "successful" evenings.

Still, I did not react particularly well to the news, several months later, that Tom and Betsy were getting married. I had run into Tom at the grocery store, and when he told me, I suddenly had that feeling you get in dreams when everyone else in the room but you is dressed. I actually had the fleeting fear that the scene was being filmed for some horrible new television program, some weird hybrid of *Divorce Court* and *This Is Your Life,* and I tried to dissociate myself from the pathetic contents of my shopping basket—yogurts and frozen food and a jumbo pack of sugarless gum—while I congratulated Tom. I could hear my own voice, squeaky and remote, like a message being played back on someone's phone machine.

At home that night I poured myself a brandy and made a list, more or less chronological, of all the men I had been involved with and why we had broken up. I had been left, I remembered, for a radio d.j., for a senior in comp. lit. at Smith, and once for the anonymous "freedom to see other people." For my part, I had once left a man who could not promise that he would not be attracted to other women (I was very young and had a rigid notion of fidelity), and later, a man who could not imagine the day that he would want children. I knew these facts by heart, but looking at them now, I saw they were explanations, not reasons—stories attached to mysterious events after the fact to make sense of them, like myths that explain the coming of winter or the sound of thunder. In fact I had no idea what the "real" reasons were, only that at some point we wanted more and more to be elsewhere when we were together, at some point we gave up talking in that flirtatious language of love, the future tense.

When Tom and I were together, we did talk about marriage a few times, but always as a kind of dare. It had the charged appeal of skydiving, a risky adventure glamorized by the slim, but nevertheless real, statistical possibility of total disaster.

It was only early June but it was already hot, and once I got to the hills, the air blowing through the car window smelled like warm wood, that sad smell of summer vacation. The sidewalks and tidy lawns gradually disappeared, giving way to pickup trucks and barking dogs. I drove slowly over the stretch of road where I had once wished for an accident, then past the gas station with the friendly rottweiler and the house where diapers were always out drying on the line, and then I was there.

Many people were arriving at once, the recently parked cars ticking in the heat. Men stood in the road, tucking in their shirts, while women squeezed out the passenger doors and picked their way like cats through the stones and high weeds at the side of the road. In the driveway, I watched a woman lean against a man's shoulder and shake something out of her shoe. She said something and the man laughed, then pulled her close and kissed the top of her head.

As I stood there, staring and thinking about climbing back into my car and driving away, I felt someone's hands close over my eyes from behind. "Tom?" I said. "Is that you?"

The hands turned my head back and forth. I pried them away and turned to look.

"Stuart," I said. "God, what are *you* doing here?"

Stuart is my former ex, my ex before Tom, my ex-ex, you could say. I like him—he lopes good-naturedly from century to century in his studies, giving one the impression that he is not yet intellectually housebroken, and he rhapsodizes about history in a way that most graduate students would consider unbecomingly naive. But whenever I see him it stuns me to remember that we were once involved, that things were ever passionate and sweaty between us, that I have seen him without his glasses on and watched him yell at his father on the phone.

I was glad to see him now, glad for the company. We walked toward the house together.

People were clustered outside, on the patio and in the yard, and the house was cool and mostly empty. It looked the way rooms look in dreams, recognizable overall somehow yet different in all their particulars: *And then suddenly I was in my house, except that it didn't look like my house and there were other people living there.* In the living room, the shiny easy chair I had made us lug to the basement had been restored to its original spot, like a dog that has finally persevered in the long fight to sleep in the house; and our couch—the one we bought at a flea market to celebrate our moving in together—was now covered with a patchwork quilt that gave the whole room a feeling of nights at home and extended family.

It took me a moment to realize that the older woman sitting there, holding a plastic cup in both hands and smiling absentmindedly, was Tom's mother, Nan.

She saw me and patted the space on the couch next to her.

"Jenny. It's so nice to see you, sweetheart. I didn't know whether . . ." When Nan is nervous, she loses confidence in the middle of a sentence and her voice drops away.

"You too, Nan. You look great."

"And Betsy? She's . . ." Nan looked at me expectantly.

"Yes she is," I said, trying to sound definite. "She certainly is." And we smiled widely, untranslatably, at each other.

Stuart was standing in the kitchen with a balding Americanist and a throaty-voiced woman who was writing her dissertation on Sylvia Plath. The Americanist was pointing at Stuart's feet, and the two of them were kidding him about his shoes. Stuart was hamming it up, pretending to be hurt. In many ways, Stuart is at his best when he is pretending.

Behind them, an inconspicuously well-dressed man was rummaging through a kitchen drawer. He was tall and handsome in a way that had nothing to do with his features—one of those men you think is in his forties who turns out to be in his sixties.

When he had unearthed a bottle opener, he gave a little cry of "Eureka!" and then looked over at me. "My dear, I don't believe we've met," he said.

In fact, we had. Charles was Tom's advisor and friend, and Tom and I had once had a swordfish dinner and three bottles of wine at his house. The two of them had argued through the meal about the efficacy of civil disobedience, stabbing the air with their forks. I remembered watching them, setting my face in an attitude of listening and letting my mind drift behind it.

While I was deciding how much of this to remind Charles of, I felt a hand fall familiarly on my shoulder from behind. "Of course," Charles said, pointing the arrowhead of the bottle opener at me. "You used to be a friend of Tom's."

Tom looked fine. He looks a little like an outlaw preparing for a court date when he dresses up, but he's a handsome man, with a moustache and bright blue eyes, and the look suits him. Right now his sleeves were turned back above his wrists, but he was wearing a tie and new leather shoes.

"Charles is going to marry us," Tom said.

"That should be fun." This remark felt a little off as I said it, and for a moment no one spoke. "Is this all legal?" I added. I was trying to keep things light, but when Charles reached for his wallet and pulled out his Universal Life minister card, I suddenly felt like the fire marshal showing up to close the circus down.

"Well," Charles offered gamely, "here's to you both." And he swept Tom and me together with a wave of his bottle. "Here's to history."

There was a line of people waiting to use the bathroom, so I walked down the hallway to the one I knew was in the back, between the study and the bedroom. Out the window I could see the far end of the yard, set up for the ceremony with a canopy woven out of lace, ribbons, and dried flowers. People stood around in knots of three or four, their laughter and cheerful curses floating in through the open window. Most of them were my friends, the same people I would have invited if it had been my wedding, and for a moment I had the strange sensation that I was watching an out-take from my own life, a scene that had been shot and was later scrapped from the film but saved, with the idea that with proper editing it could be used somewhere else.

I had rinsed my face and was pressing it with a towel when I heard Betsy's voice rise angrily from the bedroom, on the other side of the door.

"God *damn* it. I *told* you this would happen."

"What? What's happened?"

In my mind I could see Tom hooking his thumbs in his back pockets, that blameless pose.

"You said he'd be fine."

"He will."

"Jesus, Tom, look at him."

I looked out the bathroom window at Charles. He was standing close to the house, flanked by three of the older, more serious grad students, the bearded ones who always sought out the faculty at parties. One of them was holding the neck of a champagne bottle in his fist, and Charles's beer had been replaced by a whiskey glass. Something about him—maybe the way he had pushed up only one sleeve or the sharp angle at which he held his glass, almost spilling its contents—looked wrong.

Suddenly the door flew open and Betsy was standing there, wearing a pretty, flowered dress, her hair tied neatly back with a blue ribbon. She was crying.

"Oh, hi," I said. I steadied myself by focusing on the towel, refolding it with military precision.

"What are you doing back here?" she said.

"Nothing," I said, irrelevantly. Then I took in some air, what felt like all the air that was left in the room. "Tom is being a jerk," I said, hoping that it was one of those moments when you open your mouth and the right thing flies out. I wanted to feel that my history with Tom gave me permission to talk about him this way to the woman who was about to become his wife. I thought it would put us on the same side.

She just stared at me while I put the towel back on its rack, and I felt my mistake. And then I offered her that lamest of consolations: "You look beautiful."

As it turned out, Tom was right about Charles, who is the sort of man who can walk away from the brink of drunkenness the way other men can walk away from a good game on television—with regret, but not with genuine difficulty. The ceremony had the brief, anticlimactic feel that outdoor weddings sometimes have, where, because it is hard to hear and hard to see, you have to fight the feeling that you are standing around waiting for it to be over. I looked over at Nan, who now had an orchid pinned to her dress, and wondered what she was thinking. A feeling came over me that I wouldn't mistake for happiness, but that I was nevertheless happy to feel.

When Charles was finished, Tom and Betsy kissed and someone let out a piercing, taxi-hailing whistle. We all clapped and Stuart nuzzled toward my ear and said, "Well, now that Tom's happily married you can tell me. Wasn't I just a teensy bit better in the sack?"

"Gosh, Stuart," I said, clamping my chin and staring at the ground. "I really don't remember."

We stood around for a while, eating cake and drinking champagne, and Stuart went on in this absurd, flattering way, telling me every nice thing he could ever remember a man saying about me. "Bill Schubert likes the way your shirt hangs down below your sweatshirt at softball practice. Alex told me you have this adorable way of eating your salad with your fingers. As if I didn't know."

"You shouldn't be telling me this," I said. "What else have you heard?"

My friend Adele says weddings have a strange effect on men. "It's kind of a musical chairs thing," she says. "Suddenly all the unattached guys are thinking, *There goes another one, I better get moving.*"

When I was getting ready to leave, I noticed Charles sitting by himself in an aluminum-framed lawn chair that had once been mine. Somehow, in the way of such objects of indeterminate value, it had become Tom's without my ever actually giving it to him or deliberately leaving it behind.

Charles looked like the last passenger left on the deck of a cruise ship. His legs were stretched out in front of him and he was gazing out at something in the middle distance. I walked over and asked him if he needed a ride home. "My dear, that would be paradise," he said, and I held out my hand to help him up.

We waded through our goodbyes and made our way to the car. Charles settled himself into the seat next to me, and the sight of his long body tucked into the small space of my car, his head nearly brushing the roof and his knees pressed against the glove compartment, reminded me again of what it feels like to be with a man. I thought again of the men I had loved or thought I had loved, and the ones I thought had loved me. And this time I thought not of why we had parted but why we had come together: how Tom, who knew more about rock 'n' roll than anyone I had ever met, was always slipping homemade tapes into friends' pockets and tape decks and car stereos, for them to discover later; how Stuart had come up to me in class one day, before I had even learned his last name, and told me I had appeared in his dream the night before, stamping my foot and insisting that he read Thorstein Veblen.

I asked Charles how he was doing. He was breathing next to me in a noisy, drunken way, but when he spoke, the words were sweet and even. "I remember you, now," he said. "You had your hair cut short, then. You were all upset, because you and Tom had passed a bad accident on the road that night."

And then I remembered that Charles was right. But the accident had been mostly cleared by the time we got to it—we saw two mangled cars, the smoky flares and the crushed glass spread like a layer of rock salt on the road, but the ambulance had already come and gone. It had prompted me to ask Tom what he thought happens when you die, and he said, "I always imagine one of the first things is you go in this room. And all the people you ever slept with are there. Everyone looks just the way they looked when you first realized you were attracted to them, and there's plenty to eat and drink."

"Is this supposed to be heaven or hell?" I said. But what struck me was the idea, the *fact,* that we would each move on to other people. It was realizing that we both knew that would happen, even while we were together, driving to Charles's house for dinner, that had upset me.

"Well, my dear. What about you? Will you promise to love and cherish some man someday, whoever he may be, as long as you both shall live?"

Charles's voice reminded me a little of my father's, and I thought suddenly of the telephone call we ritually have on my birthday. I complain about being another year older, and my father always says, "On the other hand, consider the alternative."

And I turned to Charles and said, "I will."

What Happened to Sharon

Lesléa Newman

When I dropped my contact lens into the kitty litter, I knew it was going to be a bad day, but even that didn't indicate how bad. I mean, it could happen to anyone, right? One minute I was standing in front of the sink and the lens was balanced on the tip of my finger, and the next minute I was on my hands and knees searching the bathroom floor with a flashlight. I didn't want to admit, even to myself, that my hands were shaking, but they must have been, and why the hell do I keep the kitty litter under the sink anyway? I shone the flashlight all around the floor, illuminating dustballs, a stray marble and other such interesting items, until it dawned on me to look in Pan's box, and sure enough, there, shining like a diamond on a black velvet cushion, was my ticket to twenty-twenty vision, perched on a piece of poop.

Well, there was no way I was going to pop that piece of plastic back into my eyeball. I'm not a Virgo for nothing, you know. I barely managed to fish the lens out of there and drop it back into its little plastic case without losing my breakfast. Yeah, I was nervous all right. The day before I had put both contact lenses into the same eye and that hurt like hell, you better believe it, sister. But after about an hour I'd been able to wear the little buggers. Not today though. I'd have to sterilize them first. Nope, today I'd have to wear my glasses, and damn, today of all days, I wanted to look good. This was the day I was going to see Sharon.

Hell, maybe I really didn't want to see her. You don't have to be a Freudian analyst to figure out the significance of all that contact lens jazz. Sharon. How could one little word, six little letters hold so much emotion for me? When I think about seeing her, I get angry and sad and excited all at the same time.

I guess that's what happens when you've been with someone for seven years. Seven years! We even used to joke about the seven-year itch, how it would never happen to us, or if it did, we'd just scratch it. Ha ha, very funny. Well, the joke's sure on me, because it was exactly three days after our seven-year anniversary that Sharon said she wanted out. She said she'd been thinking about it for a while, but she didn't want to spoil our anniversary. She wanted us to have one last good time to remember. And didn't I feel like a fool.

That night was so awful—not our anniversary—that night was fine, or so I thought. I'd been sensing that Sharon felt a little off lately—she'd been a little distant, she hadn't been feeling very sexual—but I wasn't worried or anything. You know how it is after seven years, these things ebb and flow and it's no big deal. But still, I wanted our anniversary to be really special. So I told her to get all dolled up and I'd take her out to Sam's, this very fancy place complete with a piano bar, where we happened to go on our very first date.

Every year on our anniversary we'd go to Sam's, ask the gay boy at the piano to play *As Time Goes By*, drink too much champagne, eat too much food and go home and make love and fall asleep. I'd buy Sharon red roses and she'd wear this little black mini-skirt which still fit her the same as it did seven years ago: she'd worn it on our first date and that just about knocked me out—that this dyke would have the nerve to do something like that. I think that's when she got me. It was love at first sight with Sharon. She said what got her was the way I held the car door open for her and how I lit her cigarette. She thought chivalry was dead. Hell, I would have laid my jacket across a puddle for her if I'd had to. I'd have done anything, I was so taken with her. And I still felt the same way.

So imagine my surprise when three days later, Sharon said she wanted to break up. And before I could turn around, she was gone. Just like that. Now I may be a fool, but one thing I do know is that you don't find an affordable apartment in a safe neighborhood in three days. Not in this city. She must have been planning this for a long time. Shit. You'd think after seven years I would deserve a little more respect than that. She wasn't even willing to go to therapy, like any self-respecting dyke would do. She just didn't want to be with me anymore and that was that.

Maybe it was my gray hair. I looked in the mirror and started fussing with it. I look a lot older than Sharon, even though we're only a couple of months apart. Maybe my looking older reminded her she was getting older too, and who wants to be reminded about that? Maybe she wanted to be with a young chick, some suave hipless butch who mousses her hair or something. I doubt it, but then again who knows? You think you know someone pretty well after seven years and then they pull a fast one on you.

Speaking of fast—I had to move my butt along so I wouldn't be late. That would really piss Sharon off. Punctuality is not my strong point, but Sharon sure changed that. I was on time for our first date of course, and for a couple of weeks after that. But then, well, you know how it is. You try to get out of the house and then you remember the fish have to be fed and then the phone rings, and you spend ten minutes telling whoever it is that you can't talk, you have a date, and right as you're leaving, you pass the hallway mirror and decide that the shirt you're wearing doesn't really go with the pants you have on, so you pick out another shirt and of course it needs to be ironed . . . you get the picture. Sharon wouldn't stand for it. She got me a watch for our one-month anniversary and wrote on the card, *Happy Anniversary from your new girlfriend who doesn't like to be kept waiting*. She can be tough, my Sharon. My ex-Sharon, I mean.

Getting dressed, though, is easier said than done, because everything I own has some memory of Sharon attached to it. I hate buying clothes, but Sharon was born to shop. Sometimes she goes shopping just for the fun of it, if you can believe that. When I had absolutely nothing left to wear, I'd let her drag me to the mall and we'd buzz through JC Penney's, Steigers, and Jeans West and, before I could say Visa, I'd have a whole new wardrobe.

I wanted to wear something she hadn't seen, hadn't picked out, hasn't undressed me in, for Chrissakes. I wanted to show her I have a life without her. Hell, six months is long enough to get over anyone, right? Wrong. Anyone but Sharon.

All right, basic white shirt, jeans and sneakers—what the hell, it's not like this is a date or anything. I'll go casual, like, what do I care what I look like, I only have a few minutes anyway. We were meeting downtown for coffee in a "neutral" place. Shit, what did she think, I was going to rant and rave like a blithering idiot? I didn't even do that when she left. I didn't even cry. Not in front of her anyway. Except when she took Cakes.

See, for our three-year anniversary we got these two kittens and we named one of them Pan and the other one Cakes. Separately they were okay, a pan and some cakes, but together they were fabulous—Pancakes! Just like us. So when Cakes left, it really got to me. I've always been a sucker for animals. I tried to explain it to Pan, but she just moped around the house looking up at the door every ten seconds like she was waiting for Sharon and Cakes to come back. At night she slept in bed with me, under the covers even, like she was afraid I'd run out on her too if she let me out of her sight for even one second.

That was tough. God, I really feel for people who have kids—must be really hard to explain it to them. At least Sharon and I never had kids. We talked about it some. She used to bring it up more than me, all that stuff about our biological clocks ticking away. We were both pretty ambivalent about it, though. I mean, if we could just get pregnant by making love, we probably would have done it. But it was too complicated to figure it all out—known donor, unknown donor—it was just too much. And besides, we didn't have the money. And besides that, I wasn't too wild about the thought of having a boy. We decided we really wanted to be aunts, you know enjoy a kid but not be totally responsible for her. Though it was a pity that Sharon never had a kid—she'd be beautiful, just like Sharon, with long brown hair, big brown eyes, gorgeous full lips, and a body that just won't quit.

Okay, enough of that—I'm outta here. And no more crying. I took off my glasses to wipe a tear on my sleeve. I didn't know how I'd feel when I first saw Sharon. The *first* first time I saw her, my legs started shaking, my knees got weak—it was love at first sight like I told you. And sometimes I would still feel that way when I'd come home from work and she'd be sitting at the kitchen table talking on the phone, or standing at the sink doing dishes, or even sprawled on the couch pouting because I was late. I still got all trembly knowing she was mine.

Was. What a lousy word. Oh well, nothing lasts forever, I guess. I sure thought these past six months would. This no contact stuff was all Sharon's idea. I mean, how could we go from seeing each other every day for seven years to not seeing each other at all for six months? At first we tried getting together once a week and then we tried talking on the phone, but according to Sharon it didn't work because the conversations always turned into a fight about why we broke up. I mean, what did she expect me to talk about—the weather?

So six months ago, we decided we'd meet at the Eggshell Diner today at three o'clock. It was unlikely we'd bump into anyone we knew at that hour, so we'd really be able to talk, though what we had left to really talk about was beyond me. It was bizarre to think I literally hadn't laid eyes on Sharon in six months. I mean, we live in the same city even though she works in Westbrook, which is about half an hour away, and I work right downtown. I hadn't seen her at any dances, or dyke events, not even at the Alix Dobkin concert, and everyone who was anyone was there. I'd even taken this woman Dana, who I knew had a crush on me, but the only reason I went out with her was to make Sharon jealous but she wasn't even there. What a waste of twenty-four bucks.

I'd asked around a little, but no one seemed to know what happened to Sharon. No one had seen her at the bar or at the bookstore—hell, she hadn't even played softball this year. Maybe she was really depressed over our breakup and was just lying low. That's what I'd hoped anyway. It's not like I'd been Ms. Social Butterfly myself. Maybe Sharon had come to her senses over the past six months and realized that no one would ever love her as good as I would. Maybe she was going to beg me to take her back.

Well, there was only one way to find out. I got to the Eggshell early, for a change, slid into a booth way in the back, and ordered myself a cup of coffee which I hoped would dissolve the lump in my belly by the time Sharon got there. Boy, was I nervous. After about ten minutes I felt Sharon come in. Felt, I say, because the whole energy of the place changed. Every single guy stopped what he was doing to turn around and gawk at Sharon. Like I said, she's quite a looker. Guys were always staring at her when we were together, and it used to make me mad, but she'd just laugh and toss her head and tell me I was too serious. Politics was not exactly Sharon's forte. Even now I could swear she just winked at one of those guys.

I watched her make her way over to my table and I slid my hands onto my lap to hide their shaking. She looked gorgeous. She was wearing these white pants and a baggy red sweater with a black and gold scarf around her neck. Her hair was pulled back and she had some makeup on of course—Sharon would rather be caught dead than without makeup on in public. She looked, though I hate to say it, happy somehow. Happier than I'd seen her in a long time.

"Hi."

"Hi." I half rose out of my seat, then thought better of it. What were we supposed to do—kiss on the mouth, kiss on the cheek, hug, shake hands? Why hadn't anyone written the *Emily Post Guide to Lesbian Ex-Lover Etiquette* yet? Sharon, who never loses her composure, simply slid into the booth, planted her purse on the table, and stared at me.

"New glasses?"

"No, I dropped . . . ." I stopped myself, remembering that when we were together, the only times I'd ever worn my glasses in public was when we'd been up all night long making love, and I was too tired to wear my lenses. "I just didn't feel like putting my lenses in this morning," I said, staring down at my coffee. Let her wonder.

We didn't say anything for a few minutes, until the waitress came to take Sharon's order, and of all things she ordered herbal tea. I looked up at her, puzzled, and she shrugged.

"Don't you drink coffee anymore?" I asked, as the waitress gave her tea and poured me a refill.

"No, I stopped." She picked up the honey bear from the table, turned it upside down and let a smooth golden stream flow out of the top of the bear's head.

"I suppose you've given up cigarettes too." Sharon, who, not unlike Bette Davis, was usually enveloped in a cloud of smoke, hadn't lit up yet.

"Yep," she said, still dribbling honey into her tea.

"Got enough honey in there?" I wondered if she had turned into a clone of Winnie the Pooh.

She put the honey bear down and made a face. "Actually I hate tea." She picked up a spoon to stir with, and it was then that I noticed something new on her finger.

"What's that?" I asked, leaning forward to stare.

"What's what?"

"That." I pointed to her right hand.

"This?" She turned her hand towards her and studied it as though she'd never seen it before. As if some fairy godmother had magically, out of nowhere, plopped a diamond ring on the fourth finger of her right hand.

"Yeah, that."

"Just a ring." She said it as if I couldn't see her hand in front of my face.

My vision isn't that bad, even without my glasses. Sharon continued stirring her tea, and I knew by that that something was up. To Sharon, nothing is "just" a ring or "just" a coat, or "just" an anything. Everything Sharon owns has a story. Take that black and gold scarf she has around her neck, for instance. I remember the day she brought it home, and told me over supper, "Well, it was hanging in the window of this second-hand store and I made the sales clerk get it out for me and she had to climb over all these mannequins and she got really milled because there was this long line of customers waiting and then it wasn't really the style I wanted exactly, but I couldn't not buy it after she'd gone through all that trouble, and anyway it was only a dollar, so I thought I'd give it to my mother, but then I remembered she hates anything black, it makes her feel old, she says, so I guess I'll keep it; I kind of like it actually . . . et cetera." So I knew this diamond ring had a story. A story she didn't want to tell me.

"Family heirloom?" I asked.

"No." She took the spoon out of her tea and put it down on her napkin.

"Is it real?" I wondered why I insisted on knowing what would probably kill me.

"Is what real?" She picked up her spoon and licked it.

"The honey," I said, my voice dripping with sarcasm.

She put the spoon down and looked at me then, and I wished she wasn't so damn pretty. I knew I still wanted her back, and I knew I'd never tell her.

"Well, if you must know," she gave her head a little impatient shake, "it happens to be an engagement ring."

"An engagement ring!" All of a sudden the piece of toast I'd eaten for breakfast that morning felt like a cinder block in the pit of my stomach. Very, very cautiously I asked, "Sharon, why are you wearing an engagement ring?"

"Because I'm engaged."

"You're engaged?" Ask a stupid question, get a stupid answer, I reminded myself. My eyes started blinking and I took off my glasses to rub them. Be cool, I told myself. I put my glasses back on and shoved them up my nose. "So, uh, not that I really care, but who's the lucky girl?" I tried not to let on I was dying of curiosity.

"Jo . . ." She hesitated for a split second. "Jo, it's not a girl. It's a guy. His name is Rick."

I just stared at her, feeling the fist in my belly clench even tighter. Sharon was with a man? A person with a dick? A dick and a beard and a hairy chest and no tits? My Sharon? My Sharon who had buried her face between my legs more times than I could count, who had licked my breasts for hours, *hours* on end, who . . . but I didn't want to think about all that now.

"Hello?" She was waving her hand, her ringless left hand, thank God, in front of my face. "Earth to Jo, earth to Jo." I shook my head and she came back into focus. "So aren't you going to congratulate me?"

She always did have nerve.

"Hell, no," I said, staring at her. She looked like Sharon. She sounded like Sharon. She even smelled like Sharon, and I should know; I'm the one who used to buy her perfume. Maybe this was her twin sister from another planet? This couldn't possibly be the same woman whose hair I braided every night, who'd slept right next to me for seven years, as if her head was velcroed to my shoulder. "No," I repeated, almost to myself. "I can't believe this. What'd you do, get it out of a bubble gum machine? Ha, ha, very funny, Shar. You almost fooled me."

"It's not a joke, Jo." She took her purse which is the size of a small valise off the table. She dug around until she fished out her wallet and flipped through her license and charge cards. She probably was still paying for a couple of my shirts, maybe even the one I was wearing, but, hell, I wasn't going to say anything. She held something out towards me. "Here."

I took the picture and looked. It was a guy all right, an old hippy type, complete with beard, drawstring pants (turquoise or purple no doubt, though I couldn't be sure because the picture was black and white), aviator glasses and a dog.

My belly lurched, and I knew it wasn't from the coffee. "You're not kidding," I said, barely managing to get the words out. "Where did you meet this guy?"

"At work. You remember, I told you about him. We had lunch a few times when I was still living with you."

Oh yeah, Rick. Another hippy-dippy-do-good-social-worker-save-the-world type. God, how could this be happening? I handed her back the photo, wondering if she still carried around a picture of me too. I still had one of her in my wallet, but not for long, that was for damn sure. "So what's so special about this guy, what'd you say his name was, Dick?"

"Rick," she said, like she was talking to a three-year-old. "You don't have to get nasty."

"I don't have to get nasty? You get fucking engaged to a guy six months after we split up, and I don't have to get nasty?" My voice was rising and people were staring so I got a grip and lowered my voice, which came out more like a hiss. "Sharon, that was seven years of my life, remember? Seven fucking years. And since your memory is so short, let me remind you, I wanted to get married too."

She sighed and shook her head. "Ah, Jo, what good is it? A bunch of lesbians sitting in a circle passing a flower or a feather around, talking about how wonderful commitment is, and two years later they're all broken up and sleeping with someone else."

"How dare you?" I slammed my hand down on the table with more force than was really necessary, since unfortunately what she said had more than a ring of truth to it. "Straight people don't have such a great track record either, you know. One out of two break up. That's fifty per cent."

"You always were a whiz at math," she said dryly. Now I knew she was mad because Sharon hardly ever gets sarcastic. It's too unladylike.

"How's Cakes taking all of this?" I asked, trying to change the subject for two seconds anyway, to get some comic relief.

"She's fine. She just loves Rick. It took her a while to get used to Rufus, that's Rick's dog, and pretty soon . . . ." Her voice trailed off.

"Pretty soon what?"

"Oh nothing." She didn't meet my eye.

"Don't oh-nothing me." All of a sudden I felt like we were a couple again. "Are you living together?"

She nodded, and it's a good thing the table was bolted to the floor or I would have knocked the whole damn thing over. I swear I felt my blood beginning to boil, as the saying goes, and I hoped I wasn't turning beet red all over, though why I should care about the way I looked now was beyond me. Sharon was living with this guy! Dammit, she had made me wait two lousy years before she'd move in with me—two whole years of "whose house should we sleep at tonight"; two years of "but we *always* sleep at your house"; two years of never knowing where half my shit was, at home or at Sharon's. And she's living with this guy after only being with him for six months? Or . . . suddenly I felt a little sick.

"Sharon . . . " I was holding onto the edge of the table for dear life. "Tell me the truth now. Did you start seeing this guy" (I still couldn't bear saying his name) "before we broke up?"

"No." She looked me right in the eye. "Only a few lunches and I didn't hide them from you." I knew she was telling the truth by the way she looked at me, and my gut loosened, maybe one thirty-second of an inch.

I loosened my death grip on the table a little bit. "Just tell me why."

She shifted her weight and started playing with the scarf around her neck. "I don't know, Jo. I always considered myself bi."

"That's a lie," I interrupted her. "You know I would never go out with a bisexual woman."

"I know. That's why I could never tell you."

I tightened my grip on the table again, until my knuckles turned white. "You lied to me? For seven years?" I stared at this stranger sitting across the table from me, who I thought I'd once known, as my whole world crumbled.

"Not exactly." She kept playing with her scarf, untying it and retying it and tucking the ends in just so, until I wanted to strangle her with it.

"Sharon." My tone of voice said I meant business.

"Well," she finally took her hands away from her throat. "Listen. I never lied to you. I felt like I was a lesbian. I mean, coming out was so wonderful, you know, and I was with Sal for four years and when we broke up I didn't think about going out with a man at all. I thought about going out with you."

My heart raced. I wished she hadn't said that. "So?"

"So, I didn't think it mattered, because I thought we'd be together forever. You know I always got mad when the Lesbian Alliance didn't want bisexual women in it. But I never said anything about it because I knew it would make you mad."

"Sharon, you said a lot of things you knew would make me mad."

She shrugged. "Look, Jo, I know you're not going to like this, but something happened to me. For, oh, I don't know, the last eight months or so of our relationship, I kept dreaming about men. You know, it wasn't that different than coming out. I just felt my heart opening in that direction, and I knew I needed to explore it." She laughed a little and shook her head.

"What?" I asked, though I couldn't imagine what on earth could possibly be funny at this particular moment.

"You know before, when you said, 'Who's the lucky girl?' Well, I felt the same way as when people used to ask me if I was seeing anyone, and I'd say, yes, and they'd say, 'what's his name?' and I'd say, it's not a him. Her name is Johanna."

She smiled, but somehow I failed to see the humor of the situation. The irony, however, wasn't lost on me.

Sharon went on. "Don't you see, Jo, it works both ways. You remember how exciting coming out was—everything you felt for the first time, like you were being born all over again. Well, this is the same thing. I hadn't been with a man for almost thirteen years. I forgot what it felt like to be held by a man, to look up at a man, to . . . . "

"Spare me." I leaned back and crossed my arms. I couldn't stand seeing her look so . . . so goddamn dreamy about it. It wasn't the same thing at all, but I wasn't going to start that argument with Sharon. I didn't have to say anything, though. It was like Sharon could read my mind. After all, even though it was hard to believe at this particular moment, we had been together for seven years.

"Johanna," she said, and I knew something important was coming, because no one ever uses my full name. "I know you're upset, but I wish you would try to understand. I'm not like you. I wasn't satisfied with women's this and women's that and half the world hating me and not even being able to walk down the street holding your hand."

That was the last straw. "Do you hold Rick's hand on the street?" I asked, amazed I didn't choke on his name. It had always been an issue between us. I didn't give a shit what people thought, unless we were in some dangerous situation like walking by a bunch of Skinheads or Neo-Nazis or something, which wasn't too likely in this town. Sharon, on the other hand, hated even the thought of people staring at us. So we compromised by walking side by side, touching arms from the shoulder down to the elbow. Sharon even felt funny about that. She wouldn't even hold my hand at night on a deserted street or even in Provincetown where you could hold hands with an octopus and no one would notice.

Sharon was very busily not looking at me, so I answered the question for her. "So, you walk around holding this guy's hand." I didn't wait for her acknowledgment. "And you kiss him hello when you meet him downtown and you let him put his arm around you at the movies and you're going to marry him and share health insurance and tax breaks and you expect me to be happy for you?" I unfolded my arms and leaned forward, as if I were about to make a speech. "Sharon, do you know, for seven years I worried about what would happen if one of us got hurt? I worried about how I'd get in to see you if you were lying in a hospital somewhere? Seven years of that, and now, all you have to do is say 'I do' and this man will be your next of kin?"

I sat back and then leaned forward again. "I bet your mother is thrilled, isn't she? Five years, and every time I answered the phone she'd say, 'Hello, is Sharon there?' like she didn't even know who I was."

"Jo, I'm not denying anything you're saying." She was playing with her damn scarf again. "You're right. You're absolutely right. You have no idea what it feels like to be able to tell the women at work about Rick and have them get excited for me. I finally feel like I belong, and to tell you the truth, it's a big relief. They're even giving me a bridal shower, Jo. I feel so . . ." she thought for a moment, ". . . so *normal.*"

"Excuse me, I'm about to be sick," I mumbled, sliding out of the booth. I headed for the women's room, where I did in fact lose my breakfast. It never fails. Whenever I get upset, it goes right to my stomach. When my grandmother died, I cried so hard I puked, and Sharon was really good about it, stroking my hair, putting a cold washcloth on my face. God, why did I have to have so many good memories about her? And I felt so weird about what she was saying. I felt relieved and normal and like I finally belonged when I came out, and for Sharon it was just the opposite. My head was beginning to ache, so I stayed in the bathroom for a while, washing out my mouth and trying to get it together. If there had been a back door I would have exited then and there, but unfortunately this wasn't the movies. This was my life.

Slowly, and against my better judgment, I made my way back to the table. Somewhat to my surprise, Sharon was still sitting there, her hands cupped around her tea, which she still hadn't touched. Just as well, since it probably had enough honey in it to curl her hair anyway. I slid into the booth and sort of smiled. "Did you think I fell in?" I asked.

She smiled back, because despite herself, Sharon always did appreciate my junior-high sense of humor. "Are you okay?"

"Better now. I did get sick, though."

"Poor baby." She almost reached for my hand. Out of habit, I suppose. Her right hand, the one with the ring on it, edged towards my end of the table, stopped, and then retreated. "I got sick this morning, too."

I was touched. "Were you that nervous about seeing me?" I asked, and this time it was my hand that started creeping across the table, as though it had a mind of its own.

"Well . . ." She hesitated, and my intuition told me to brace myself. "Not exactly. Jo, I'm pregnant."

"Whoa." I lurched back as if I'd been punched in the face. Pregnant! She was really going the whole nine yards with this guy. "You're pregnant?" I stared at her face, and then my eyes travelled down her body, which still looked exactly the same to me, though of course a good part of it was hiding under the table. Maybe I was on a bad acid trip. I hadn't taken drugs in over fifteen years but still, maybe this was a flashback? I couldn't seem to comprehend the fact that there was not one, but two people sitting across from me, one inside the other.

The one who was visible to the naked eye (behind my glasses of course) was now really smiling. I could see she'd been holding back, because happiness was just oozing out of her now. That pregnant glow, I suppose.

"You're having a baby?" I asked like an idiot, since that is, after all, what being pregnant implies. "I never knew you were that serious about having a baby."

"I wasn't. It just happened."

"It just happened?" All I could do, at this point, was repeat everything she said.

"The rubber broke." She sort of giggled, and I could have killed her. I couldn't believe the words that had just come out of her mouth. The rubber broke. Rubber meant dick. I could not for the life of me bear to imagine her beautiful cunt with all its delicious folds and crevices being hammered away at by some prick. Not to mention all the lesbians I knew who spent months, years even, trying to get pregnant. And then to Sharon, it "just happens."

"Aren't you happy you're finally going to be an aunt?" she asked. I saw the waitress out of the corner of my eye start to approach the table and then think better of it. You probably could have cut the vibe between me and Sharon with a knife.

"An aunt?" I still couldn't manage much more than being Sharon's echo.

"Of course." Sharon leaned forward, pushing her tea aside so she wouldn't drag the end of her scarf through it. "You were the most important person in my life for seven years. Of course I want you to be an aunt."

Were. There it was again, that lousy past tense. You were. Boy, did that hurt. I couldn't believe she thought we could just let bygones be bygones and live happily ever after, her and the kid and the husband, and good old Aunt Johanna.

"What about what's-his-face? Does he approve of his child having a lesbian aunt?"

"Of course." Sharon chose to ignore my temporary memory loss concerning names. Or rather one name. His. "I've told him all about you."

I groaned. I could just see the two of them lying in bed side by side, with Sharon telling him all about me. All about us. Some guys get turned on by that stuff, you know. Sharon would probably tell him what we used to do, and then he'd get a hard-on, and then . . . Oh God, I felt like I was going to get sick again.

"He's very understanding, Jo. In fact, he even had an affair with a man once."

"He's bi too?" My voice and eyebrows shot up. "Has he been tested for AIDS?"

"Of course." Sharon waved her hand as if she was shooing away a fly. "That was right after high school, when he was just playing around. But, yes, he did get tested, and everything's fine."

Just playing around? Is that what Sharon considered the last seven years?

"Jo." Now her hand was definitely seeking mine. I slid my hands off the table onto my lap, safely out of reach.

"Shit," she mumbled under her breath. "Jo," she said again. She always was persistent. "Listen to me. I'm still the same person. I'm still woman-identified. I still love women. In fact, I still think women are smarter, more creative, more passionate, more . . . more everything than men. You don't have to be a lesbian to be a feminist, you know. It's just . . . . " She let out a deep sigh. "Never mind. You wouldn't understand."

"Sharon." I decided to try the voice of reason. "If you think women are better than men in every way, how can you have your most intimate relationship with someone you think is inferior to you?"

"I never said inferior. Men are human beings, you know." I knew it. I was just waiting for the men-are-people-too line. "Besides," she went on, "it's not what I *think*, it's what I *feel.*" She pointed to her heart with the hand that had that damn ring on it. "When you were a teenager, you thought you had to be with men, right, but you *felt* you wanted to be with women. No one made you change. You couldn't *force* yourself to be attracted to men. Well, it's the same thing. During our last year together, I knew I should want to be with women, but I felt myself changing, being drawn towards men. And I couldn't stop it or deny it. I wanted to be with a man."

"It's not the same thing." My voice was coming out low and even. "It's not the same thing at all." I looked down at my lap and ran my fingers through my hair. For a second I felt like Sharon had been brainwashed by some cult, and I was the hired deprogrammer, out to save her. I knew logic wasn't going to work, but I had to try it anyway. "Sharon," I looked up at her. "Everyone tried to make me change. My parents, my teachers, hell, even some of the women I slept with."

"Exactly." She looked triumphant. "You see Jo, you're different than me. I'm not a fighter. *You pays your money, you makes your choice,* that's what my father used to say. You made your choice, I'm making mine, and each one has its price." She looked down at her hands then which were folded on the table. "The price of being a lesbian was just too high for me," she said, and I swear I thought I saw a tear leak out of her eye.

"Sharon." I leaned forward, resting my elbows on the table and trying to meet her gaze. "Don't you see?" I asked gently. "If the world didn't make it so hard for lesbians, you'd still be with me." I even reached across the table and stroked her arm. "We can make it, Babe. Sure, it's tough, but if we love each other enough, it doesn't matter. Just because the world hates lesbians is no reason to deny your own happiness. That's way too high a price." I squeezed her arm and waited. Two fat tears definitely streaked down her face. I decided to go all out. "Hey, listen. Ditch the guy and I'll be your co-mother."

"No." She jerked her arm away. "I'm not going to have my kid go through this. I can just see her bringing her little friends home and they'll ask a few questions and the next thing you know it'll be all over her school and no one will be allowed to play with her. No, Jo," she shook her head, "I made my choice."

Well, at least I had tried. I studied her face, tempted to wipe the tears from her cheeks, as I had done so many times before. "But won't you miss women?" I asked.

She shrugged. "I'm bi, not straight, remember? Maybe I'll have an affair. Married people do all the time."

Now I was confused. "Didn't you say a minute ago that you weren't attracted to women anymore?"

She shrugged again. "Things can change, you know."

"But what about your husband?" I asked, pronouncing the two syllables distinctly.

She waved her hand, brushing aside that invisible fly again. "Rick lets me do whatever I want."

"He *lets* you?" God, she was even talking like a straight woman. "Sharon, Sharon, Sharon." Oh I just wanted to shake her. "What are you going to do, put an ad in the classifieds: 'Married woman looking for same, for discreet afternoon pleasure?' What do you think, Rick's gonna watch the baby while you trot off to Michigan next summer to have an affair? You're getting *married*. That means a lifetime commitment."

"So? You think lesbians have cornered the market on nonmonogamy?"

"Sharon, you can't have everything. You can't live a straight life and have one foot in the lesbian world too."

"Jo, you're just as bad as my straight friends who dumped me when I came out, you know that? It's the same exact thing."

"Will you stop saying that? It's not the same thing." My voice rose, and this time I didn't care. "Sharon, do I have to give you a crash course in Oppression 101? You are joining the dominant culture. Are you still going to fight for gay rights? No. Are you going to make a statement at your wedding about straight privilege? No. Are you going to take your child to gay pride marches? It sure as hell doesn't sound like it. So have a nice life." I rose to go but I was stopped by Sharon's hand on my arm. I hate to admit that even now the touch of her skin still sent electric shocks through me, but it did.

"Don't leave," she said, and I made the mistake of looking into her eyes. "Jo, I miss you."

My heart started pounding and I slid back into the booth. Once a fool, always a fool, I suppose.

"Sharon, for the last time, listen to me. I still love you. I'm still *in* love with you. I would take you back in a minute. You and the baby." I'd never felt so vulnerable in my entire life.

She looked right at me and our eyes filled at the same time. She reached for my hand and I let her take it. Her skin was so soft and warm, I almost kissed her palm. Bi my ass, I thought to myself. Sharon was a woman's woman through and through.

"I can't, Jo," she said, her voice barely a whisper. "But I'd like you to be my baby's godmother."

I sighed deeply. That's some consolation prize, I thought, taking my hand back and standing to go, for real this time. I fished around in my pocket for some cash and tossed a buck on the table for my coffee, hearing Sharon's words echo in my brain: *"You pays your money, you makes your choice."*

"Jo?" She looked up at me.

I held my hands out, palms up, and lifted my shoulders, as if I was pleading for mercy. "Sharon, how in the world can you expect me to answer that question right now?"

She didn't give an inch. "Jo, it's important to me."

I lowered my hands in defeat. "I don't know, Sharon. Maybe. I have to think about it. Hey." A light bulb went on over my head.

"What?"

"What if you have a daughter and she grows up to be a lesbian?"

Sharon's eyes filled again. "I'd be awful proud," she whispered. And I tell you, I left a mighty big piece of my heart sitting at that table as I turned and walked out the door.

Contributors' Notes

Kim Addonizio is the author of *The Philosopher's Club,* a book of poems published by BOA Editions in 1993. After receiving an NEA Fellowship in 1990 and signing the "anti-obscenity" clause she began working on a collection of indecent stories, *In the Box Called Pleasure.* She lives in San Francisco.

Alta is publisher of Shameless Hussy Press in Berkeley, the oldest feminist press in America. Her most recent collection of poems is *Deluged with Dudes: Platonic & Erotic Love Poems.*

Reneé Ashley won the Brittingham Prize in Poetry for her collection, *Salt* (University of Wisconsin Press, 1991). Her poetry and prose have appeared in *The Kenyon Review, Poetry,* and *New England Review.* She lives in New Jersey.

Louise A. Blum teaches English at Mansfield University in Pennsylvania. Her stories have been published in *The Cream City Review, The Sonora Review,* and in the anthologies *Lovers* and *Love's Shadow.* She is currently working on a collection of stories about lesbian lifestyles and relationships in small, rural towns.

Alice K. Boatwright has published stories in *Penumbra, Maelstrom,* and *Love's Shadow.* She holds degrees in writing from Syracuse and Columbia and teaches for UC Berkeley Extension.

Kate Braverman lives in Los Angeles and is the author of four books of poetry, the short story collection, *Squandering the Blue,* and the novels, *Lithium For Medea, Palm Latitudes* and *Wonders of the West.* She won the O. Henry Award in 1992.

Claire Braz-Valentine is a widely published poet and playwright. Her plays on Susan B. Anthony, Frida Kahlo and Amelia Earhart have been produced in theatres throughout the United States. She teaches creative writing at Soledad Prison and lives in Santa Cruz.

Maria Bruno is an assistant professor of women's studies and writing at Michigan State University. She has published fiction in *Earth's Daughters, MidAmerican Review, Ms.* and in the anthologies, *The Time of Our Lives: Women Write on Sex after 40, Eating Our Hearts Out* and *Women's Friendships.*

Thea Caplan lives in Toronto and has published stories in *Oxford Magazine, Emrys Journal, Other Voices, Snake Nation Review,* and in the anthologies *The Time of Our Lives* and *Love's Shadow.*

Kathryn Chetkovich lives in Oakland, California. Her work has appeared in *The Georgia Review, New England Review, The Missouri Review,* and in the anthology *Love's Shadow.*

Lin Florinda Colavin says, "Breaking up is the pits. I chalk it up to mistaken beliefs and inexperience. I still have not discovered how to change my beliefs or a less painful way to gain experience." She lives with her two adolescents in an old Victorian close to the Pacific Ocean.

Martha Collins is the author of three collections of poetry, including *A History of Small Life on a Windy Planet,* which was published in 1993 by University of Georgia Press. She teaches creative writing at University of Massachusetts in Boston.

Carolyn Cooke lives in Point Arena, California. Her fiction has appeared in *StoryQuarterly* and *The American Voice,* and was nominated for a 1991 Pushcart Prize.

Silvia Curbelo was born in Cuba and currently resides in Tampa where she has received creative writing fellowships from the NEA and the Cintas Foundation. Her award-winning collection of poems, *The Geography of Leaving,* was published by Silverfish Review Press.

Terry Ehret is the author of *Lost Body* (Copper Canyon, 1993) which was selected by Carolyn Kizer for the National Poetry Series. Her work has appeared in *Five Fingers Review, Suspensions* and *Feminist Aesthetics.* She lives in Petaluma, California, where she teaches English and creative writing.

Deborah Fruin has worked as a magazine editor and writer in New York and Los Angeles. She now writes from her home in Calistoga, California, where her children have reached the "take no prisoners" stage of development. She has published fiction in the anthology, *Lovers.*

Pamela Gray is a Jewish lesbian poet, playwright, screenwriter and comedian living in Santa Monica. Her work appears in *Politics of the Heart, Naming the Waves* and *Love's Shadow*. She has an "embarrassingly large collection" of break-up poems and continues to be astonished that she survives her breakups and actually gets material out of them.

Patricia Halloff lives in New Jersey and has published fiction in *The Cream City Review, Gargoyle* and *Short Fiction by Women*. She recently completed *Self-Validation,* a short story collection.

Ann Harleman is the author of *Happiness,* a collection of short fiction which won the 1993 Iowa Short Fiction Award. She has published in *The Southern Review, Shenandoah, American Fiction* and *Love's Shadow*. She lives in Rhode Island and works at Brown University.

June Hudson teaches art and creative writing to a group of home-schooled children in Sonoma, California. Her poetry and fiction appear in *New Letters, Calyx, Poets On* and *The Time of Our Lives.* She won a Los Angeles Poetry Festival Award in 1993.

Susan Ito holds an MFA from the Creative Writing Program at Mills College and teaches an Asian-American Women Writers' Workshop in Oakland, California. Her fiction and poetry have appeared in over a dozen magazines and anthologies.

Lynn Kanter lives in Washington, DC. Her novel, *On Lill Street,* was published in 1992 by Third Side Press. Her work has appeared in *Common Lives/Lesbian Lives, The Time of Our Lives, Confronting Cancer, Constructing Change* and other anthologies.

J. Deborah Klein lives in Boulder, Colorado, where she is working on a novel, *Storm Windows,* and a collection of short fiction, *Casual Acquaintances.*

Marilyn Krysl teaches at the University of Colorado, Boulder. She has published two short story collections, five books of poetry, and has recently completed a novel, *Atomic Open House.*

Daniela Kuper lives in Boulder, Colorado, with her two teenagers. She has published in *The Sun, Amaranth Review* and *Rough Translations* and is working on a collection of short-short stories.

Dorianne Laux is the author of *Awake* (Boa Editions, 1991) and is working on a second collection of poetry, *What We Carry.* She lives in Petaluma and teaches writing workshops in Northern California.

Candida Lawrence lives with her dog in Corralitos, California and is the author of two recent books of creative nonfiction, *Change of Circumstance* and *Reeling and Writhing*. Her work appears in *The Time of Our Lives* and *Women of the 14th Moon*.

Diane Lefer teaches in the Writing Program at Vermont College and has published dozens of stories in literary magazines and anthologies including *Vogue, Boulevard, Women's Glib* and *Women's Glibber*.

Janice Levy was nominated twice for the 1993 Pushcart Prize for her fiction, which has appeared in *The American Voice, Alaska Quarterly, The Sun, If I Had My Life To Live Over, I Would Pick More Daisies, Lovers* and *The Time of Our Lives*. She lives in New York.

Susan Lewis teaches fiction writing at SUNY, Purchase. She received her MFA in fiction from Sarah Lawrence College and has published in *Global City Review, New Press Literary Quarterly* and *One Mead Way*.

Lynn Luria-Sukenick teaches at San Diego State University and has a private practice in writing and healing in La Jolla. Her most recent books of poetry are *Houdini Houdini* and *The Hue Everyone Living Knows*. Her fiction has appeared in *New Letters, Yellow Silk, Fiction International* and *Touching Fire: Erotic Writing by Women*.

Cris Mazza is the author of five books of fiction including *Exposed*, a novel (Coffee House Press) and *Revelation Countdown*, short stories (Fiction Collective Two). Her other books are *Animal Acts, Is It Sexual Harassment Yet* and *How to Leave a Country*.

Margaret McMullan teaches creative writing at the University of Evansville, Indiana. She is the author of the novel, *When Warhol Was Still Alive* (The Crossing Press) and has been published in *Glamour, New England Living, The Greensboro Review* and *Eating Our Hearts Out*.

Patricia Meyers has an MFA in creative writing from Memphis State University where she currently teaches part-time. Her short story collection is titled *Searching for Ivory*. She has recently completed a novel, *The Cruel Shoe*.

Lesléa Newman is the author of sixteen books for adults and children; the most recent ones are *In Every Laugh A Tear*, a novel, and a non-fiction book, *Writing From The Heart: Inspiration and Exercises for Women Who Want to Write*. Her latest children's books are *Remember That* and *Too Far Away To Touch, Close Enough To See* (Clarion Books).

Ellen Orleans lives in Colorado where "Amendment 2 is an even bigger drag than breaking up." She is the author of *Can't Keep A Straight Face: A Lesbian Looks and Laughs at Life* and has been published in the *Women's Glib* series, *Funny Times,* and *Common Lives/Lesbian Lives.*

Nita Penfold has published work in *Love's Shadow, Catholic Girls, The Womansleuth Anthology, Cries of the Spirit* and *If I Had My Life To Live Over, I Would Pick More Daisies.* She lives in Milton, Massachusetts, where she is working on a novel.

Vicky Phillips is a free-lance writer from Indiana. Her fiction has appeared in *Ms., Common Lives/Lesbian Lives, The Berkeley Fiction Review* and *Love's Shadow.* Her nonfiction educational writing has been published by Simon and Shuster.

Carol Potter is the author of *Before We Were Born* (Alice James Books) and has published poetry in *Lovers, The Time of Our Lives, Field* and *Sojourner.* She lives in western Massachusetts.

Trudy Riley lives in Sonoma, California, where she is currently working on a novel. Her short stories appear in *Catholic Girls, Women of the 14th Moon: Writings on Menopause* and *The Time of Our Lives: Women Write on Sex after 40.*

Elaine Romaine is a book reviewer for *Belles Lettres* and has published in *Georgia Review, Texas Review, New Letters* and *The Dream Book: Italian American Women Writers.* Her poetry manuscript, *Necessary Misters,* was a semi-finalist for the 1993 Barnes Award.

A.D. Ross lives in Northern California. She has published fiction in *Hayden's Ferry Review, Reed, The American Literary Review* and *The Time of Our Lives.* She is working on a novel.

Anita Santiago grew up in Caracas, Venezuela and presently lives in Southern California, where she owns an advertising company. Her fiction has appeared in *The Pacific Review.*

Elizabeth Searle is the author of *My Body to You,* a story collection that won the 1992 Iowa Short Fiction Prize. Her fiction has been published in *Ploughshares, Redbook, The Kenyon Review, Lovers* and *The Time of Our Lives.* She teaches in the graduate writing program at Emerson College in Massachusetts.

Joanne Seltzer has published in literary journals and anthologies including *Kalliope, The Croton Review, The Village Voice, When I Am An Old Woman I Shall Wear Purple* and *Women of the 14th Moon.* She has also published short fiction, literary essays, translations of French poetry and three poetry chapbooks.

Judith Serin teaches English at California College of Arts and Crafts in San Francisco. Her work appears in *What's a Nice Girl Like You Doing in a Relationship Like This?*

Robbi Clipper Sethi is an associate professor of English at Rider College in Lawrenceville, New Jersey. Her stories have been published in *Mademoiselle, California Quarterly* and *Atlantic.*

Enid Shomer is the author of *This Close to the Earth,* a collection of new poems and *Imaginary Men,* a short story collection which won the Iowa Short Fiction Award. Her work has appeared in *The New Yorker, Poetry* and *The Paris Review.* She is Writer-in-Residence at the Thurber House in 1994.

Deborah Shouse lives in Kansas. Her fiction has appeared in *The Sun, New Letters, Good Housekeeping, Love's Shadow* and *The Time of Our Lives.*

Kelly Simon lives in San Francisco, where she is working on a collection of stories about the lighter side of degradation and another about her travels in the third world. Her work has appeared in *The Quarterly, Ellery Queen Magazine, Furious Fictions* and *The Washington Post.* Her Thai cookbook was published by *Weldon Press.*

Amber Coverdale Sumrall is grateful for all her previous breakups, without which she wouldn't have met Wally. She has edited or co-edited ten collections of writing by women and has published poetry, fiction and nonfiction in numerous literary journals and anthologies.

Christina Sunley teaches composition and creative writing at San Francisco State and is completing a collection of short fiction. Her work has appeared in *Love's Shadow, The Time of Our Lives, Conditions, Common Lives/Lesbian Lives* and *Nimrod.*

Ellen Treen lives, works and writes, knits and gardens in Santa Cruz. Sister, daughter, ex-wife and mother, she likes to write short fiction about relationships from these viewpoints. Her work has appeared in *Catholic Girls, Kalliope* and *Women of the 14th Moon.*

Sherrie Tucker has recently acquired a Master's degree in women's studies at San Francisco State, where she also earned an MA in creative writing. Her fiction has appeared in *Transfer, Zebra, The San Francisco Bay Guardian* and *Lovers.* Breaking up is one of her favorite topics of obsession.

Karen X. Tulchinsky is a Jewish lesbian political activist writer living in Vancouver. Her work has appeared in *Love's Shadow, Getting Wet, Lovers, Sister/Stranger* and *Out Rage.*

Barbara Louise Ungar teaches creative writing at Queens College and the City Center for Workers Education in New York. Her poetry and fiction have appeared in *Cream City Review, Kalliope* and *Thema.* She is for romance in spite of reason.

Jodi Varon teaches English and writing at Eastern Oregon State College. Her fiction and translations from the Chinese of the poet Li He appear in *Northwest Review, Seattle Review, Translations* and *Colorado Review.*

Patrice Vecchione is co-editor of *Catholic Girls* and the forthcoming *Catholic Girls and Boys.* She is the editor of *Fault Lines: Children's Earthquake Poetry* and teaches poetry to children in Monterey Bay Area schools. Her work has appeared in *Puerto del Sol, IKON,* and *Quarry West.*

Lisa Vice was raised in rural Indiana and now resides in a small town on the Pacific Coast where she teaches writing. Her work appears in *Love's Shadow* and *The Time of Our Lives.* Her first novel, *Reckless Driver,* is forthcoming in 1994 from Dutton.

Shelley Washburn lives in Portland, Oregon, where she works as a free-lance writer. Her award-winning story, "The Nighthawk," appeared in the anthology, *Lovers.* She is currently working on a novel.

Wendy White-Ring has published in *Fiction Network, Sun Dog* and *Hayden's Ferry Review.* She lives in Arizona and is at work on a short story collection, *Periodic Sightings.*

Cecilia Woloch is the Los Angeles coordinator for the California Poets in the Schools program. Her poems have appeared in *Catholic Girls, Zyzzyva* and *On The Bus.*

Gene Zeiger lives and writes in western Massachusetts. Her poems have appeared in *The Georgia Review, The Massachusetts Review,* and *Word of Mouth.* A collection of poems, *Sudden Dancing,* was published in the Amherst Writers & Artists Chapbook Series.

Continued from page ii

"After Repeated Attempts" by Pamela Gray originally appeared in *New Lesbian Writing* (Grey Fox Press, 1984).

"Someone Else" by Ann Harleman was first published in *The Chicago Tribune.*

"Whatever Happened to Harry" by Susan Ito is reprinted by permission of the author from *Growing Up Asian American* (William Morrow & Co, 1993).

"Fever" by Lynn Kanter originally appeared in *Common Lives/Lesbian Lives,* Spring 1991.

"Macroscopic Phenomena" by Marilyn Krysl is reprinted by permission of the author from *Mozart, Westmoreland and Me* (Thunder's Mouth Press, 1985).

"Italian Supper" by Daniela Kuper first appeared in *The Sun,* February, 1992.

"Romance" by Dorianne Laux first appeared in *American Poetry Review,* July/August 1993.

"Silver Bullets" by Diane Lefer originally appeared in *Boulevard,* Spring 1988.

"Hole In The Wind" by Janice Levy first appeared in *Prism International.*

"Adrenalin" by Cris Mazza first appeared in *North Dakota Quarterly.*

"What Happened To Sharon" by Lesléa Newman is reprinted by permission of the author from *Secrets* (New Victoria Publishers, 1990).

"It's Only a Phase" by Ellen Orleans first appeared in *Quest Magazine,* August 1991.

"Losing Weight" by Elizabeth Searle is reprinted by permission of the author from *My Body to You* (University of Iowa Press, 1993).

"The End of a Marriage" by Joanne Seltzer first appeared in *Verve,* Fall 1989.

"Grace" by Robbi Clipper Sethi first appeared in *Atlantic.*

"Her Michelangelo" by Enid Shomer is reprinted by permission of the author from *Imaginary Men* (University of Iowa Press,1993).

"Jackie Boy" by Jodi Varon first appeared in *The High Plains Literary Review,* Spring 1990.

"Norway" by Wendy White-Ring first appeared in *Great Stream Review,* Spring 1991.

"Post and Beam Construction" by Gene Zeiger was previously published in *Swamp Root,* 1989.